THE MECHANICS OF THE ATOM

MAX BORN

THE MECHANICS OF THE ATOM

Translated from the German by
J. W. FISHER, Ph.D.

and revised by
D. R. HARTREE, Ph.D.

FREDERICK UNGAR PUBLISHING CO.
NEW YORK

Republished 1960
by arrangement with
G. Bell and Sons, Ltd., London

Second Printing, 1967

Printed in the United States of America

Library of Congress Catalog Card No. 60-9102

DEDICATED IN ALL GRATEFULNESS

TO

MR HENRY GOLDMAN

OF NEW YORK

A FRIEND OF GERMAN LEARNING

WHO STANDS ALWAYS READY TO AID

PREFACE TO THE GERMAN EDITION

THE title "Atomic Mechanics,"[1] given to these lectures which I delivered in Göttingen during the session 1923–24, was chosen to correspond to the designation "Celestial Mechanics." As the latter term covers that branch of theoretical astronomy which deals with the calculation of the orbits of celestial bodies according to mechanical laws, so the phrase "Atomic Mechanics" is chosen to signify that the facts of atomic physics are to be treated here with special reference to the underlying mechanical principles; an attempt is made, in other words, at a deductive treatment of atomic theory. It may be argued that the theory is not yet sufficiently developed to justify such a procedure; to this I reply that the work is deliberately conceived as an attempt, an experiment, the object of which is to ascertain the limits within which the present principles of atomic and quantum theory are valid and, at the same time, to explore the ways by which we may hope to proceed beyond these boundaries. In order to make this programme clear in the title, I have called the present book "Vol. I"; the second volume is to contain a closer approximation to the "final" mechanics of the atom. I know that the promise of such a second volume is bold, for at present we have only a few hazy indications as to the departures which must be made from the classical mechanics to explain atomic phenomena. Chief among these indications I include Heisenberg's conception of the laws of multiplets and the anomalous Zeeman effect; some features of the new radiation theory of Bohr, Kramers, and Slater, such as the notion of "virtual oscillators"; the subsequent advances of Kramers towards a quantum theory of dispersion phenomena; as well as some general considerations, which I have recently published, relating to the application of the theory of perturbations to the quantum theory. This mass of material, however, in spite of its

[1] The German title "Atommechanik" corresponds to the title "Himmelsmechanik" (celestial mechanics); the title "Mechanics of the Atom" appeared, however, preferable for this book, although, in the text, the clumsier expression atomic mechanics has often been employed.

extensive range, is not nearly enough for the foundation of a deductive theory. The second volume may, in consequence, remain for many years unwritten. In the meantime let its virtual existence serve to make clear the aim and spirit of this work.

This book is not intended for those who are taking up atomic problems for the first time, or who desire merely to obtain a survey of the theoretical problems which it involves. The short introduction, in which the most important physical foundations of the new mechanics are given, will be of little service to those who have not previously studied these questions ; the object of this summary is not an introduction to this field of knowledge, but a statement of the empirical results which are to serve as a logical foundation for our deductive theory. Those who wish to obtain a knowledge of atomic physics, without laborious consultation of original literature, should read Sommerfeld's *Atombau und Spektrallinien*.[1] When they have mastered this work they will meet with no difficulties in the present volume, indeed a great deal of it will be already familiar. The fact that many portions of this book overlap in subject-matter with sections of Sommerfeld's is of course unavoidable, but, even in these portions, a certain difference will be discernible. In our treatment prominence is always given to the mechanical point of view ; details of empirical facts are given only where they are essential for the elucidation, confirmation, or refutation of theoretical deductions. Again, with regard to the foundations of the quantum theory, there is a difference in the relative emphasis laid on certain points ; this, however, I leave for the reader to discover by direct comparison. My views are essentially the same as those of Bohr and his school ; in particular I share the opinion of the Copenhagen investigators, that we are still a long way from a " final " quantum theory.

For the fact that it has been possible to publish these lectures in book form I am indebted in the first place to the co-operation of my assistant, Dr. Friedrich Hund. Considerable portions of the text have been prepared by him and only slightly revised by me. Many points, which I have only briefly touched on in the lectures, have been worked out in detail by him and expounded in the text. In this connection I must mention, in the first place, the principle of the uniqueness of the action variables which, in my opinion, constitutes the basis of the present-day quantum theory ; the proof worked out by Hund plays an important part in the second chapter (§ 15). Further, the account of Bohr's theory of the periodic system, given in the third

[1] English translation of third edition, 1923, by H. L. Brose, Methuen & Co., Ltd., London.

chapter, has, for the most part, been put together by Hund. I also wish to thank other collaborators and helpers. Dr. W. Heisenberg has constantly helped us with his advice and has himself contributed certain sections (as, for example, the last on the helium atom); Dr. L. Nordheim has assisted in the presentation of the theory of perturbations, and Dr. H. Kornfeld has verified numerous calculations.

MAX BORN.

GÖTTINGEN, *November* 1924.

AUTHOR'S PREFACE TO THE ENGLISH EDITION

SINCE the original appearance of this book in German, the mechanics of the atom has developed with a vehemence that could scarcely be foreseen. The new type of theory which I was looking for as the subject-matter of the projected second volume has already appeared in the new quantum mechanics, which has been developed from two quite different points of view. I refer on the one hand to the quantum mechanics which was initiated by Heisenberg, and developed by him in collaboration with Jordan and myself in Germany, and by Dirac in England, and on the other hand to the wave mechanics suggested by de Broglie, and brilliantly worked out by Schrödinger. There are not two different theories, but simply two different modes of exposition. Many of the theoretical difficulties discussed in this book are solved by the new theory. Some may be found to ask if, in these circumstances, the appearance of an English translation is justified. I believe that it is, for it seems to me that the time is not yet arrived when the new mechanics can be built up on its own foundations, without any connection with classical theory. It would be giving a wrong view of the historical development, and doing injustice to the genius of Niels Bohr, to represent matters as if the latest ideas were inherent in the nature of the problem, and to ignore the struggle for clear conceptions which has been going on for twenty-five years. Further, I can state with a certain satisfaction that there is practically nothing in the book which I wish to withdraw. The difficulties are always openly acknowledged, and the applications of the theory to empirical details are so carefully formulated that no objections can be made from the point of view of the newest theory. Lastly, I believe that this book itself has contributed in some small measure to the promotion of the new theories, particularly those parts which have been worked out here in Göttingen. The discussions with my collaborators Heisenberg, Jordan and Hund which attended the writing of this book have prepared the way for the critical step which we owe to Heisenberg.

It is, therefore, with a clear conscience that I authorise the English translation. It does not seem superfluous to remark that this book is not elementary, but supposes the reader to have some knowledge of the experimental facts and their explanation. There exist excellent books from which such knowledge can easily be acquired. In Germany Sommerfeld's *Atombau und Spektrallinien* is much used: an English translation has appeared under the title *Atomic Structure and Spectral Lines*. I should like also to direct attention to Andrade's book, *The Structure of the Atom*, in which not only the theories but also the experimental methods are explained.

I desire to offer my warmest thanks to Professor Andrade for suggesting an English edition of my book. I also owe my thanks to Mr. Fisher, who prepared the translation in the first place; Professor Andrade, Professor Appleton and Dr. Curtis, who read it over; and finally to Dr. Hartree, who revised the translation, read the proof-sheets, and made many helpful suggestions for elucidating certain points. I also offer my sincere thanks to the publishers for the excellent manner in which they have produced the book.

MAX BORN.

GÖTTINGEN, *January* 1927.

NOTE

The chief departures from the German text which have been made by Professor Born or with his approval are (1) some modifications in §§ 1, 2 concerning the mechanism of radiation, in view of the experiments of Geiger and Bothe, and of Compton and Simon, (2) a modification of the derivation, on the lines suggested by Bohr, of the Rydberg-Ritz series formula in § 26, and (3) various alterations in §§ 24 and 30–32, made in view of the development of ideas and the additional experimental data acquired since the German edition was written.

D. R. H.

CONTENTS

INTRODUCTION

PHYSICAL FOUNDATIONS

FIRST CHAPTER

THE THEORY OF HAMILTON AND JACOBI

SECOND CHAPTER

PERIODIC AND MULTIPLY PERIODIC MOTIONS

THIRD CHAPTER

SYSTEMS WITH ONE RADIATING ELECTRON

FOURTH CHAPTER

THEORY OF PERTURBATION

APPENDIX

THE MECHANICS OF THE ATOM

INTRODUCTION

PHYSICAL FOUNDATIONS

§ 1.—Development of the Quantum Theory of the Oscillator from the Theory of Radiation

BEFORE dealing with the mathematical theory of atomic mechanics we shall give a brief account of its physical foundations. There are two sources to be considered : on the one hand the theory of thermal radiation, which led to the discovery of the quantum laws ; on the other, investigations of the structure of atoms and molecules.

Among all the characteristics of the atom which can be inferred from the physical and chemical properties of bodies, the radiation phenomena are distinguished by the fact that they provide us with the most direct information regarding the laws and structure of the ultimate constituents of matter. The most universal laws of matter are those manifested in such phenomena as are independent of the nature of the particular substance with which we are dealing. This constitutes the importance of Kirchhoff's discovery that the thermal radiation in an enclosure is independent of the nature of the material forming the walls of the enclosure, or contained in its interior. In an enclosure uniformly filled with radiation in equilibrium with the surroundings, the energy density, for a range of frequency $d\nu$, is equal to $\rho_\nu d\nu$, where ρ_ν is a universal function of ν and the temperature T. From the standpoint of the wave theory the macroscopic homogeneous radiation is to be regarded as a mixture of waves of every possible direction, intensity, frequency, and phase, which is in statistical equilibrium with the particles existing in matter which emit or absorb light.

For the theoretical treatment of the mutual interaction between radiation and matter it is permissible, by Kirchhoff's principle, to replace the actual atoms of the substances by simple models, so long as these do not contradict any of the known laws of nature. The harmonic oscillator has been used as the simplest model of an atom emitting or absorbing light; the moving particle is considered to be an electron, which is bound by the action of quasi-elastic forces to a position of equilibrium at which a positive charge of equal magnitude is situated. We thus have a doublet, whose moment (charge × displacement) varies with time. H. Hertz showed, when investigating the propagation of electric waves, how the radiation from such a doublet may be calculated on the basis of Maxwell's equations. It is an even simpler matter to calculate the excitation of such an oscillator by an external electromagnetic wave, a process which is utilised to explain refraction and absorption in the classical theory of dispersion. On the basis of these two results the mutual interaction between such resonators and a field of radiation may be determined. M. Planck has carried out the statistical calculation of this interaction. He found that the mean energy $\overline{W}$ of a system of resonators of frequency ν is proportional to the mean density of radiation ρ_ν, the proportionality factor depending on ν but not on the temperature T:

$$\rho_\nu = \frac{8\pi\nu^2}{c^2}\overline{W}. \tag{1}$$

The complete determination of $\rho_\nu(T)$ is thus reduced to the determination of the mean energy of the resonators, and this can be found from the laws of the ordinary statistical mechanics.

Let q be the displacement of a linear oscillator and χq the restoring force for this displacement; then $p = m\dot{q}$ is the momentum, and the energy is

$$W = \frac{m}{2}\dot{q}^2 + \frac{\chi}{2}q^2 = \frac{1}{2m}p^2 + \frac{\chi}{2}q^2.$$

The force-coefficient χ is connected with the angular frequency ω and the true frequency ν[1] by the relation

$$\frac{\chi}{m} = \omega^2 = (2\pi\nu)^2.$$

According to the rules of statistical mechanics, in order to calculate the mean value of a quantity depending on p and q the quantity must be multiplied by the weighting factor $e^{-\beta W}$, where $\beta = 1/kT$, and then averaged over the whole of the "phase space" (p, q) corresponding to possible motions. Thus the mean energy becomes

---

[1] In the following ω will always be used to denote the number of oscillations or rotations of a system in 2π secs. (the angular frequency), ν will be used to denote the number in 1 sec. (the true frequency).

$$\overline{W}=\frac{\iint We^{-\beta W}dp\,dq}{\iint e^{-\beta W}dp\,dq}.$$

This can clearly also be written

$$\overline{W}=-\frac{\partial}{\partial\beta}\log Z,$$

where

$$Z=\iint e^{-\beta W}dp\,dq$$

is the so-called partition function (Zustandsintegral). The evaluation of Z gives

$$Z=\int_{\infty}^{\infty}e^{-\frac{\beta}{2m}p^2}dp\int_{-\infty}^{\infty}e^{-\frac{\beta\chi}{2}q^2}dq\,;$$

and since

$$\int_{-\infty}^{\infty}e^{-x^2}dx=\sqrt{\pi}$$

we get

$$Z=2\pi\sqrt{\frac{m}{\chi}}\frac{1}{\beta}=\frac{1}{\nu\beta}.$$

Hence

(2) $$\overline{W}=\frac{1}{\beta}=kT.$$

This leads to the following formula for the density of radiation :

(3) $$\rho_\nu=\frac{8\pi\nu^2}{c^3}kT,$$

the so-called Rayleigh-Jeans formula. It is at variance not only with the simple empirical fact that the intensity does not increase continually with the frequency, but also leads to the impossible consequence that the total density of radiation

$$\int_0^\infty \rho_\nu d\nu$$

is infinite.

The formula (3) is valid only in the limiting case of small ν (long waves). W. Wien put forward a formula which represents correctly the observed decrease in intensity for high frequencies. A formula which includes both of these others as limiting cases was found by Planck, first by an ingenious interpolation, and shortly afterwards derived theoretically. It is

(4) $$\rho_\nu=\frac{8\pi\nu^2}{c^3}\frac{h\nu}{e^{\frac{h\nu}{kT}}-1},$$

where h is a new constant, the so-called Planck's Constant. Since it is the fundamental constant of the whole quantum theory, its numerical value will be given without delay, viz.:

$$h = 6{\cdot}54 \,.\, 10^{-27} \text{ erg sec.}$$

Comparison of (4) with (1) shows that this radiation formula corresponds to the following expression for the energy of the resonators:

$$\overline{W} = \frac{h\nu}{e^{\frac{h\nu}{kT}} - 1}. \tag{5}$$

To derive this formula theoretically, a complete departure from the principles of classical mechanics is necessary. Planck discovered that the following assumption led to the required result: *the energy of an oscillator can take not all values, but only those which are multiples of a unit of energy* W_0.

According to this hypothesis of Planck, the integral formula for Z is to be replaced by the sum

$$Z = \sum_{n=0}^{\infty} e^{-\frac{nW_0}{kT}}. \tag{6}$$

The summation of this geometric series gives

$$Z = \frac{1}{1 - e^{-\frac{W_0}{kT}}}.$$

From this it follows that

$$\overline{W} = \frac{\partial}{\partial\beta} \log(1 - e^{-\beta W_0}) = \frac{W_0 e^{-\beta W_0}}{1 - e^{-\beta W_0}},$$

thus

$$\overline{W} = \frac{W_0}{e^{\frac{W_0}{kT}} - 1}. \tag{7}$$

This agrees with Planck's formula (5) if we put $W_0 = h\nu$. This last relation can be established with the help of Wien's displacement law, which can be deduced from thermo-dynamical considerations combined with the Doppler principle. Wien's law states that the density of radiation must depend on the temperature and frequency in the following way:

$$\rho_\nu = \nu^3 f\left(\frac{\nu}{T}\right),$$

the energy of the resonator has therefore the form

$$\overline{W} = \nu F\left(\frac{\nu}{T}\right).$$

Comparison with (7) shows that W_0 must be proportional to ν.

Einstein showed that the behaviour of the specific heat of solid bodies furnished valuable support for Planck's bold hypothesis of energy quanta. The crudest model of a solid consisting of N atoms is a system of 3N linear oscillators, each of which more or less represents the vibration of an atom in one of the three directions of space. If the energy content of such a system be calculated on the assumption of a continuous energy distribution, we get from (2)

$$E=3NkT.$$

If we consider one gram molecule, then $Nk=R$, the absolute gas constant, and we have the law of Dulong and Petit in the form

$$c_v=\frac{dE}{dT}=3R=5{\cdot}9 \text{ calories per degree C.}$$

Experiment shows, however, that this is the case at high temperatures only, while, for low temperatures, c_v tends to zero. Einstein took Planck's value (5) for the mean energy instead of the classical one and obtained for one gram molecule :

$$E=3RT\frac{\frac{h\nu}{kT}}{e^{\frac{h\nu}{kT}}-1}.$$

This represents, with fair accuracy, the decrease in c_v at low temperatures for monatomic substances (*e.g.* diamond). The further development of the theory, taking into account the coupling of the atoms with one another, has confirmed Einstein's fundamental hypothesis.

Whereas Planck's assumption of energy quanta for resonators is well substantiated by this result, a serious objection may be brought against his deduction of his radiation formula, namely, that the relation (1) between the density of radiation ρ_ν and the mean energy $\overline{W}$ of the resonators is derived from classical mechanics and electrodynamics, whereas the statistical calculation of $\overline{W}$ is based on the quantum principle, which cannot be reconciled with classical considerations. Planck has endeavoured to remove this contradiction by the introduction of modified quantum restrictions ; but further developments have shown that the classical theory is inadequate to explain numerous phenomena, and plays rather the rôle of a limiting case (see below), whereas the real laws of the atomic world are pure quantum laws.

Let us recapitulate clearly the points in which the quantum principles are absolutely irreconcilable with the classical theory.

According to the classical theory, when a resonator oscillates, it emits an electromagnetic wave, which carries away energy; in consequence the energy of the oscillation steadily decreases. But according to the quantum theory, the energy of the resonator remains constant during the oscillation and equal to $n.h\nu$; a change in the energy of the resonator can occur only as the result of a process in which n changes by a whole number, a " quantum jump."

A radically new connection between radiation and the oscillation of the resonator must therefore be devised. This may be accomplished in two ways. We may either assume that the resonator does not radiate at all during the oscillation, and that it gives out radiation of frequency ν only when a quantum jump takes place, there being some yet unexplained process by which energy lost or gained by the resonator is given to or taken away from the ether. The energy principle is then satisfied in each elementary process. Or we may assume that the resonator radiates during the oscillation, but retains its energy in spite of this. The energy principle is then no longer obeyed by the individual processes; it can only be maintained on an average provided that a suitable relation exists between the radiation and the probabilities of transitions between the states of constant energy.

The first conception was long the prevailing one; the second hypothesis was put forward by Bohr, Kramers, and Slater,[1] but new experiments by Bothe and Geiger,[2] and by Compton and Simon,[3] have provided strong evidence against it. The investigations of this book will, in general, be independent of a decision in favour of either of these two assumptions. The existence of states of motion with constant energy (Bohr's " stationary states ") is the root of the problems with which we are concerned in the following pages.

§ 2.—General Conception of the Quantum Theory

By consideration of Planck's formula $W_0=h\nu$, Einstein was led to interpret phenomena of another type in terms of the quantum theory, thus giving rise to a new conception of this equation which has proved very fruitful. The phenomenon in question is the photoelectric effect. If light of frequency $\tilde{\nu}$ falls on a metallic surface,[4] electrons are set free and it is found that the intensity of the light influences

[1] *Zeitschr. f. Physik*, vol. xxiv, p. 69, 1924; *Phil. Mag.*, vol. xlvii, p. 785, 1924.
[2] W. Bothe and H. Geiger, *Zeitschr. f. Physik*, vol. xxxii, p. 639, 1925.
[3] A. H. Compton and W. Simon, *Phys. Rev.*, vol. xxv, p. 306, 1925.
[4] When the symbols ν and $\tilde{\nu}$ are employed concurrently, $\tilde{\nu}$ always refers to the frequency of the radiation, the symbol ν to a frequency within the atom. (Translator's note.)

the number of electrons emitted but not their velocity. The latter depends entirely on the frequency of the incident light. Einstein suggested that the velocity v of the emitted electrons should be given by the formula

$$\tfrac{1}{2}mv^2=h\tilde{\nu},$$

which has been verified for high frequencies (X-rays), while for low frequencies the work done in escaping from the surface must be taken into consideration.

We have then an electron, loosely bound in the metal, ejected by the incident light of frequency $\tilde{\nu}$ and receiving the kinetic energy $h\tilde{\nu}$; the atomic process is thus entirely different from that in the case of the resonator, and does not contain a frequency at all. The essential point appears to be, that the alteration in the energy of an atomic system is connected with the frequency of a light-wave by the equation

$$h\tilde{\nu}=W_1-W_2, \tag{1}$$

no matter whether the atomic system possesses the same frequency $\tilde{\nu}$ or some other frequency, or indeed has any frequency at all.

Planck's equation

$$W=n\,.\,W_0\,;\;W_0=h\nu$$

gives a relation between the frequency of oscillation ν of a resonator and its energy in the stationary states, the Einstein equation (1) gives a relation between the change in the energy of an atomic system for a transition from one state to another and the frequency $\tilde{\nu}$ of the monochromatic light with the emission or absorption of which the transition is connected.

Whereas Einstein applied this relation solely to the case of the liberation of electrons by incident light and to the converse process, viz. the production of light (or rather X-rays) by electronic bombardment, Bohr recognised the general significance of this quantum principle for all processes in which systems with stationary states interact with radiation. In fact the meaning of the equation is independent of any special assumptions regarding the atomic system. Since Bohr demonstrated its great fertility in connection with the hydrogen atom, equation (1) has been called Bohr's Frequency condition.

Taking into account the new experiments by Bothe and Geiger, and by Compton and Simon, which have been mentioned above, we have to assume that the frequency $\tilde{\nu}$ is radiated during the transition and the waves carry with them precisely the energy $h\tilde{\nu}$

(light quantum); there is at present no theoretical indication of the detailed nature of the transition process.

If Bohr's frequency relation (1) be applied to the resonator we are faced by alternatives which will now be considered. The change of energy which takes place when the resonator passes from the state with the energy $n_1 h\nu$ to that with the energy $n_2 h\nu$, viz.:

$$(n_1 - n_2)h\nu,$$

is, in general, a multiple of the energy quantum, $h\nu$, of the resonator. According now to Bohr and Einstein, this change in energy must be connected with the frequency $\tilde{\nu}$ of the emitted monochromatic radiation by the equation

$$h\tilde{\nu} = (n_1 - n_2)h\nu.$$

This admits of two possibilities only: either we may require that, as in the classical theory, the radiated frequency shall correspond with that of the radiator, in which case only transitions between neighbouring states, for which

$$n_1 - n_2 = 1$$

are possible, or we may assume that the frequency of the radiation differs from that of the resonator, being a multiple of it. In the latter case the emitted light will not be monochromatic, on account of the possibility of different transitions. The decision between these two possibilities has been attained in the course of the further development of Bohr's atomic theory, the conclusion being that the emitted radiation is strictly monochromatic, with the frequency given by the condition (1), but that the agreement between the frequency of the radiation and the frequency of oscillation of the resonator (*i.e.* $n_1 - n_2 = 1$) is brought about by an additional principle, which provides a criterion for the occurrence of transitions between the different states, and is called the Correspondence Principle.

A fundamental difference between the quantum theory and the classical theory is that, in the present stage of our knowledge of the elementary processes, we cannot assign a "cause" for the individual quantum jumps. In the classical theory, the transition from one state to another occurs causally, in accordance with the differential equations of mechanics or electrodynamics. The only connection in which probability considerations find a place on the older theory is in the determination of the probable properties of systems of many degrees of freedom (*e.g.* distribution laws in the kinetic theory of gases). In the quantum theory, the differential equations for the transitions between stationary states are given up, so that in this case special rules must be sought. These transitions are analogous to the processes of radioactive disintegration. All experiments go to show that the radioactive transformation processes occur spontaneously and are not capable of being influenced in any way. They appear to obey only statistical laws. It is not possible to say when a given radioactive atom will disintegrate, but it is possible to say what percentage of a given number will disintegrate in a given period; or, what comes to the same thing, a probability can be assigned for each radioactive transformation (which is called *a priori* since we are not at present in a position to express it in terms of anything more fundamental). We transfer this conception to the states of an atomic system. We ascribe to each transition between two stationary states an *a priori* probability.

The theoretical determination of this *a priori* probability is one of the most fundamental problems of the quantum theory. The only method of attack so far available is to consider processes in which the energy transformed in the course of a single transition is small in comparison to the total energy, in which case the results of the quantum theory must tend to agree with those of the classical theory. One theorem based on this idea is the Correspondence Principle of Bohr mentioned above; here the transitions between states with large quantum numbers (*e.g.* for large n in the case of a resonator) are compared with the corresponding classical processes. The rigorous formulation of this principle will be given later.

Another application of this idea occurs in a new derivation of Planck's radiation formula; this is due to Einstein, and has given effective support to the ideas of the quantum theory and in particular to Bohr's frequency condition.

In this case no assumptions are made regarding the radiating system except that it possesses different stationary states of constant energy. From these we select two with the energies W_1 and W_2 ($W_1 > W_2$), and suppose that, when statistical equilibrium exists, atoms in these states are present in the numbers N_1 and N_2 respectively. Then, by Boltzmann's Theorem

$$\frac{N_2}{N_1}=\frac{e^{-\frac{W_2}{kT}}}{e^{-\frac{W_1}{kT}}}=e^{\frac{W_1-W_2}{kT}}.$$

According to the classical theory, the mutual interaction between an atomic system and radiation consists of three kinds of processes:

1. If the system exists in a state of higher energy, it radiates energy spontaneously.

2. The field of radiation gives up energy to or takes away energy

from the system according to the phases and amplitudes of the waves of which it is composed. We call these processes

(*a*) positive in-radiation,[1] if the system absorbs energy;

(*b*) negative in-radiation (out-radiation), if it gives up energy.

In the cases 2 (*a*) and 2 (*b*) the contributions of the processes to the alteration of the energy are proportional to the energy density of the radiation.

In an analogous manner we assume for the quantum interaction between radiation and atomic systems the three corresponding processes. Between the two energy levels W_1 and W_2 there are then the following transitions:

1. Spontaneous decrease in energy by transition from W_1 to W_2. The frequency with which this process occurs is proportional to the number N_1 of the systems at the higher level W_1, but will also depend on the lower energy state W_2. We write for this frequency of occurrence

$$A_{12}N_1.$$

2*a*. Increase in energy on account of the field of radiation (*i.e.* transition from W_2 to W_1). We write in a corresponding way for its frequency of occurrence

$$B_{21}N_2\rho_\nu.$$

2*b*. Decrease in energy on account of the radiation field (transition from W_1 to W_2) with the frequency of occurrence

$$B_{12}N_1\rho_\nu.$$

We leave open the question whether the energy gained or lost by the atomic system is subtracted from or given up to the radiation during each individual process, or whether the energy principle is satisfied statistically only.

Now the statistical equilibrium of the states N_1 and N_2 requires that

$$A_{12}N_1=(B_{21}N_2-B_{12}N_1)\rho_\nu.$$

This gives

$$\rho_\nu=\frac{A_{12}}{B_{21}\frac{N_2}{N_1}-B_{12}}=\frac{A_{12}}{B_{21}e^{\frac{W_1-W_2}{kT}}-B_{12}}.$$

It is necessary now to make use of the frequency condition

$$W_1-W_2=h\tilde{\nu}$$

[1] Einstrahlung is here translated in-radiation, as there seems to be no exact English equivalent. E. A. Milne (*Phil. Mag.*, xlvii, 209, 1924) has already used in English the terms "in-radiation" and "out-radiation" in this connection.

in order that the formula for ρ_ν should be consistent with Wien's displacement law. Then

$$(2) \qquad \rho_\nu = \frac{A_{12}}{B_{21}e^{\frac{h\tilde{\nu}}{kT}} - B_{12}}.$$

At this stage Einstein makes use of the general consideration mentioned above, that the quantum laws must reduce to the classical ones as a limiting case. Clearly in the present problem the limiting case is that of high temperatures, where $h\tilde{\nu}$ is small compared to kT. In this case our formula (2) must become the Rayleigh-Jeans formula (3) of § 1, required by the classical theory (and verified by experiment for high temperatures), namely,

$$\rho_\nu = \frac{8\pi\tilde{\nu}^2}{c^3}kT.$$

Since, for large values of T, our ρ_ν becomes

$$\rho_\nu = \frac{A_{12}}{B_{21} - B_{12} + B_{21}\frac{h\tilde{\nu}}{kT} + \ldots},$$

the agreement is possible only if

$$B_{12} = B_{21}$$

and

$$\frac{A_{12}}{B_{12}} = \frac{8\pi}{c^3}\tilde{\nu}^3 h.$$

We arrive in fact at Planck's radiation formula

$$(3) \qquad \rho_\nu = \frac{8\pi h}{c^3}\frac{\tilde{\nu}^3}{e^{\frac{h\nu}{kT}} - 1}.$$

Collecting our results together, we see that Planck's original formulation of the quantum principles for the resonator embodies two essentially different postulates:

1. The determination of the stationary states (constant energy): this is done in the case of the resonator by the equation

$$W = nh\nu.$$

We shall generalise this equation later for any periodic system.

2. The Bohr Frequency condition

$$h\tilde{\nu} = W_1 - W_2,$$

which determines the frequency of the light emitted or absorbed in the transition between two stationary states. The frequency $\tilde{\nu}$ so defined is positive for emission and negative for absorption.

In addition to this there are certain statistical principles bearing on the frequency of occurrence of the stationary states and of the transitions between them, chief among which is the Correspondence Principle already referred to.

§ 3.—The Conceptions of Atomic and Molecular Structure

Having now considered the development of the special principles underlying the quantum mechanics of the atom, we shall indicate briefly the development of our knowledge regarding the material substratum to which they apply.

The phenomena of electrolysis first led to the hypothesis of the atomic structure of electricity. Subsequently the carriers of negative electricity were detected in the free state as the cathode rays and the β-rays of radioactive substances. From the deviation of these rays in electromagnetic fields, the ratio e/m, of charge to mass of the particles, could be determined. It was found that

$$e/m = 5{\cdot}31 \,.\, 10^{17} \text{ E.S.U. per gram.}$$

On the assumption that the same elementary quantum of electricity is concerned both here and in electrolysis (which can be verified approximately by experiment), we are led to the conclusion that the mass of these negative particles of electricity is about an 1830th part of that of a hydrogen atom. These carriers of negative electricity are called electrons and it can be shown, by optical and electrical experiments, that they exist as structural units in all matter. By making use of the fact that it is possible to produce on very small (ultra-microscopic) metal particles, and oil drops, a charge of only a few electrons, and to measure it, very accurate values have been found for the charge carried by an electron. Millikan found

$$e = 4{\cdot}77 \,.\, 10^{-10} \text{ E.S.U.}$$

Positive electricity has only been found associated with masses of atomic magnitude. Positive rays have been produced and studied: it will suffice to mention α-rays of radioactive substances, anode rays and canal rays. The determination of e/m from deviation experiments gave the mass of the α-particles to be that of the helium atom; for the particles of the anode rays the mass is that of the atom of the anode material, while for the particles of the canal rays the mass is that of an atom of the gas in the tube. We must therefore assume that each atom consists of a positive particle, at which is concentrated most of its mass, and of a number of electrons. In the neutral atom the number of the elementary charges of the positive particle is equal to the number of electrons; positive ions result from loss of electrons, negative ions from capture of extra electrons.

As regards the size of the electrons we can do nothing but make doubtful theoretical deductions, which lead to an order of magnitude of 10^{-13} cm. Lenard was the first to obtain definite conclusions regarding the size of the positive particles, which he called dynamids (Dynamiden). From experiments on the penetration of matter by cathode rays, he found that only a vanishingly small fraction of the space occupied by matter is impenetrable to fast cathode rays. Subsequently Rutherford arrived at analogous conclusions, as the result of experiments on the penetration of matter by α-rays. From a study of the range and scattering of these rays he was able to establish the fact that the linear dimensions of the positive particles, which he named nuclei, are at least 10,000 times smaller than those of an atom; up to this limit the observed deviations can be ascribed to Coulomb forces between the charged particles. The measurements also provided information regarding the charge of the positive particles, and gave for the number of the elementary charges about half the value of the atomic weight; the number of electrons in the neutral atom must be the same. This result was supported by investigations of the scattering of X-rays; the amount of the scattering depends principally, at any rate in the case of loosely bound electrons, on their number only.

When we come to regard all the possible types of atoms we must turn for guidance to the periodic system, which has been set up as the result of chemical experience. By this, the elements are arranged in an absolutely definite order; the magnitudes of the atomic weights give in the main the same order, but there are certain discrepancies (*e.g.* argon and potassium). The result obtained above, that the nuclear charge is approximately equal to half the atomic weight, led van den Broek to the hypothesis that the number of elementary nuclear charges is the same as the ordinal number of the atom in the periodic system (atomic number or order number). When, following Laue's discovery, X-ray spectroscopy had been begun by Bragg, van den Broek's hypothesis was confirmed by Moseley's investigations on the characteristic X-ray spectra of the elements. Moseley found that all elements possess essentially the same type of X-ray spectrum, but that with increasing atomic number the lines are displaced in the direction of higher frequencies and, moreover, that the square root of the frequency always increases by nearly the same amount from one element to the next. This established the fundamental character of the atomic number, as contrasted with the atomic weight. Further, the similarities of the X-ray spectra suggest the similarity of certain features of atomic structure. If now we assume that the structure of the atom, *i.e.* number and arrangement of its electrons, is determined essentially by the nuclear charge, we are led to the conclusion that there must be a close relationship between the nuclear charge and the atomic number; in fact, with the assumption that the two quantities are equal, the more precise theory of the X-ray spectra, which we shall give later, leads to Moseley's law.

Collecting together the results bearing on atomic structure, we have then the following picture of an atom with the order number Z; it consists of a nucleus with the charge Z,[1] with which is associated practically the whole mass of the atom, and (in the neutral state) Z electrons. In the model atom imagined by Rutherford it is supposed that these circulate round the nucleus in much the same way as the planets round the sun, and that the forces holding them together are essentially the electrostatic attractions and repulsions of the charged particles.

But if, on the basis of these conceptions and the classical principles, we now attempt to develop a mechanical theory of the atom, we encounter the following fundamental difficulty: a system of moving electric charges, such as is pictured in this model, would continually lose energy owing to electromagnetic radiation and must therefore gradually collapse. Further, all efforts to deduce the characteristic structure of the series spectra on the basis of the classical laws have proved fruitless.

Bohr has succeeded in overcoming these difficulties by rejecting the classical principles in favour of the quantum principles discussed in § 1 and § 2. He postulates the existence of discrete stationary states, fixed by quantum conditions, the exchange of energy between these states and the radiation field being governed by his frequency condition (1), § 2. The existence of a stationary state of minimum energy, which the atom cannot spontaneously abandon, provides for the absolute stability of atoms which is required by experience. Further,

[1] Later researches, chiefly by J. J. Thomson, Rutherford, Aston, and Dempster, have shown that the nucleus itself is further built up of electrons and hydrogen nuclei, called protons. As a consequence of these investigations the old hypothesis of Prout regains significance, in a somewhat different form. The deviations of the atomic weights from whole-number values, which previously ruled out this hypothesis, can be accounted for by the conception of isotopes and energy-mass variations. Not much is definitely known on the subject of nuclear mechanics, and it will not be discussed in this book.

in the case of the hydrogen atom, he succeeded in calculating the energy levels by a rational generalisation of Planck's hypothesis, in such a way that the frequency condition leads at once to the observed spectrum (Balmer's formula). He has also given the principles whereby the quantum conditions may be formulated in more complicated cases; this will be dealt with in the following pages.

Bohr's fundamental concepts of discrete stationary states and a quantum frequency condition receive their most direct confirmation from a class of investigations initiated by Franck and Hertz, and subsequently extended and refined by these and other investigators. The fundamental idea of these experiments is that definite amounts of energy can be communicated to atoms by bombarding them with electrons of known velocity. As the velocity of the bombarding electrons is increased, the abrupt occurrence of the stationary states is indicated on the one hand by the sudden appearance of electrons which have lost some of their incident energy, and on the other by the sudden production of radiation of those frequencies which are associated with transitions from the stationary state in question to other stationary states of lower energy.

Analogous phenomena are observed in the domain of the X-rays, where the occurrence of emission lines and absorption edges is bound up with the attainment of definite energy levels, consequent on electronic bombardment. In both the optical and the X-ray region values for the constant h can be determined by means of the frequency condition by measuring the energy supplied and the frequency of the consequent radiation. These values are independent of the atom and the particular quantum transition used to derive them, and are found to be in good agreement with the values obtained from heat radiation measurements.

Not only the structure of atoms but also their combination to form molecules and extended bodies, and the laws of motion of the latter, are governed by the same quantum laws. We may mention, for example, the more precise development of the theory of specific heats of solid bodies already referred to, and further the theory of the band spectra of molecules, which we shall deal with in detail in this book.

We give in conclusion a brief formulation of the ideas which have led to Bohr's atomic theory. There are two observations which are fundamental: firstly the stability of atoms, secondly the validity of the classical mechanics and electrodynamics for macroscopic processes. The application of the classical theory to atomic processes leads, however, to difficulties in connection with the stability. The problem arises, therefore, of developing a mechanics of the atom free from these contradictions. This new mechanics is characterised by the fact that the classical continuous manifold of states is replaced by a discrete manifold, defined by quantum numbers.

FIRST CHAPTER

THE THEORY OF HAMILTON AND JACOBI

§ 4.—Equations of Motion and Hamilton's Principle

NEWTON's equations of motion for a system of free particles form the starting-point for all the following considerations : [1]

$$\frac{d}{dt}(m_k\mathbf{v}_k)=\mathbf{K}_k, \tag{1}$$

where m_k denotes the mass of the kth particle, $\mathbf{v}_k$ its velocity, and $\mathbf{K}_k$ the force acting on it. The product $m_k\mathbf{v}_k$ is called the impulse or momentum.

In this form the equations (1) still hold if the mass is dependent on the magnitude of the velocity, as is required by Einstein's relativity theory.

In many cases the system of equations (1) is equivalent to a variation principle, known as Hamilton's Principle, viz. :

$$\int_{t_1}^{t_2} \mathrm{L}dt=\text{stationary value.} \tag{2}$$

Here L is a certain function of the co-ordinates and velocities of all the particles, and, in certain circumstances, also an explicit function of the time, and equation (2) as an expression of Hamilton's Principle is to be interpreted as follows: the configuration (co-ordinates) of the system of particles is given at the times t_1 and t_2 and the motion is sought (*i.e.* the co-ordinates as function of the time) which will take the system from the first configuration to the second in such a way that the integral will have a stationary value.[2] The chief advantage of such a variation principle is its independence of the system of co-ordinates.

---

[1] Heavy type is used to indicate vector quantities. Vector products are indicated by square brackets, and scalar products by round brackets or by absence of brackets.

[2] It does not matter whether it is a maximum or a minimum or a saddle-point value.

Lagrange's equations[1]

$$\frac{d}{dt}\frac{\partial L}{\partial \dot{x}_k}-\frac{\partial L}{\partial x_k}=0 \tag{3}$$

can be derived directly from the variation principle (2). We have to determine L so that these equations agree with the Newtonian equations (1).

If the forces $\mathbf{K}_k$ have a potential U, *i.e.* if

$$\mathbf{K}_{kx}=-\frac{\partial U}{\partial x_k}$$

we determine a function T^* of the velocity components so that

$$\frac{\partial T^*}{\partial \dot{x}_k}=m_k\dot{x}_k$$
$$\frac{\partial T^*}{\partial \dot{y}_k}=m_k\dot{y}_k$$
$$\frac{\partial T^*}{\partial \dot{z}_k}=m_k\dot{z}_k.$$

The equations (1) can then be written in the form

$$\frac{d}{dt}\frac{\partial T^*}{\partial \dot{x}_k}-\frac{\partial(-U)}{\partial x_k}=0$$

or

$$\frac{d}{dt}\frac{\partial(T^*-U)}{\partial \dot{x}_k}-\frac{\partial(T^*-U)}{\partial x_k}=0.$$

We put therefore in our variation principle (2)

$$L=T^*-U. \tag{4}$$

If, taking no account of the theory of relativity, we regard m_k as constant, T^* is equal to the kinetic energy T. If we write, in accordance with the special theory of relativity,

$$m=m_0\left\{1-\left(\frac{v}{c}\right)^2\right\}^{-\frac{1}{2}},$$

where m_0 is the "rest mass" and c is the velocity of light, we have (for one particle)

$$T^*=m_0c^2\left[1-\left\{1-\left(\frac{v}{c}\right)^2\right\}^{\frac{1}{2}}\right], \tag{5}$$

which, for the limiting case $c=\infty$, reduces to the expression $\frac{1}{2}m_0v^2$.

---

[1] In the following we shall usually write down only the first of the three equations corresponding to the co-ordinates x, y, z.

This function differs from the kinetic energy

$$T = m_0 c^2 \left[\left\{ 1 - \left(\frac{v}{c} \right)^2 \right\}^{-\frac{1}{2}} - 1 \right], \tag{6}$$

which, of course, also reduces to $\frac{1}{2} m_0 v^2$ in the limiting case where $c = \infty$.

Besides a component **K**, which can be derived from a potential U, the forces often contain a component **K*** depending on the velocities (as in the case of magnetic forces acting on electric charges). A function M is then determined so that

$$\frac{d}{dt} \frac{\partial M}{\partial \dot{x}} - \frac{\partial M}{\partial x} = \mathbf{K}_x^*, \tag{7}$$

and the expression

$$L = T^* - U - M \tag{8}$$

is substituted in the variation principle (2).

The Lagrangian equations (3) then become

$$\frac{d}{dt} \frac{\partial T^*}{\partial \dot{x}} + \frac{\partial U}{\partial x} - \frac{d}{dt} \frac{\partial M}{\partial \dot{x}} + \frac{\partial M}{\partial x} = 0,$$

and our variation principle is, in fact, equivalent to the Newtonian equations of motion

$$\frac{d}{dt}(m\dot{x}) - \mathbf{K}_x - \mathbf{K}_x^* = 0.$$

Hamilton's Principle is also valid when the particles are constrained in a manner defined by equations

$$f_h(x_1, y_1, z_1, x_2, y_2, z_2 \ . \ . \ .) = 0$$

between the co-ordinates.[1] In accordance with the rules of the calculus of variations, additional forces of the form

$$\mathbf{K}_k^{(h)} = \lambda_h \frac{\partial f_h}{\partial x_k}$$

must be added to the original forces, where the λ_h's, which are functions of the co-ordinates, are the "undetermined multipliers" of Lagrange. These multipliers, together with the co-ordinates, are to be regarded as unknowns; the number of determining equations, *i.e.* differential equations and equations of constraint, is then equal to the number of unknowns.

As already mentioned, the chief advantage of Hamilton's Principle is that it represents the laws of motion in a manner independent of any special choice of co-ordinates. If a number of equations of con-

[1] Such conditions, which do not involve the velocity components, are called holonomous.

straint be given, an equal number of co-ordinates can be eliminated with their help. There remains then a certain number of independent co-ordinates $$q_1 q_2 \dots q_f.$$
The number f is known as the number of degrees of freedom. The Lagrangian function will then be a function of the q's and of their time derivatives; the time may also appear explicitly:

$$L = L(q_1, \dot{q}_1, q_2, \dot{q}_2 \dots q_f, \dot{q}_f, t);$$

the variation principle (2) then leads to the Lagrangian equations

$$(9) \qquad \frac{d}{dt}\frac{\partial L}{\partial \dot{q}_k} - \frac{\partial L}{\partial q_k} = 0 \qquad k=1, 2, \dots f.$$

These are also valid if the co-ordinates q_k refer to arbitrarily moving, or even deformed, systems of reference.

§ 5.—The Canonical Equations

Each of Lagrange's equations is a differential equation of the second order. In many cases, particularly for work of a general character, it is desirable to replace them by a system of twice as many differential equations of the first order. The simplest way of accomplishing this is to put $\dot{q}_k = s_k$, and then to take these additional equations into account, treating the s_k's, as well as the q_k's, as unknown quantities. A much more symmetrical form is obtained as follows:

In place of the $\dot{q}_k$'s the new variables

$$(1) \qquad p_k = \frac{\partial L}{\partial \dot{q}_k},$$

known as momenta, are introduced; the Lagrangian equations (9) of § 4 now become

$$(2) \qquad \dot{p}_k = \frac{\partial L}{\partial q_k},$$

where L is still to be regarded as a function of the q_k's and $\dot{q}_k$'s. Equations (1) can now be expressed in a similar form by introducing in place of the function $L(q_1 \dot{q}_1 \dots t)$ a new function $H(q_1 p_1 \dots t)$, by means of a Legendre Transformation [1]

$$(3) \qquad H = \sum_k \dot{q}_k p_k - L.$$

[1] A Legendre Transformation transforms, in general, a function $f(x, y)$ into a function $g(x, z)$, where $z = \frac{\partial f}{\partial y}$, in such a way that the derivative of g with respect to the new variable z is equal to the old variable y. Such transformations play a considerable part in all branches of physics; in thermodynamics, for example, the energy and the free energy are related in the same way as two functions connected by a Legendre Transformation.

If now we form the total differential

$$dH=\sum_k \dot{q}_k dp_k+\sum_k p_k d\dot{q}_k-\sum_k \frac{\partial L}{\partial q_k}dq_k-\sum_k \frac{\partial L}{\partial \dot{q}_k}d\dot{q}_k-\frac{\partial L}{dt}dt,$$

the terms in $d\dot{q}_k$ cancel out on account of (1). For the partial derivatives of $H(q_1 p_1 \ldots t)$ with respect to p_k and q_k we have therefore

$$\frac{\partial H}{\partial p_k}=\dot{q}_k$$

(4)

$$\left(\frac{\partial H}{\partial q_k}\right)_p=-\left(\frac{\partial L}{\partial q_k}\right)_{\dot{q}},$$

where the indices outside the brackets denote which variable is independent. Now with the help of the new variables we can write (2) and (4) (which is an expression of (1)) as follows :

$$\dot{q}_k=\frac{\partial H}{\partial p_k}$$

(5)

$$\dot{p}_k=-\frac{\partial H}{\partial q_k}.$$

This is the so-called canonical form of the equations of motion. $H(q_1, p_1, q_2, p_2 \ldots t)$ is called the Hamiltonian function. The variables q_k and p_k are said to be canonically conjugated.

The same equations are obtained if the momenta are defined by (1) in the same way, and the function L in the variation principle (2), § 4, is expressed in terms of H by means of equation (3). We have

(6) $$\int_{t_1}^{t_2}\left[\sum_k p_k\dot{q}_k-H(q_1 p_1 \ldots t)\right]dt=\text{stationary value},$$

for the same possible variations as before, *i.e.* variations for which the configurations at fixed times t_1 and t_2 are themselves fixed ; here the q_k and p_k are to be regarded as the functions required. It is easily seen that the Lagrangian equations are equivalent to (5), and it should be noted that the derivatives of the p_k's do not occur explicitly in the integrand ; for this reason only the values of the q_k's at the times t_1 and t_2 can be prescribed as limiting conditions, not those of the p_k's.

All of these considerations remain valid if the function L, and with it the function H, depends explicitly on the time t. The latter case will occur, for example, either if external influences depending on the time are present (U depending on t), or if, in the case of a self-contained system, a system of reference is employed which itself performs a prescribed non-uniform motion. If, however, H does not involve the time explicitly, we have

$$\frac{dH}{dt}=\sum_k\left[\frac{\partial H}{\partial q_k}\dot{q}_k+\frac{\partial H}{\partial p_k}\dot{p}_k\right].$$

Substituting for $\dot{q}_k$ and $\dot{p}_k$ from the equations of motion (5), it follows that

$$\frac{dH}{dt}=0,$$

so that

(7) $$H(p_1q_1\ldots)=\text{constant}$$

is a first integral of the equations of motion (5).

We inquire now as to the mechanical significance of the quantity H and consider first the case of the classical (non-relativistic) mechanics. With any co-ordinates, in a stationary system of reference, the kinetic energy is a homogeneous quadratic function T_2 of the velocities $\dot{q}_k$; in moving co-ordinate systems additional linear terms, and terms not involving $\dot{q}_k$, will occur, so that we can write :

$$T=T_0+T_1+T_2.$$

Here T_n denotes a homogeneous function of the nth degree of the $\dot{q}_k$'s, which may, moreover, depend on the q_k's. By Euler's Theorem we have

$$nT_n=\sum_k\frac{\partial T_n}{\partial\dot{q}_k}\dot{q}_k,$$

thus

(8) $$\sum_k p_k\dot{q}_k=\sum_k\frac{\partial T}{\partial\dot{q}_k}\dot{q}_k=T_1+2T_2.$$

If we suppose that an ordinary potential energy U exists, in which case

$$L=T-U,$$

we have

$$\begin{aligned}H&=T_1+2T_2-(T_0+T_1+T_2)+U\\&=-T_0+T_2+U.\end{aligned}$$

In the case of a co-ordinate system at rest ($T=T_2$)

(9) $$H=T+U$$

is the total energy. If the time does not occur explicitly in H, this gives, in conjunction with equation (7), the law of the conservation of energy.

In the case of moving co-ordinate systems, where T_0 and T_1 are not 0, it may happen that H is independent of the time, thus

$$H = \text{const.}$$

is an integral, but not the energy integral.

Example.—We consider a system of co-ordinates (ξ, η) rotating with the angular velocity ω round the axis of z. We transform to this from the stationary system (x, y) by means of the formulæ

$$\begin{aligned} x &= \xi \cos \omega t - \eta \sin \omega t \\ y &= \xi \sin \omega t + \eta \cos \omega t \\ z &= \zeta. \end{aligned}$$

The kinetic energy then becomes

$$T = \sum \frac{m}{2}[\omega^2(\xi^2+\eta^2) + 2\omega(\xi\dot{\eta} - \eta\dot{\xi}) + \dot{\xi}^2 + \dot{\eta}^2 + \dot{\zeta}^2].$$

The momenta corresponding to the co-ordinates ξ and η are then

$$\begin{aligned} p_\xi &= m(\dot{\xi} - \omega\eta) \\ p_\eta &= m(\dot{\eta} + \omega\xi) \\ p_\zeta &= m\dot{\zeta}, \end{aligned}$$

so that we can also write

$$T = \sum \frac{1}{2m}(p_\xi^2 + p_\eta^2 + p_\zeta^2).$$

For H we obtain

$$H = \sum \left[\dot{\xi} p_\xi + \dot{\eta} p_\eta + \dot{\zeta} p_\zeta - \frac{1}{2m}(p_\xi^2 + p_\eta^2 + p_\zeta^2) \right] + U,$$

or

$$H = \sum \left[\omega(\eta p_\xi - \xi p_\eta) + \frac{1}{2m}(p_\xi^2 + p_\eta^2 + p_\zeta^2) \right] + U.$$

If U is symmetrical around the axis of z, H does not contain the time explicitly and is therefore constant. The integral

$$H = \text{const.}$$

is called the Jacobian Integral. It is, however, different from the energy

$$E = T + U = \sum \frac{1}{2m}(p_\xi^2 + p_\eta^2 + p_\zeta^2) + U,$$

which is likewise constant.

From both integrals it follows that

$$E - H = \text{const.}$$

This gives the law of conservation of angular momentum. We have, in fact,

$$E - H = \omega \cdot \Sigma(\xi p_\eta - \eta p_\xi) = \omega \cdot \Sigma m(\xi\dot{\eta} - \eta\dot{\xi}) + \omega^2 \Sigma m(\xi^2 + \eta^2).$$

If we transform back to x, y, we have

$$E - H = \omega \Sigma m(x\dot{y} - y\dot{x}).$$

We consider now the case of relativistic mechanics. By (4) and (5), § 4, we have for a particle

$$L=T^*-U=m_0c^2\left[1-\left(1-\frac{v^2}{c^2}\right)^{\frac{1}{2}}\right]-U,$$

thus

$$(10) \qquad p_x=m_0\dot{x}\left(1-\frac{v^2}{c^2}\right)^{-\frac{1}{2}}$$

and

$$\begin{aligned} H&=\dot{x}p_x+\dot{y}p_y+\dot{z}p_z-L\\ &=m_0c^2\left[\left(1-\frac{v^2}{c^2}\right)^{-\frac{1}{2}}-1\right]+U\\ (11) \qquad &=T+U, \end{aligned}$$

so that in this case also H is the total energy. This result is independent of the co-ordinate system so long as this is at rest.

§ 6.—Cyclic Variables

Before dealing with the general theory of the integration of the canonical equations, we will, first of all, consider some simple cases. If the Hamiltonian function H does not contain one co-ordinate, *e.g.* q_1, *i.e.* if

$$H=H(p_1q_2p_2\ldots t),$$

it follows from the canonical equations that

$$\dot{p}_1=0$$
$$p_1=\text{constant}.$$

Thus we arrive immediately at one integral of these equations. The co-ordinate q_1 is called, after Helmholtz, a cyclic co-ordinate (since it often corresponds to a rotation about an axis).

Clearly this case always arises if the mechanical system is not affected by an alteration of the co-ordinate q_1 (*e.g.* by a single translation or rotation).

If, for example, a system of massive particles $(\mathbf{r}_1\mathbf{r}_2\ldots\mathbf{r}_n)$ moves under the action of mutual forces only, the potential energy will depend solely on the differences

$$\mathbf{s}_2=\mathbf{r}_2-\mathbf{r}_1,\quad \mathbf{s}_3=\mathbf{r}_3-\mathbf{r}_1,\quad\ldots\quad \mathbf{s}_n=\mathbf{r}_n-\mathbf{r}_1.$$

We introduce as co-ordinates the components $x_1y_1z_1$ of $\mathbf{r}_1$, and the components $\xi_k\eta_k\zeta_k$ of these differences $\mathbf{s}_k$. Since U is independent of $x_1y_1z_1$, it follows that $p_{x_1}p_{y_1}p_{z_1}$ are constant. Now the kinetic energy is

$$T=\sum_k \tfrac{1}{2}m_k(\dot{x}_k^2+\dot{y}_k^2+\dot{z}_k^2) \qquad (k=1, 2\ldots n).$$

Since

$$\dot{x}_k=\dot{x}_1+\dot{\xi}_k \qquad (k=2, 3 \ldots n)$$

it follows that

$$p_{x_1}=\frac{\partial T}{\partial \dot{x}_1}=\sum_k m_k \dot{x}_k \qquad (k=1, 2 \ldots n).$$

The three integrals give therefore the principle of the conservation of momentum.

Another important case is that in which the potential energy remains unaltered by a rotation of the whole system about an axis fixed in space. If $\phi_1, \phi_2 \ldots$ are the azimuths of the particles of the system about this axis, we introduce as co-ordinates the magnitudes

$$\Phi_1=\phi_1\,; \qquad \Phi_k=\phi_k-\phi_1 \qquad (k=2, 3 \ldots)$$

and certain others, depending only on the relative positions of the particles with respect to one another and to the axis (for example, cylindrical co-ordinates r_k, z_k or polar co-ordinates r_k, θ_k). Since the Hamiltonian function does not depend on Φ_1, Φ_1 is a cyclic variable (in this case in the true sense of the word) and the momentum p_{Φ_1} conjugate to it, is constant. Since

$$\dot{\phi}_k=\dot{\Phi}_1+\dot{\Phi}_k \qquad (k=2, 3 \ldots n)$$

and

$$T=\sum_{k=1}^{n}\tfrac{1}{2}m_k(r_k^2\dot{\phi}_k^2+\ldots),$$

where r_k is the distance from the axis, p_{Φ_1} has the value

$$p_{\Phi_1}=\frac{\partial T}{\partial \dot{\Phi}_1}=\sum_{k=1}^{n}\frac{\partial T}{\partial \dot{\phi}_k}=\sum_{k=1}^{n} m_k r_k^2 \dot{\phi}_k,$$

and is therefore the angular momentum about the axis of symmetry.

If the massive particles move under the action of mutual forces only, our considerations are valid for every fixed direction in space. Since the quantity p_{Φ_1} is the component of the total angular momentum

$$\sum_{k=1}^{n} m_k[\mathbf{r}_k\dot{\mathbf{r}}_k]$$

in an arbitrary direction, and is always constant, the constancy of the angular momentum follows.

It may happen that H depends only on the p_k's, *i.e.*

$$H=H(p_1 p_2 \ldots).$$

In this case the canonical equations admit of immediate integration. We have

$$\dot{p}_k=0, \qquad p_k=\alpha_k$$
$$\dot{q}_k=\frac{\partial H}{\partial p_k}=\omega_k, \qquad q_k=\omega_k t+\beta_k.$$

Here the ω_k's are constants characteristic of the system and α_k, β_k are constants of integration. It will be seen from this that a mechanical problem is solved as soon as we have found co-ordinates for which the Hamiltonian function depends only on the canonically conjugated momenta. The methods treated in this book will usually follow this course. In general, such variables cannot be found by a simple point transformation of the q_k's into new co-ordinates, but rather the totality (q_k, p_k) of the co-ordinates and momenta must be transformed to new conjugated variables.

We shall, however, first consider some more examples.

1. *The Rotator.*—By this we understand a rigid body which can rotate about an axis fixed in space. If ϕ denotes the angle of rotation and A the moment of inertia about the axis, then

$$T=\tfrac{1}{2}A\dot{\phi}^2,$$

and the momentum corresponding to ϕ is

$$p=A\dot{\phi}.$$

For motion under no forces (U=0).

(1) $$H=T=\frac{1}{2A}p^2,$$

ϕ is therefore cyclic, and consequently

$$p=\text{constant},$$

and

$$\dot{\phi}=\omega=\frac{p}{A}, \qquad \phi=\omega t+\beta.$$

The motion under no forces is therefore a uniform rotation about the axis.

2. *The Symmetrical Top.*—If A_x denotes the moment of inertia about an axis perpendicular to the axis of symmetry (z), A_z the moment of inertia about the axis of symmetry, and $\mathbf{d}_x$, $\mathbf{d}_y$, $\mathbf{d}_z$ the components of the angular velocity in the system of reference (x, y, z) rigidly fixed in the body, then

$$T=\tfrac{1}{2}[A_x(\mathbf{d}_x^2+\mathbf{d}_y^2)+A_z\mathbf{d}_z^2].$$

We introduce as co-ordinates the Eulerian angles θ, ϕ, ψ defined as follows :— Rectangular axes $\bar{x}$, $\bar{y}$, $\bar{z}$ are taken fixed in space; θ is the angle between the axis of symmetry (z) and the $\bar{z}$-axis, ϕ is the angle between the x-axis and the nodal line (line of intersection between the (x, y) plane and the plane ($\bar{x}$, $\bar{y}$)), and ψ is the angle between the $\bar{x}$-axis and nodal line. The components of the angular velocity will then be

$$\mathbf{d}_x=\dot{\theta}\cos\phi+\dot{\psi}\sin\theta\sin\phi,$$

(2) $$\mathbf{d}_y=\dot{\theta}\sin\phi-\dot{\psi}\sin\theta\cos\phi$$

$$\mathbf{d}_z=\dot{\phi}+\dot{\psi}\cos\theta$$

and the kinetic energy

$$\mathrm{T}+\tfrac{1}{2}[\mathrm{A}_x(\dot{\theta}^2+\dot{\psi}^2\sin^2\theta)+\mathrm{A}_z(\dot{\phi}+\dot{\psi}\cos\theta)^2].$$

The momenta corresponding to θ, ϕ, ψ are

$$p_\theta=\frac{\partial\mathrm{T}}{\partial\dot{\theta}}=\mathrm{A}_x\dot{\theta},$$

(3) $$p_\phi=\frac{\partial\mathrm{T}}{\partial\dot{\phi}}=\mathrm{A}_z(\dot{\phi}+\dot{\psi}\cos\theta),$$

$$p_\psi=\frac{\partial\mathrm{T}}{\partial\dot{\psi}}=(\mathrm{A}_x\sin^2\theta+\mathrm{A}_z\cos^2\theta)\dot{\psi}+\mathrm{A}_z\cos\theta\dot{\phi}.$$

In order to make the physical significance of these momenta clear, we use (2) to replace the $\dot{\theta}$, $\dot{\phi}$, $\dot{\psi}$ by the components of $\mathbf{d}$: then

$$p_\theta=\mathrm{A}_x(\mathbf{d}_x\cos\phi+\mathbf{d}_y\sin\phi),$$
$$p_\phi=\mathrm{A}_z\mathbf{d}_z,$$
$$p_\psi=\mathrm{A}_x(\mathbf{d}_x\sin\phi-\mathbf{d}_z\cos\phi)\sin\theta+\mathrm{A}_z\mathbf{d}_z\cos\theta,$$

in which $(\mathbf{d}_x\cos\phi+\mathbf{d}_y\sin\phi)$ clearly denotes the angular velocity about the nodal line and $(\mathbf{d}_x\sin\phi-\mathbf{d}_y\cos\phi)$ the angular velocity about a perpendicular direction in the (x, y) plane. We see then from the equations, that

p_θ is the angular momentum about the nodal line,
p_ϕ is the angular momentum about the axis of symmetry,
p_ψ is the angular momentum about the direction $\bar{z}$ fixed in space.

For motion under no forces (U=0), a simple calculation gives

$$\mathrm{H}=\mathrm{T}=\frac{1}{2\mathrm{A}_x}\left[p_\theta^2+\left(\frac{p_\psi-p_\phi\cos\theta}{\sin\theta}\right)^2\right]+\frac{p_\phi^2}{2\mathrm{A}_z}.$$

In this expression ϕ and ψ do not appear; they are therefore cyclic, and consequently

$$p_\phi=\text{constant},\qquad p_\psi=\text{constant}.$$

Since we have in addition the principle of the conservation of the total angular momentum at our disposal the integration can be completely carried out. We can take the hitherto arbitrary axis of $\bar{z}$ in the direction of the resultant angular momentum. Since the nodal line is perpendicular to this, the angular momentum about the nodal line will be

$$p_\theta=0.$$

The canonical equations give firstly

$$\theta=\text{constant},$$

and then

$$\frac{\partial\mathrm{H}}{\partial\theta}=0,$$

which leads to

$$(p_\phi - p_\psi \cos\theta)(p_\psi - p_\phi \cos\theta) = 0.$$

Since p_ψ is essentially greater than or equal to p_ϕ, it follows that

$$p_\phi - p_\psi \cos\theta = 0,$$

as can also be seen immediately. The Hamiltonian function now takes the simple form

$$\mathrm{H} = \frac{1}{2\mathrm{A}_x} p_\psi^2 + \frac{1}{2}\left(\frac{1}{\mathrm{A}_z} - \frac{1}{\mathrm{A}_x}\right) p_\phi^2;$$

ψ and ϕ therefore execute uniform rotations with the angular velocities

$$\dot{\phi} = \omega_\phi = \frac{\partial \mathrm{H}}{\partial p_\phi} = \left(\frac{1}{\mathrm{A}_z} - \frac{1}{\mathrm{A}_x}\right) p_\phi$$

$$\dot{\psi} = \omega_\psi = \frac{\partial \mathrm{H}}{\partial p_\psi} = \frac{1}{\mathrm{A}_x} p_\psi.$$

The motion under no forces of the symmetrical top therefore consists of a uniform rotation about the axis of symmetry, together with a uniform precession of this axis about the direction of the resultant angular momentum.

§ 7.—Canonical Transformations

As already mentioned, the integration of the equations of motion can be effected by introducing new co-ordinates having a cyclic character if such can be found. We shall therefore quite generally seek a transformation

$$p_k = p_k(\bar{q}_1 \bar{q}_2 \ldots \bar{p}_1 \bar{p}_2 \ldots t)$$
$$q_k = q_k(\bar{q}_1 \bar{q}_2 \ldots \bar{p}_1 \bar{p}_2 \ldots t)$$

such that the new variables again satisfy the canonical equations of motion. For this to be the case it is necessary and sufficient that the variation principle (6) of § 5

$$\int \Big[\sum_k p_k \dot{q}_k - \mathrm{H}(q_1 p_1 \ldots t) \Big] dt = \text{stationary value}$$

shall transform into

$$\int \Big[\sum_k \bar{p}_k \dot{\bar{q}}_k - \bar{\mathrm{H}}(\bar{q}_1 \bar{p}_1 \ldots t) \Big] dt = \text{stationary value.}$$

This will be the case if, and only if, the difference of the integrands is the complete derivative $\frac{d\mathrm{V}}{dt}$ of a function of $2f$ of the old and new variables and of the time; for, if V be regarded as a function of the q_k and $\bar{q}_k$, the values of V at the limits of integration will be fixed. According now as we take V to be a function of q_k, $\bar{q}_k$, t, or of q_k, $\bar{p}_k$, t, or of $\bar{q}_k$, p_k, t, or finally of p_k, $\bar{p}_k$, t, we obtain four principal forms for canonical transformations.

We choose therefore an arbitrary function $V(q_1, \bar{q}_1 \ldots t)$. The condition

$$\sum_k p_k\dot{q}_k - H(q_1, p_1 \ldots t) = \sum_k \bar{p}_k\dot{\bar{q}}_k - \bar{H}(\bar{q}_1, \bar{p}_1 \ldots t) + \frac{d}{dt}V(q_1, \bar{q}_1 \ldots t)$$

is fulfilled, if the coefficients of $\dot{q}_k$ and $\dot{\bar{q}}_k$, and of terms independent of these quantities, are the same on both sides, that is if

$$p_k = \frac{\partial}{\partial q_k}V(q_1, \bar{q}_1 \ldots t)$$

(1) $$\bar{p}_k = -\frac{\partial}{\partial \bar{q}_k}V(q_1, \bar{q}_1 \ldots t)$$

$$H = \bar{H} - \frac{\partial}{\partial t}V(q_1, \bar{q}_1 \ldots t).$$

Since in general the q_k's can be calculated from the equations of the second line, and then the p_k's can be calculated from the equations of the first line as functions of the $\bar{q}_k$ and $\bar{p}_k$, the system (1) replaces the equations of transformation.

Again, in order to obtain a canonical transformation by means of an arbitrary function $V(q_1, \bar{p}_1 \ldots t)$, we write our condition in the form :

$$\sum_k p_k\dot{q}_k - H(q_1, p_1 \ldots t) = \sum_k \bar{p}_k\dot{\bar{q}}_k - \bar{H}(\bar{q}_1, \bar{p}_1 \ldots t) + \frac{d}{dt}\left(V - \sum_k \bar{p}_k\bar{q}_k\right),$$

or, what comes to the same thing :

$$\sum_k p_k\dot{q}_k - H(q_1, p_1 \ldots t) = -\sum_k \bar{q}_k\dot{\bar{p}}_k - \bar{H}(\bar{q}_1, \bar{p}_1 \ldots t) + \frac{d}{dt}V(q_1, \bar{p}_1 \ldots t).$$

Comparison of the coefficients of $\dot{q}_k$ and $\dot{\bar{p}}_k$ gives

$$p_k = \frac{\partial}{\partial q_k}V(q_1, \bar{p}_1 \ldots t)$$

(2) $$\bar{q}_k = \frac{\partial}{\partial \bar{p}_k}V(q_1, \bar{p}_1 \ldots t)$$

$$H = \bar{H} - \frac{\partial}{\partial t}V(q_1, \bar{p}_1 \ldots t).$$

These equations can also be regarded as equations of transformation.

The third form we obtain by simply interchanging the old and new variables, and replacing V by $-$V, in order to obtain the simplest possible correspondence between the four forms. We obtain :

$$
\begin{aligned}
\bar{p}_k &= -\frac{\partial}{\partial \bar{q}_k} V(\bar{q}_1, p_1 \ldots t), \\
q_k &= -\frac{\partial}{\partial p_k} V(\bar{q}_1, p_1 \ldots t), \qquad (3) \\
H &= \bar{H} - \frac{\partial}{\partial t} V(\bar{q}_1, p_1 \ldots t).
\end{aligned}
$$

Finally, in order to arrive at the fourth form, we write the condition in the form :

$$
\sum_k p_k \dot{q}_k - H(q_1, p_1 \ldots t) = \sum_k \bar{p}_k \dot{\bar{q}}_k - \bar{H}(\bar{q}_1, \bar{p}_1 \ldots t) + \frac{d}{dt}\left(V - \sum_k \bar{p}_k \bar{q}_k + \sum_k p_k q_k\right)
$$

or :

$$
-\sum q_k \dot{p}_k - H(q_1, p_1 \ldots t) = -\sum \bar{q}_k \dot{\bar{p}}_k - \bar{H}(\bar{q}_1, \bar{p}_1 \ldots t) + \frac{d}{dt} V(p_1, \bar{p}_1 \ldots t),
$$

and obtain :

$$
\begin{aligned}
q_k &= -\frac{\partial}{\partial p_k} V(p_1, \bar{p}_1 \ldots t), \\
\bar{q}_k &= \frac{\partial}{\partial \bar{p}_k} V(p_1, \bar{p}_1 \ldots t), \qquad (4) \\
H &= \bar{H} - \frac{\partial}{\partial t} V(p_1, \bar{p}_1 \ldots t).
\end{aligned}
$$

We can express all four forms at once in the following manner : In the arbitrary function $V(x_1, \bar{x}_1, x_2, \bar{x}_2 \ldots t)$ let x_k be one of the variables q_k and p_k, $\bar{x}_k$ one of the variables $\bar{q}_k$, $\bar{p}_k$; then the equations

$$
\begin{aligned}
y_k &= \pm \frac{\partial V}{\partial x_k}, \\
\bar{y}_k &= \mp \frac{\partial V}{\partial \bar{x}_k}, \qquad (5) \\
H &= \bar{H} - \frac{\partial V}{\partial t}
\end{aligned}
$$

give a canonical transformation. Here y_k is conjugated to x_k and $\bar{y}_k$ to $\bar{x}_k$; the upper sign applies to the case where the differentiation is taken with respect to a co-ordinate and the lower one to the case of differentiation with respect to a momentum. The function V we shall call the generating function, or shortly, the generator, of the canonical transformation.

Further, it must be emphasised that the canonical property of a transformation depends in no way on the special mechanical problem; if a transformation is canonical, it remains so for every form of the function H. We now give some transformations which we shall need later:

The function

$$V = q_1\bar{p}_1 + q_2\bar{p}_2 + \dots$$

leads to the identical transformation

$$\begin{array}{ll} q_1 = \bar{q}_1 & p_1 = \bar{p}_1 \\ q_2 = \bar{q}_2 & p_2 = \bar{p}_2. \\ \dots & \dots \end{array}$$

The function

$$V = q_1\bar{p}_1 \pm q_1\bar{p}_2 + q_2\bar{p}_2$$

gives, after solving (2) for p_k and q_k, the transformation

$$\begin{array}{ll} q_1 = \bar{q}_1 & p_1 = \bar{p}_1 \pm \bar{p}_2 \\ q_2 = \bar{q}_2 \mp \bar{q}_1 & p_2 = \bar{p}_2 \end{array} \tag{6}$$

and the function

$$V = q_1\bar{p}_1 + q_1\bar{p}_2 + q_2\bar{p}_1 - q_2\bar{p}_2$$

leads to

$$\begin{array}{ll} q_1 = \tfrac{1}{2}(\bar{q}_1 + \bar{q}_2) & p_1 = \bar{p}_1 + \bar{p}_2 \\ q_2 = \tfrac{1}{2}(\bar{q}_1 - \bar{q}_2) & p_2 = \bar{p}_1 - \bar{p}_2. \end{array} \tag{7}$$

A transformation for three pairs of variables is provided by

$$V = q_1\bar{p}_1 + q_1\bar{p}_2 + q_1\bar{p}_3 + q_2\bar{p}_2 + q_2\bar{p}_3 + q_3\bar{p}_3$$

namely

$$\begin{array}{ll} q_1 = \bar{q}_1 & p_1 = \bar{p}_1 + \bar{p}_2 + \bar{p}_3 \\ q_2 = \bar{q}_2 - \bar{q}_1 & p_2 = \bar{p}_2 + \bar{p}_3 \\ q_3 = \bar{q}_3 - \bar{q}_2 & p_3 = \bar{p}_3. \end{array} \tag{8}$$

In all of these examples the co-ordinates and the momenta are kept separate in the transformation. The general necessary and sufficient condition for this is clearly, that V shall be linear in the q's and $\bar{p}$'s:

$$V = \sum_{i,k} \alpha_{ik} q_i \bar{p}_k + \sum_k \beta_k q_k + \sum_k \gamma_k \bar{p}_k.$$

This function gives

$$\begin{aligned} p_i &= \sum_k \alpha_{ik} \bar{p}_k + \beta_i \\ \bar{q}_i &= \sum_k \alpha_{ki} q_k + \gamma_i. \end{aligned} \tag{9}$$

If the constants β_i and γ_i are zero we have a transformation which transforms the q_k's and p_k's linearly and homogeneously into the $\bar{q}_k$ and $\bar{p}_k$, viz.:

$$\sum_k p_k q_k = \sum_{k,l} a_{kl} \bar{p}_l q_k = \sum_l \bar{q}_l \bar{p}_l.$$

The necessary and sufficient condition that the q_k's shall transform among themselves is the linearity of V in the $\bar{p}_k$'s. In fact

$$V = \sum_k f_k(q_1, q_2 \ldots) \bar{p}_k + g(q_1, q_2 \ldots)$$

provides the transformation:

$$p_k = \sum_l \frac{\partial f_l}{\partial q_k} \bar{p}_l + \frac{\partial g}{\partial q_k} \tag{10}$$
$$\bar{q}_k = f_k(q_1, q_2 \ldots).$$

Linearity of V in the q_k's gives, on the other hand, a transformation of the momenta between themselves;

$$V = \sum_k f_k(\bar{p}_1, \bar{p}_2 \ldots) q_k + g(\bar{p}_1, \bar{p}_2 \ldots)$$

leads to

$$p_k = f_k(\bar{p}_1, \bar{p}_2 \ldots)$$
$$\bar{q}_k = \sum_l \frac{\partial f_l}{\partial \bar{p}_k} q_l + \frac{\partial g}{\partial \bar{p}_k}. \tag{11}$$

It appears if the variables of the one kind transform among themselves, the new variables of the second kind will be linear functions of the old variables of the second kind, the coefficients of which will be determined functions of the variables of the first kind, and the free terms arbitrary functions of the variables of the first kind.

Transformations of the co-ordinates among themselves which are frequently employed are those which transform rectangular co-ordinates into cylindrical or polar co-ordinates, and also those which correspond to rotations of the co-ordinate system.

The function

$$V = p_x r \cos\phi + p_y r \sin\phi + p_z z$$

transforms rectangular co-ordinates into cylindrical co-ordinates. It gives

$$\begin{aligned} x &= r\cos\phi & p_r &= p_x \cos\phi + p_y \sin\phi \\ y &= r\sin\phi & p_\phi &= -p_x r \sin\phi + p_y r \cos\phi \\ z &= z & p_z &= p_z. \end{aligned} \tag{12}$$

The expression

$$p_x^2 + p_y^2$$

then becomes

$$p_r^2+\frac{1}{r^2}p_\phi^2.$$

In transforming to spatial polar co-ordinates we take

$$V=p_x r\cos\phi\sin\theta+p_y r\sin\phi\sin\theta+p_z r\cos\theta.$$

This function leads to the transformation

$$(13)\qquad \begin{aligned} x&=r\cos\phi\sin\theta\\ y&=r\sin\phi\sin\theta\\ z&=r\cos\theta\\ p_r&=p_x\cos\phi\sin\theta+p_y\sin\phi\sin\theta+p_z\cos\theta\\ p_\phi&=-p_x r\sin\phi\sin\theta+p_y r\cos\phi\sin\theta\\ p_\theta&=p_x r\cos\phi\cos\theta+p_y r\sin\phi\sin\theta-p_z r\sin\partial \end{aligned}$$

and transforms the expression

$$p_x^2+p_y^2+p_z^2$$

into

$$p_r^2+\frac{1}{r^2}p_\theta^2+\frac{1}{r^2\sin^2\theta}p_\phi^2.$$

A rotation of the rectangular co-ordinate system (x, y, z) involves a linear transformation of the co-ordinates with constant coefficients. The momenta transform then contravariantly. In this case, where the coefficients α_{ik} defining the rotation fulfil the conditions

$$\sum_j \alpha_{ij}\alpha_{kj}=\begin{cases}1 & (i=k)\\ 0 & (i\neq k)\end{cases}$$

the contravariant transformation is equivalent to the original one. The momenta transform like the co-ordinates ; we have

$$(14)\qquad \begin{aligned} \bar{x}&=\alpha_{11}x+\alpha_{12}y+\alpha_{13}z & \bar{p}_x&=\alpha_{11}p_x+\alpha_{12}p_y+\alpha_{13}p_z\\ \bar{y}&=\alpha_{21}x+\alpha_{22}y+\alpha_{23}z & \bar{p}_y&=\alpha_{21}p_x+\alpha_{22}p_y+\alpha_{23}p_z\\ \bar{z}&=\alpha_{31}x+\alpha_{32}y+\alpha_{33}z & \bar{p}_z&=\alpha_{31}p_x+\alpha_{32}p_y+\alpha_{33}p_z, \end{aligned}$$

and

$$p_x^2+p_y^2+p_z^2=\bar{p}_x^2+\bar{p}_y^2+\bar{p}_z^2.$$

We give two further transformations, for which V depends on q_k and $\bar{q}_k$. The function

$$V=\sum_k q_k\bar{q}_k$$

gives, by (1),

$$\begin{aligned} q_k&=-\bar{p}_k\\ p_k&=\bar{q}_k. \end{aligned}$$

It therefore interchanges co-ordinates and momenta.

A transformation frequently employed is given by

$$V=\tfrac{1}{2}q^2\cot\bar{q}\,;$$

it leads to

(15)
$$q=\sqrt{2\bar{p}}\sin\bar{q}$$
$$p=\sqrt{2\bar{p}}\cos\bar{q}$$

and transforms the expression q^2+p^2 into $2\bar{p}$. The somewhat more general function

(16)
$$V=\frac{m}{2}\omega q^2\cot\bar{q}$$

gives

(16′)
$$q=\sqrt{\frac{2\bar{p}}{m\omega}}\sin\bar{q}$$
$$p=\sqrt{2m\omega\bar{p}}\cos\bar{q}$$

and transforms

$$\frac{1}{2m}p^2+\frac{m\omega^2}{2}q^2$$

into $\omega\bar{p}$.

We shall illustrate now, by means of an example, how the canonical substitutions can be used to integrate the equations of motion.

Linear Harmonic Oscillator.—In this case

$$T=\frac{m}{2}\dot{q}^2, \qquad U=\frac{\chi}{2}q^2;$$

where q denotes the displacement, m the mass, and χ the elastic constant. Introducing the momentum

$$p=m\dot{q}$$

and putting

$$\frac{\chi}{m}=\omega^2,$$

we get

(17)
$$H=\frac{1}{2m}p^2+\frac{m\omega^2}{2}q^2.$$

The transformation last mentioned (16) applies then to this case. We call the new variables ϕ and a and write:

(18)
$$q=\sqrt{\frac{2a}{m\omega}}\sin\phi$$
$$p=\sqrt{2m\omega a}\cos\phi.$$

The Hamiltonian function then becomes

$$H=\omega a;$$

and the equations of motion give

$$\alpha = \text{constant}$$
$$\phi = \omega t + \beta.$$

The displacement q will therefore be given by

$$q = \sqrt{\frac{2\alpha}{m\omega}} \sin(\omega t + \beta).$$

The canonical transformations are characterised by the fact that they leave invariant the form of the equations of motion, or the stationary character of the integral [(6) of § 5] expressing Hamilton's principle. This raises the question whether there are still other invariants in the case of canonical transformations. This is in fact the case, and we shall give here a series of integral invariants introduced by Poincaré.[1]

We can show that the integral

$$J_1 = \iint \sum_k dp_k dq_k, \tag{19}$$

taken over an arbitrary two-dimensional manifold of the $2f$-dimensional (p, q) space, is such an invariant. If we represent the two-dimensional manifold by taking p_k and q_k as functions of two parameters u and v, then

$$J_1 = \iint \sum_k \begin{vmatrix} \dfrac{\partial p_k}{\partial u} & \dfrac{\partial q_k}{\partial u} \\ \dfrac{\partial p_k}{\partial v} & \dfrac{\partial q_k}{\partial v} \end{vmatrix} du\, dv.$$

We prove the invariant character of J_1 by showing that

$$\sum_k \begin{vmatrix} \dfrac{\partial \bar{p}_k}{\partial u} & \dfrac{\partial \bar{q}_k}{\partial u} \\ \dfrac{\partial \bar{p}_k}{\partial v} & \dfrac{\partial \bar{q}_k}{\partial v} \end{vmatrix} = \sum_k \begin{vmatrix} \dfrac{\partial p_k}{\partial u} & \dfrac{\partial q_k}{\partial u} \\ \dfrac{\partial p_k}{\partial v} & \dfrac{\partial q_k}{\partial v} \end{vmatrix}$$

provided that $\bar{p}_k$ and $\bar{q}_k$ are derived from q_k, p_k by a canonical transformation. We write the transformation in the form (2)

$$p_k = \frac{\partial V(q_1, \bar{p}_1 \ldots t)}{\partial q_k}$$
$$\bar{q}_k = \frac{\partial V(q_1, \bar{p}_1 \ldots t)}{\partial \bar{p}_k}$$

[1] H. Poincaré, *Méthodes nouvelles de la mécanique céleste*, vol. iii. ch. xxii–xxiv (Paris, 1899); proof of the invariance by E. Brody, *Zeitschr. f. Physik*, vol. vi, p. 224, 1921.

and replace q_k, p_k by $q_k, \bar{p}_k$ with the help of the first equation; then

$$\sum_k \begin{vmatrix} \frac{\partial p_k}{\partial u} & \frac{\partial q_k}{\partial u} \\ \frac{\partial p_k}{\partial v} & \frac{\partial q_k}{\partial v} \end{vmatrix} = \sum_k \begin{vmatrix} \sum_i \frac{\partial^2 V}{\partial q_k \partial \bar{p}_i} \cdot \frac{\partial \bar{p}_i}{\partial u} & \frac{\partial q_k}{\partial u} \\ \sum_i \frac{\partial^2 V}{\partial q_k \partial \bar{p}_i} \cdot \frac{\partial \bar{p}_i}{\partial v} & \frac{\partial q_k}{\partial v} \end{vmatrix}$$

$$= \sum_{ik} \frac{\partial^2 V}{\partial q_k \partial \bar{p}_i} \begin{vmatrix} \frac{\partial \bar{p}_i}{\partial u} & \frac{\partial q_k}{\partial u} \\ \frac{\partial \bar{p}_i}{\partial v} & \frac{\partial q_k}{\partial v} \end{vmatrix}.$$

Interchanging the indices k, i, this becomes

$$\sum_{ik} \frac{\partial^2 V}{\partial q_i \partial \bar{p}_k} \begin{vmatrix} \frac{\partial \bar{p}_k}{\partial u} & \frac{\partial q_i}{\partial u} \\ \frac{\partial \bar{p}_k}{\partial v} & \frac{\partial q_i}{\partial v} \end{vmatrix},$$

and we now transform $q_k, \bar{p}_k$ into $\bar{q}_k, \bar{p}_k$ by means of the second equation of transformation; the integrand becomes equal to

$$\sum_k \begin{vmatrix} \frac{\partial \bar{p}_k}{\partial u} & \sum_i \frac{\partial^2 V}{\partial \bar{p}_k \partial q_i} \cdot \frac{\partial q_i}{\partial u} \\ \frac{\partial \bar{p}_k}{\partial v} & \sum_i \frac{\partial^2 V}{\partial \bar{p}_k \partial q_i} \cdot \frac{\partial q_i}{\partial v} \end{vmatrix} = \sum_k \begin{vmatrix} \frac{\partial \bar{p}_k}{\partial u} & \frac{\partial \bar{q}_k}{\partial u} \\ \frac{\partial \bar{p}_k}{\partial v} & \frac{\partial \bar{q}_k}{\partial v} \end{vmatrix},$$

proving the invariance of the integral (19).

The invariance of the integral

$$J_2 = \iiiint \sum dp_i dp_k dq_i dq_k$$

in which every combination of two indices occurs in the integrand, may be proved in a precisely similar way. The same holds true for

$$J_3 = \iiiiiint \sum dp_i dp_k dp_l dq_i dq_k dq_l$$

and so on. The last integral of the series is

$$J_f = \int \dots \int dp_i \dots dp_f dq_i \dots dq_f.$$

The volume in the phase space is consequently invariant with respect to a canonical transformation.

§ 8.—The Hamilton-Jacobi Differential Equation

The idea underlying the method of integration which is so particularly suited to the problems of atomic mechanics (just as it is to those of celestial mechanics) will be clear from the example of the oscillator given in § 7. Although it appears very awkward in this case, yet, on the other hand, it is powerful enough to lead to the required end even for some quite complicated (particularly periodic) motions. We shall now give a general formulation for the case in which the Hamiltonian function does not contain the time explicitly: We endeavour to transform the variables q_k, p_k, by means of a canonical transformation, into new variables ϕ_k, α_k in such a way that the Hamiltonian function depends only on the quantities α_k, which correspond to the momenta. For this purpose the most suitable form of the canonical transformations is (2), § 7. We seek therefore to determine a function

$$S(q_1, q_2 \ldots \alpha_1, \alpha_2 \ldots)$$

such that, by means of the transformation

$$(1) \qquad \begin{aligned} p_k &= \frac{\partial}{\partial q_k} S(q_1, q_2 \ldots \alpha_1, \alpha_2 \ldots) \\ \phi_k &= \frac{\partial}{\partial \alpha_k} S(q_1, q_2 \ldots \alpha_1, \alpha_2 \ldots) \end{aligned}$$

H is transformed into a function

$$W(\alpha_1, \alpha_2 \ldots)$$

depending only on the α_k's. The ϕ_k's are then cyclic variables and the equations of motion lead at once to the solution

$$(2) \qquad \begin{aligned} &\alpha_k = \text{constant} \\ &\phi_k = \omega_k t + \beta_k, \qquad \omega_k = \frac{\partial W}{\partial \alpha_k}. \end{aligned}$$

The determination of the function S can be made to depend on the solution of a partial differential equation of the first order. A particular case of some importance is given by taking W equal to α_1; let each p_k in H be replaced by the corresponding $\frac{\partial S}{\partial q_k}$, then S has to satisfy the condition

$$(3) \qquad H\left(q_1, q_2 \ldots q_f, \frac{\partial S}{\partial q_1}, \frac{\partial S}{\partial q_2}, \ldots, \frac{\partial S}{\partial q_f}\right) = \alpha_1.$$

This equation is known as the Hamilton-Jacobi differential equation. The problem is now to find a complete solution, *i.e.* a solution which involves α_1 and $f-1$ other constants of integration $\alpha_2, \alpha_3 \ldots \alpha_f$, apart from the purely additive constant in S. This function S provides a transformation (1) of the kind desired; at the same time the following special relations hold,

$$\omega_1=\frac{\partial W}{\partial \alpha_1}=1\,; \qquad \omega_2=\omega_3=\cdots=\omega_f=0.$$

The solution of the equations of motion will then be given by the solution of (1) in terms of q_k and p_k, if the substitutions

$$\begin{aligned} &\alpha_k=\text{constant}\\ &\phi_1=t+\beta_1\\ (4)\qquad &\phi_2=\beta_2\\ &\cdot\quad\cdot\quad\cdot\quad\cdot\\ &\phi_f=\beta_f \end{aligned}$$

are made.

The problem of solving the system of $2f$ *ordinary* differential equations of the first order, *i.e.* the canonical equations, is therefore equivalent to that of finding a complete solution of the *partial* differential equation (3) (f being greater than 1). This is a special case of general theorems on the relation between ordinary and partial differential equations.

For many purposes it is more advantageous not to single out one of the α's, as has just been done. A canonical transformation may be carried out, in which the α_k's transform into a like number of new variables, which we shall also call $\alpha_1 \ldots \alpha_f$, in such a way that the ϕ_k's do not enter into the relations between the old and new α_k's. α_1 is transformed into

$$W(\alpha_1, \alpha_2 \ldots \alpha_f).$$

According to a theorem proved in § 7 (equation (11)), new variables ϕ_k can be introduced, which are conjugated with the α_k's and are linear functions of the old ϕ_k's with coefficients depending only on the constants α_k. Thus the new ϕ_k's are likewise linear functions of the time and the equations of motion hold in the form (2).

The function S may be regarded as a solution of the differential equation

$$(5)\qquad H\left(q_1, q_2 \ldots \frac{\partial S}{\partial q_1}, \frac{\partial S}{\partial q_2} \ldots\right)=W,$$

depending on f constants $\alpha_1 \ldots \alpha_f$, between which and W a relation

$$W=W(\alpha_1 \ldots \alpha_f)$$

exists. By (5) the transformation (1) transforms the function H into the function $W(\alpha_1 \ldots \alpha_f)$, and we have here also

$$\omega_k=\frac{\partial W}{\partial \alpha_k}.$$

An important property of the function S can be derived from (1), namely, that for a path defined by fixed values of the α_k's

$$dS=\sum_k \frac{\partial S}{\partial q_k} dq_k=\sum_k p_k dq_k.$$

S is therefore the line integral

$$S=\int_{Q_0}^{Q} \sum_k p_k dq_k \tag{6}$$

taken along the path, where Q_0 denotes a fixed and Q a moving point of the path.

In the case of classical mechanics, and for a system of co-ordinates at rest, this integral has a simple significance. For in this case we have (see (8), § 5)

$$2T=\sum_k p_k \dot{q}_k,$$

and thus

$$S=2\int_{t_0}^{t} T dt. \tag{7}$$

In the case of the theory of relativity, if we take a single particle, 2T must be replaced by

$$T+T^*=m_0 v^2\left(1-\frac{v^2}{c^2}\right)^{-\frac{1}{2}}.$$

It will be seen that in both cases S is a function continuously increasing with the time, it is called the Principal Function of the system.

We will now consider the simplest case, namely, that of one degree of freedom. Then the differential equation (5) becomes an ordinary one

$$H(q, p)=H\left(q, \frac{\partial S}{\partial q}\right)=W.$$

Solving for p as a function of q and W, and integrating with respect to q, since

$$p=\frac{\partial S}{\partial q},$$

we find

$$S=\int_{q_0}^{q} p(q, W) dq.$$

This can also be regarded as a special case of the general formula (6). The function S determined in this way, which contains no constants apart from W, providès the general solution of the equations of motion; we have

$$\phi=\int_{q_0}^{q}\frac{\partial p(q, W)}{\partial W}dq=t-t_0,$$

which, on solution, gives q as a function of the time with the constants of integration W and t_0.

For co-ordinate systems at rest T has the form

$$T=\frac{p^2}{2\mu},$$

where μ denotes mass, moment of inertia, or some such quantity. We have then

$$H=\frac{p^2}{2\mu}+U(q)=W,$$

so the solution for p in terms of q and W is

$$p=\sqrt{2\mu}\sqrt{W-U(q)}, \tag{8}$$

and

$$S=\int_{q_0}^{q}p(q, W)dq=\sqrt{2\mu}\int_{q_0}^{q}\sqrt{W-U(q)}dq$$

$$t-t_0=\sqrt{\frac{\mu}{2}}\int_{q_0}^{q}\frac{dq}{\sqrt{W-U(q)}}. \tag{9}$$

Example 1.—*Particle falling freely or projected vertically.* Here q denotes the height of the moving body and μ the mass. The potential energy is

$$U=\mu gq,$$

where g is the constant of gravitational acceleration. Then we have

$$t-t_0=\sqrt{\frac{\mu}{2}}\int_{q_0}^{q}\frac{dq}{\sqrt{W-\mu gq}}=-\frac{\sqrt{2}}{g\sqrt{\mu}}\sqrt{W-\mu gq},$$

where q_0 is taken equal to $\frac{W}{\mu g}$; q_0 obviously denotes the maximum height attained, and t_0 the instant at which it is attained. On solving for q we obtain the well-known formula

$$q-q_0=-\frac{g}{2}(t-t_0)^2.$$

Example 2.—*The Pendulum.* Here q denotes the angular displacement and μ=A the moment of inertia of the pendulum. The potential energy, reckoned from $q=\pi/2$ as zero, is

$$U=-D\cos q.$$

We find

(10) $$p=\sqrt{2A}\sqrt{W+D\cos q},$$

$$t-t_0=\sqrt{\frac{A}{2}}\int_0^q\frac{dq}{\sqrt{W+D\cos q}}=\sqrt{\frac{A}{2}}\int_0^q\frac{dq}{\sqrt{W+D-2D\sin^2\frac{1}{2}q}},$$

and if we put

$$W+D=2D\sin^2\frac{a}{2},$$

then

$$t-t_0=\frac{1}{2}\sqrt{\frac{A}{D}}\int_0^q\frac{dq}{\sqrt{\sin^2\frac{a}{2}-\sin^2\frac{q}{2}}}.$$

The solution of this equation, which involves an elliptic integral, gives q as a function periodic in time, and oscillating between $+a$ and $-a$. For sufficiently small values of a we can write

$$t-t_0=\sqrt{\frac{A}{D}}\int_0^q\frac{dq}{\sqrt{a^2-q^2}}$$

and obtain the solution in a simple form. We have

$$t-t_0=\sqrt{\frac{A}{D}}\sin^{-1}\frac{q}{a}$$

or

$$q=a\sin\left[\sqrt{\frac{D}{A}}(t-t_0)\right].$$

Clearly all problems for which every co-ordinate, with the exception of one, is cyclic, reduce to the case of one degree of freedom. Let

$$H=H(q_1, p_1, p_2 \ldots p_f),$$

the solution will then be represented by

$$p_2=\alpha_2 \ldots p_f=\alpha_f$$

and

$$S=\int p_1(q_1, W, \alpha_2 \ldots \alpha_f)dq_1,$$

where p_1 is found by solving

(11) $$H(q_1, p_1, \alpha_2 \ldots \alpha_f)=W.$$

Therefore

(11′)
$$t-t_0=\int\frac{\partial}{\partial W}p_1(q_1, W, \alpha_2 \ldots \alpha_f)dq_1$$
$$\beta_k=\int\frac{\partial}{\partial\alpha_k}p_1(q_1, W, \alpha_2 \ldots \alpha_f)dq_1 \quad (k=2, 3 \ldots f).$$

Example 3.—*Projectile Motion.* Let $q_1=z$ be the vertical co-ordinate, reckoned positively upwards, and $q_2=x$, $q_3=y$ the horizontal co-ordinates, then

$$T=\frac{m}{2}(\dot{x}^2+\dot{y}^2+\dot{z}^2)$$

$$U=mgz,$$

and

$$W=H=\frac{1}{2m}(p_x{}^2+p_y{}^2+p_z{}^2)+mgz.$$

Since x and y are cyclic variables, we put

$$p_x=\alpha_2, \qquad p_y=\alpha_3$$

and obtain

$$p_z=[2m(W-mgz)-\alpha_2{}^2-\alpha_3{}^2]^{\frac{1}{2}}$$

$$t-t_0=\int_{z_0}^{z}\frac{mdz}{[2m(W-mgz)-\alpha_2{}^2-\alpha_3{}^2]^{\frac{1}{2}}}=-\sqrt{\frac{2}{g}}(z_0-z)^{\frac{1}{2}},$$

z_0 being given by

$$2mW-\alpha_2{}^2-\alpha_3{}^2=2m^2gz_0.$$

It follows from this that

$$z-z_0=-\frac{g}{2}(t-t_0)^2.$$

The two other equations of motion follow most simply from

$$m\dot{x}=p_x=\alpha_2, \qquad m\dot{y}=p_y=\alpha_3.$$

We find

$$x-x_0=\frac{\alpha_2}{m}(t-t_0)$$

$$y-y_0=\frac{\alpha_3}{m}(t-t_0).$$

Elimination of t from the three equations of motion gives the equations of the path, which is, of course, a parabola :

$$z-z_0=-\frac{g}{2}\frac{m^2}{\alpha_2{}^2}(x-x_0)^2$$

$$z-z_0=-\frac{g}{2}\frac{m^2}{\alpha_3{}^2}(y-y_0)^2.$$

These results could also have been found from the second of equations (11′), without making use of relations involving the time.

Example 4.—*Heavy Symmetrical Top.* In § 6 we found for the kinetic energy

$$T=\frac{1}{2A_x}\left[p_\theta{}^2+\left(\frac{p_\psi-p_\phi\cos\theta}{\sin\theta}\right)^2\right]+\frac{p_\phi{}^2}{2A_z};$$

and now, in addition to this, let there be the potential energy

$$U=D\cos\theta,$$

so that

$$H=\frac{1}{2A_x}\left[p_\theta{}^2+\left(\frac{p_\psi-p_\phi\cos\theta}{\sin\theta}\right)^2\right]+\frac{p_\phi{}^2}{2A_z}+D\cos\theta.$$

Since ϕ and ψ are cyclic variables, we have

(12) $$p_\phi = \alpha_2, \quad p_\psi = \alpha_3$$

and

$$p_\theta = \left[2A_x W - \left(\frac{\alpha_3 - \alpha_2 \cos\theta}{\sin\theta}\right)^2 - \frac{\alpha_2{}^2 A_x}{A_z} - 2A_x D\cos\theta\right]^{\frac{1}{2}}.$$

In the equation for t we put $\cos\theta = u$, and obtain

(13) $$t - t_0 = -\int \frac{du}{F^{\frac{1}{2}}},$$

where

$$F = \frac{1}{A_x{}^2}\left[(1-u^2)\left(2A_x W - \frac{A_x}{A_z}\alpha_2{}^2 - 2A_x Du\right) - (\alpha_3 - \alpha_2 u)^2\right];$$

this is a cubic in u, so the solution of (13) involves elliptic integrals.

The Eulerian angles ϕ and ψ may be expressed by similar elliptic integrals. If, for example, we solve the equations (3), § 6, for $\dot\phi$ and $\dot\psi$, we obtain, taking (12) into account,

$$\dot\phi = \alpha_2\left(\frac{1}{A_z} - \frac{1}{A_x}\right) + \frac{\alpha_2 - \alpha_3\cos\theta}{A_x \sin^2\theta}$$

$$\dot\psi = \frac{\alpha_3 - \alpha_2\cos\theta}{A_x\sin^2\theta}.$$

and

(14) $$\phi = \int \dot\phi\, dt = \alpha_2\left(\frac{1}{A_z} - \frac{1}{A_x}\right)t - \int \frac{\alpha_2 - \alpha_3 u}{A_x(1-u^2)}\frac{du}{F^{\frac{1}{2}}}$$
$$\psi = \int \dot\psi\, dt = \int \frac{\alpha_3 - \alpha_2 u}{A_x(1-u^2)}\frac{du}{F^{\frac{1}{2}}}.$$

The evaluation the integral type (13) gives $u = \cos\theta$ as a periodic function of the time. It oscillates backwards and forwards between two zero points of F, which enclose an interval in which F is positive. If α_2 is not precisely equal to α_3, we have

$$F(-1) = -\frac{1}{A_x{}^2}(\alpha_3 + \alpha_2)^2$$

and

$$F(1) = -\frac{1}{A_x{}^2}(\alpha_3 - \alpha_2)^2$$

both negative. If a motion is to be possible at all it follows that, somewhere in the interval $(-1, +1)$, F must not be negative; it has then two zero points u_1 and u_2 which may coincide. If the zero points are different, it means that the point of intersection of the axis of the top with a sphere, described about the centre of the top, oscillates backwards and forwards between two parallel circles. It describes a curve shown in fig. 1. In the case of the double root our equations (13) and (14) fail, but the motion can be easily calculated in an elementary manner: θ is then a constant, and we have the case of a regular precession.

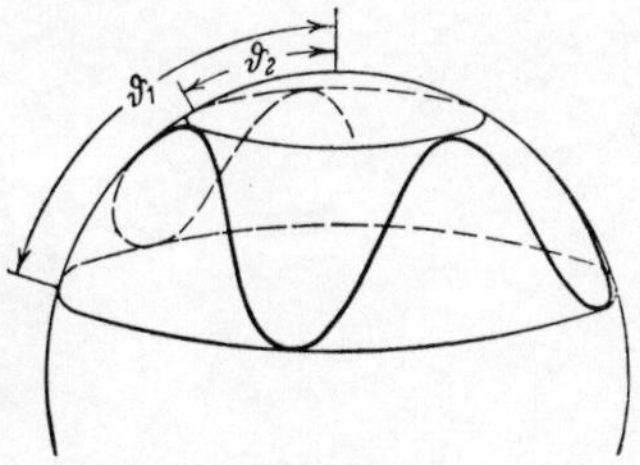

FIG. 1.

A general rule for the rigorous solution of the Hamilton-Jacobi differential equation (5) cannot be given. In many cases a solution is obtained on the supposition that S can be represented as the sum of f functions, each of which depends on only one of the co-ordinates q (and, of course, on the integration constants $\alpha_1 \ldots \alpha_f$):

$$S = S_1(q_1) + \ldots + S_f(q_f). \tag{15}$$

The partial differential equation (5) then resolves into f ordinary differential equations of the form

$$F_k\left(\frac{dS_k}{dq_k}, q_k\right) = \alpha_k,$$

or, if we solve for $\frac{dS_k}{dq_k}$,

$$\frac{dS_k}{dq_k} = p_k(q_k, \alpha_k).$$

The differential equation (5) is said in this case to be soluble by separation of the variables, or, for short, to be separable.

The case dealt with above, where all co-ordinates with the exception of one (q_1) are cyclic, can be regarded as a special case of this. We make the hypothesis

$$S = S_1(q_1, \alpha_1 \ldots \alpha_f) + \alpha_2 q_2 + \ldots + \alpha_f q_f,$$

and the differential equation becomes

$$H\left(q_1, \frac{\partial S}{\partial q_1} \ldots \frac{\partial S}{\partial q_f}\right) = H\left(q_1, \frac{dS_1}{dq_1}, \alpha_2 \ldots \alpha_f\right) = W,$$

which agrees exactly with (11).

SECOND CHAPTER

PERIODIC AND MULTIPLY PERIODIC MOTIONS

§ 9.—Periodic Motions with One Degree of Freedom

We have seen that, in the case of systems of one degree of freedom, new variables ϕ, α can be introduced in place of the variables q, p, such that α is constant and ϕ is a linear function of the time. The variables ϕ and α are not, however, determined uniquely in this way; we can in fact replace α by an arbitrary function of α, whilst ϕ is multiplied by a factor dependent on α.

For periodic motions it is an advantage to make a perfectly definite choice of ϕ and α. Now there are two kinds of periodicity. Either different values of q correspond to different positions of the system and q and p are periodic functions of the time, and also of the variable ϕ which is linearly connected with the time, in which case there is a quantity $\tilde{\omega}$ such that

$$q(\phi+\tilde{\omega})=q(\phi),$$

for all values of q; or else the configuration of the system is the same for any two values of q differing by a constant quantity, which we shall take to be 2π. This increase in q of amount 2π always takes place during the same time, and then

$$q(\phi+\tilde{\omega})=q(\phi)+2\pi.$$

In the first case we speak of libration, in the second of rotation. Examples of these are the oscillating pendulum and the rotating pendulum respectively (see below).

In both cases we shall choose ϕ in a particular way, namely, in such a way that it increases by 1 during one period of the motion, in which case we shall denote it by w. Let the corresponding conjugated variable be J. We call w an angle variable and J an action variable.

If we consider S to be a function of q and J, then

$$w=\frac{\partial S(q, J)}{\partial J}$$

(*cf.* (1), § 8, remembering that w and J are particular examples of the quantities there written ϕ and α), and the differential quotient of w along the path is

$$\frac{dw}{dq}=\frac{\partial}{\partial J}\left(\frac{\partial S}{\partial q}\right).$$

That the period of w shall be 1 therefore implies that

$$\oint dw=\frac{\partial}{\partial J}\oint\frac{\partial S}{\partial q}dq=\frac{\partial}{\partial J}\oint pdq=1,$$

where the symbol $\oint$ denotes that the integration is to be extended over one period, *i.e.* in the case of libration, over one back and forward motion of q, and in the case of a rotation, over a path of length 2π.

We can clearly satisfy this requirement by putting

$$J=\oint\frac{\partial S}{\partial q}dq=\oint pdq, \tag{1}$$

or, in other words, by making J equal to the increase of S during one period.[1]

The variables w, J may therefore be introduced in the following way. If H is given as a function of some canonical variables q, p, the action function

$$S=S(q,\ \alpha)$$

is determined by integration of the Hamilton-Jacobi equation, and the integral

$$J=\oint\frac{\partial S}{\partial q}dq$$

is calculated as a function of α or W. J is then introduced into S in place of α or W.

By means of the transformation

$$p=\frac{\partial S(q,\ J)}{\partial q}, \qquad w=\frac{\partial S(q,\ J)}{\partial J} \tag{2}$$

[1] $\oint pdq=J+\text{constant}$ would also satisfy the condition. The general transformation

$$(\phi,\ \alpha)\rightarrow(w,\ J)$$

which satisfies the periodicity conditions postulated contains in fact another arbitrary constant in addition to the phases constant for w. Its generator is

$$V=\pm\frac{\phi J}{\bar{\omega}}+c_1\phi+c_2J.$$

The method for determining J given above is equivalent to putting $c_1=0$; it is particularly useful in the quantum theory.

p and q will become periodic functions of w with the period 1, and H will be a function W of J alone. From the canonical equations it follows that for any one possible motion of the system

$$J = \text{constant}$$

and

$$\dot{w} = \frac{dW}{dJ} = \nu \tag{3}$$

$$w = \nu t + \beta.$$

Since we have chosen w so that it increases by 1 during each period of the motion, it follows that W is a function which increases continuously with J; ν must be a positive number, it is equal to the number of periods in unit time, or the frequency of the motion.

If the variable ϕ conjugate to α is already known, J can be found from the equation

$$J = \oint \alpha d\phi = \pm \alpha \tilde{\omega}.$$

The equations of transformation are then

$$J = \pm \tilde{\omega} \alpha, \qquad w = \pm \frac{\phi}{\tilde{\omega}}.$$

A consequence of the above determination of J as the increase in S during one period, is that the function

$$S^* = S - wJ \tag{4}$$

is a periodic function of w with the period 1. Conversely this requirement may also be used for the unique determination of the magnitude J, which is fixed except for an additive constant by $\oint dw = 1$, in which case equation (1) is obtained. In place of S the function S* can be regarded as the generator of the canonical transformation which transforms q and p into w and J. Comparing the transformation equations (2) with equations (2) of § 7, it will be seen that S satisfies the equation

$$p\dot{q} = -w\dot{J} + \frac{dS}{dt},$$

whence

$$p\dot{q} = J\dot{w} + \frac{dS^*}{dt},$$

and this implies that S* is the generator of the transformation

$$\begin{aligned} p &= \frac{\partial}{\partial q} S^*(q, w) \\ J &= -\frac{\partial}{\partial w} S^*(q, w). \end{aligned} \tag{5}$$

The calculation of the integral J necessitates study of the connection between q and p as given by the equation

$$\text{H}(q, p)=\text{W}. \tag{6}$$

Let this relation be represented by a family of curves with the parameter W in the (p, q) plane. The cases of libration and rotation are then represented by two typical figures (figs. 2 and 3).

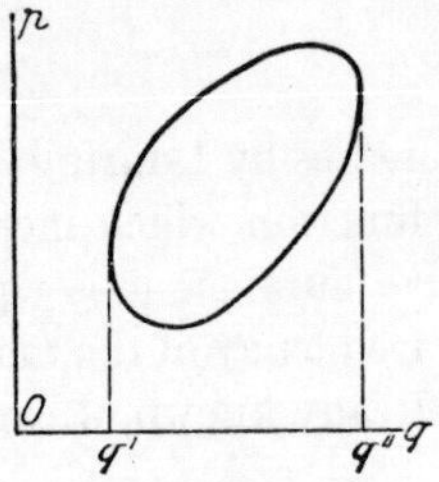

FIG. 2.

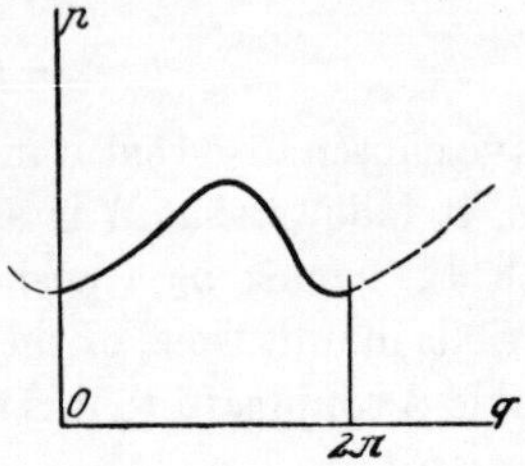

FIG. 3.

In the case of libration a closed branch of the curve (6) must exist, and J denotes the enclosed area, which, by (19), § 7, is a canonical invariant.

For rotation, p must be a periodic function of q with period 2π, and J denotes the area between the curve, the q-axis, and two ordinates at a distance 2π apart.

For the purpose of illustration we shall deal with the case of classical mechanics on the assumption of a co-ordinate system at rest. By (8), § 8,

$$p=\sqrt{2\mu}\sqrt{\text{W}-\text{U}(q)}.$$

In order that libration may occur, the expression under the square root must have two zeros, q' and q'' between which it is positive ; then p vanishes only at the limits of the interval (q', q''). In order that a closed loop may be formed from the two branches of the curve (6), it is further necessary that $\frac{dp}{dq}$ shall be infinite at q' and q''. Now

$$\frac{dp}{dq}=-\sqrt{\frac{\mu}{2}}\{\text{W}-\text{U}(q)\}^{-\frac{1}{2}}\cdot\frac{d\text{U}}{dq};$$

the condition is therefore fulfilled, provided $\frac{d\text{U}}{dq}$ is not at the same time zero, *i.e.* provided q', q'' are simple roots of the expression under the root sign. In this case the resulting curve, which is symmetrical about the q axis, will be traversed completely, and always in the same sense. Then, by (8), § 5,

$$p\dot{q}=2\text{T},$$

and thus pdq is always positive ; therefore on the outward journey ($dq>0$) the upper branch ($p>0$) will be traversed, and in the return journey ($dq<0$) the lower branch ($p<0$) will be followed. The co-ordinate q traverses the whole region between the zero points q' and q'' ; these zero points form the limits of libration.

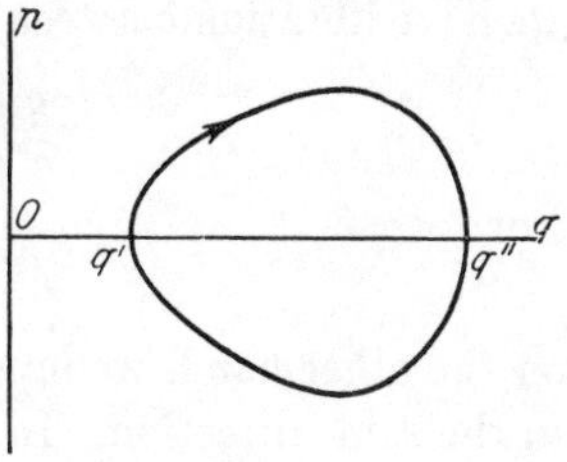

FIG. 4.

If W be varied, the corresponding curves lie within one another, without intersecting. If W be decreased, the zero points move towards one another and converge to a point, provided no new zero points occur between them. This point we call the libration centre ; at it

$$\frac{dU}{dq}=0.$$

It corresponds to a state of stable equilibrium of the system, since the movement resulting from slight alteration of the initial conditions remains in its vicinity. If new zero points occur between q' and q'', they coincide at their first appearance as W is decreased, and here too

$$\frac{dU}{dq}=0.$$

In this case the state of equilibrium is unstable, since, for a small variation of W, the motion does not remain in the immediate vicinity of the equilibrium position.

If W be increased it may happen that at q' or q'' the derivative $\frac{dU}{dq}$ vanishes, in which case we again have a condition of unstable equilibrium. For such values of W it may also happen that the motion approaches the state of unstable equilibrium asymptotically with the time. The motion is then said to be one of limitation.

In order that rotational motion may occur, U must first of all be periodic in q, and we assume as period 2π ; further, the quantity under the root sign must always be positive.

In order to illustrate these ideas we consider the pendulum, for which all three possibilities—rotation, libration, and limitation—occur. We have (see (10), § 8)

$$p=\sqrt{2A}\sqrt{W+D\cos q} \qquad D>0\,;$$

the curves (6) have therefore the form shown in fig. 5.

For

$$W=-D$$

the curves contract on the libration centre $q=0$. For

$$-D<W<D$$

we have libration between the limits

$$q'=\cos^{-1}(-D/W)$$
$$q''=-\cos^{-1}(-D/W).$$

For

$$W>D,$$

on the other hand, we have rotation, the pendulum rotating always in the same direction. In the limiting case

$$W=D$$

it approaches asymptotically the position $q=\pi$.

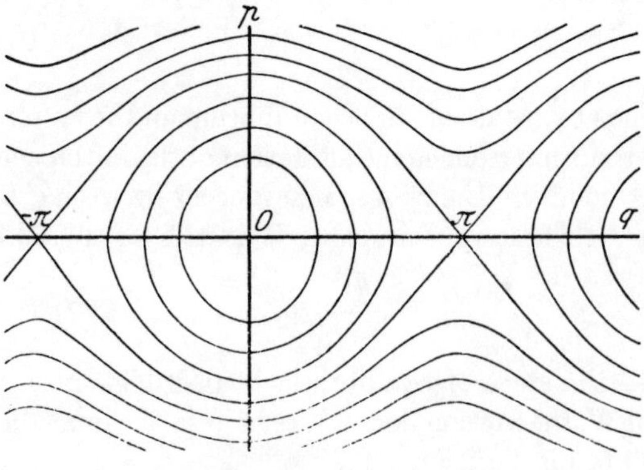

FIG. 5.

In this case the integral

$$\text{(7)} \qquad J=\oint\sqrt{2A}\sqrt{W+D\cos q}\,dq$$

for the libration motion is an elliptic integral. Only in the case when the libration limits lie close together (on the two sides of the libration centre) can it be approximated to by a simple integral. The calculation then corresponds to that for the linear harmonic oscillator, to which we now turn.

Example.—Linear Harmonic Oscillator. In § 7 we have already found the variables ϕ and a, and according to (18), § 7, q has the period $\tilde{\omega}=2\pi$ in ϕ. The variables w and J are introduced in accordance with the formulæ.

$$J=\int_0^{2\pi} a\,d\phi=2\pi a$$

and

$$w=\frac{\phi}{2\pi}=\nu t+\delta,$$

where

$$\nu=\frac{\omega}{2\pi}, \qquad \delta=\frac{\beta}{2\pi}.$$

The motion will now be represented by

$$q=\frac{1}{2\pi}\left(\frac{2J}{m\nu}\right)^{\frac{1}{2}}\sin 2\pi w$$

$$p=(2m\nu J)^{\frac{1}{2}}\cos 2\pi w.$$

The energy becomes

$$H=W=\nu J,$$

from which the relation

$$\nu=\frac{\partial W}{\partial J}$$

is at once evident.

In order to show how the change to angle and action variables can be made without a knowledge of ϕ and a, we shall once again carry out the calculations for the oscillator, starting out from

$$H=\frac{p^2}{2m}+\frac{m}{2}\omega^2q^2.$$

If we put this expression equal to W, then

$$p=(2mW-m^2\omega^2q^2)^{\frac{1}{2}}=\left\{2mW\left(1-\frac{q^2}{a^2}\right)\right\}^{\frac{1}{2}},$$

where, for shortness, we write

$$\frac{2W}{m\omega^2}=a^2.$$

From this it will be seen that the libration limits are situated at $q=+a$ and $q=-a$. We calculate the integral

$$J=(2mW)^{\frac{1}{2}}\oint\left(1-\frac{q^2}{a^2}\right)^{\frac{1}{2}}dq$$

by introducing the auxiliary variable ϕ, by means of the equation

$$q=a\sin\phi$$

ϕ goes from 0 to 2π during one period of the motion. We obtain

$$J=\frac{2W}{\omega}\int_0^{2\pi}\cos^2\phi d\phi=\frac{2\pi}{\omega}W$$

and, consequently, the energy or the Hamiltonian function is given by

(8) $$W=H=\nu J,$$

where we have put

$$\omega=2\pi\nu.$$

To express the co-ordinate q in terms of the new variables w, J, and hence in terms of the time, we do not need to calculate S itself. We have

$$w=\frac{\partial}{\partial J}S(q, J)=\int\frac{\partial p}{\partial J}dq,$$

in which p is to be considered as a function of q and J:

$$p=(2m\nu J-4\pi^2\nu^2m^2q^2)^{\frac{1}{2}}.$$

We obtain

$$w=\int\frac{m\nu dq}{(2m\nu J-4\pi^2\nu^2m^2q^2)^{\frac{1}{2}}}=\frac{1}{2\pi}\sin^{-1}\left(\frac{2\pi^2\nu m}{J}\right)^{\frac{1}{2}}q,$$

or

(9) $$q=\left(\frac{J}{2\pi^2\nu m}\right)^{\frac{1}{2}}\sin 2\pi w,$$

where

$$w=\nu t+\delta.$$

We then have for p

(10) $$p=(2m\nu J)^{\frac{1}{2}}\cos 2\pi w.$$

For the pendulum with small amplitude the corresponding formulæ are :

$$W=\nu J$$

(11) $$q=\frac{1}{2\pi}\left(\frac{2J}{A\nu}\right)^{\frac{1}{2}}\sin 2\pi w$$

$$p=(2A\nu J)^{\frac{1}{2}}\cos 2\pi w.$$

§ 10.—The Adiabatic Invariance of the Action Variables and the Quantum Conditions for One Degree of Freedom

Now that we have considered in detail the mechanics of periodic systems with one degree of freedom we can pass on to the question how, and how far, the mechanical principles may be applied to the mechanics of the atom, the chief characteristic of which is the existence of discrete stationary states.

We have a typical example of this application in Planck's treatment of the simple linear oscillator (see § 1). The stationary states were defined there by the condition that the energy should have only the discrete values

(1) $$W=n\,.\,h\nu \qquad (n=0,\ 1,\ 2\ .\ .\ .).$$

The question now occurs whether it is possible to deal in a similar way with the general case of periodic systems of one degree of freedom.

In the development of the mechanics of the atom the method of discovery has been to retain the classical mechanics as far as possible. Planck's theory of the oscillator, for example, is based on the view that the motion of the vibrating particle takes place entirely in accordance with the classical principles. Not all motions, however, with arbitrary initial conditions, *i.e.* values of the energy, are equally permissible ; certain motions, characterised by the energy values (1), occupy a preferential position in the interaction with radiation, on account of a certain inherent " stability " ; these motions constitute the " stationary states."

The endeavour to retain the classical mechanics as far as possible having proved to be a fertile method, we take as our first requirement that the stationary states of an atomic system shall be calculated, as far as possible, in accordance with the laws of classical mechanics, but the classical theory of radiation is disregarded. For this requirement to be fulfilled it is essential that the motion shall be of such a nature that the term " state " is applicable to it. This would not be the case, for example, if the path went off to infinity or if it approached a limiting curve asymptotically. In the case of periodic motions, however, the system may well be said to be in a definite state. We shall see later that there is still a further class of motions, the so-called multiply periodic systems, to which the same applies. On the other hand, the development of the quantum theory has shown that these probably exhaust the types of motion for which classical mechanics gives a valid description of the stationary states ; we shall restrict ourselves in this book essentially to this domain.

The next question concerns the manner in which the stationary motions are to be selected from the continuous manifold of those mechanically possible motions. We shall first try to give an answer to this in the case of periodic systems with one degree of freedom.

At first sight we might be inclined to apply to the general case the formula (1) established for the oscillator. Since, in general, ν is a function of W, a transcendental equation would have to be solved to determine W. This method of procedure must, however, be rejected ; it leads in certain instances to results which are in contradiction with observation (*e.g.* in the case of diatomic molecules, the atoms of which are coupled non-harmonically with one another) and, further, it cannot be sustained theoretically.

The quantum conditions by means of which the stationary orbits are selected can be expressed in the form that a certain mechanically defined magnitude is an integral multiple of Planck's constant h. In the case of the oscillator this magnitude is W/ν ; the question is, what is to take the place of this quantity in the case of other systems ?

We now examine the conditions to be satisfied by a magnitude in order that it may be "quantised" in this manner. In the first place it must be uniquely determined and independent of the co-ordinate system. This, however, would do but little to narrow the choice, and, if nothing more was known, the results of a comparison of the theory with observation would be our sole guide. In this connection Ehrenfest has, however, done much for the development of the quantum theory by advancing a postulate which makes possible a purely theoretical determination of the quantum magnitudes.

The novelty of Ehrenfest's idea lies in regarding the atoms not as isolated systems, but as subject to external influences. We have postulated above that classical mechanics shall be valid for isolated systems in the stationary states; following Ehrenfest, we now require that classical mechanics shall also be retained as far as possible in the presence of external influences.

We must now investigate to what extent this is possible without coming into conflict with the principles of the quantum theory. According to these the magnitude to be quantised can change only by integral multiples of h. If, therefore, an external influence is not sufficient to cause an alteration of magnitude h, the quantum magnitude must remain absolutely unaltered.

It is first necessary to find the conditions which determine whether the external influence is capable of causing such an alteration (known as a quantum transition or jump) or not. It is known from experience that quantum transitions can be caused by light and by molecular impacts. In these cases we have to deal with influences which vary very rapidly. If we consider, on the other hand, actions which change very slowly—slowly, that is to say, in comparison with the processes occurring within atomic systems—*e.g.* the switching on of electric or magnetic fields, experience teaches us that in this case no quantum transitions are excited; neither emission of light nor other processes associated with quantum transitions are observed in such cases.

The quantum transitions certainly take place in a non-mechanical manner. The maintenance of the classical mechanics, required by Ehrenfest in the case of external influences, is then possible only if no quantum transitions are excited by these influences, *i.e.* only in the case of processes which vary very slowly.

Ehrenfest calls this postulate, that, in the limiting case of infinitely slow changes, the principles of classical mechanics remain valid, the adiabatic hypothesis, by analogy with the terminology of thermodynamics [1]; Bohr speaks of the principle of mechanical transformability.

This postulate severely restricts the arbitrariness in the choice of the magnitude to be quantised. For now only those quantities are to be taken into account which, according to the laws of classical mechanics, remain invariant for slow variations of external influences; following Ehrenfest, we name them "adiabatic invariants."

---

[1] *Proc. Kon. Akad. Amsterdam*, vol. xvi, p. 591, 1914, and *Ann. d. Physik*, vol. li, p. 327, 1916. Ehrenfest found his "adiabatic hypothesis" in an altogether different way, namely, by an examination of the statistical foundations of Planck's radiation formula.

In order to make clear the conception of adiabatic invariance, we consider the example of a simple pendulum consisting of a bob of mass m on a thread whose length l is slowly decreased by drawing the thread up through the point of suspension. This shortening causes an alteration of the energy W and the frequency ν of the pendulum; we can show, however, that for small oscillations the magnitude W/ν remains invariant.

The force which keeps the thread of the pendulum taut consists of a gravity component $mg \cos \phi$, and the centrifugal force $ml\dot{\phi}^2$, the angular displacement being ϕ. The work done then during a shortening of the thread is

$$A=-\int mg \cos \phi dl-\int ml\dot{\phi}^2 dl.$$

If this shortening occurs so that its progress in time has no relation to the period of oscillation, and sufficiently slowly for us to be able to ascribe an amplitude to each single period, we can write

$$dA=-mg\,\overline{\cos \phi}\,dl-ml\overline{\dot{\phi}^2}dl,$$

where the bar denotes an average taken over one period. For small oscillations we can write

$$\cos \phi=1-\frac{\phi^2}{2}.$$

If this is substituted, dA resolves into an expression $-mgdl$, which represents the work done in raising the position of equilibrium of the bob of the pendulum, and a second expression

$$dW=\left(\frac{mg}{2}\overline{\phi^2}-ml\overline{\dot{\phi}^2}\right)dl$$

which denotes the energy communicated to the oscillation. The mean values of the kinetic and potential energy of the pendulum are the same, and are thus equal to half the total energy W:

$$\frac{W}{2}=\frac{m}{2}l^2\overline{\dot{\phi}^2}=\frac{m}{2}gl\overline{\phi^2}.$$

Substituting, we have

$$dW=-\frac{W}{2l}dl.$$

Since now the frequency ν is proportional to $\frac{1}{\sqrt{l}}$, and therefore

$$\frac{d\nu}{\nu}=-\frac{dl}{2l}$$

it follows that

$$\frac{dW}{W}=\frac{d\nu}{\nu}.$$

This differential equation expresses the way in which the energy of oscillation is connected with the frequency for an adiabatic shortening, and it follows by integration that

$$\frac{W}{\nu}=\text{constant}$$

as asserted.

A similar argument applies when ν is slowly varied by some other external influence. Since the harmonic oscillator is mathematically equivalent to a pendulum with an infinitely small amplitude of oscillation, W/ν is constant in that case also ; Planck's quantum condition (1) is consequently in agreement with the adiabatic hypothesis. It can be shown, on the other hand, that for other periodic systems of one degree of freedom W/ν is not an adiabatic invariant.

We remember that, according to (8), § 9, in the case of the harmonic oscillator the magnitude W/ν is also the action variable J. This suggests

$$J=nh \tag{2}$$

as a general quantum condition for systems of one degree of freedom. The quantity J fulfils the requirement of uniqueness, since it is independent of the co-ordinate system (on account of the invariance of $\iint dpdq$, cf. § 7), and we shall show now that it is an adiabatic invariant.

The general proof of the theorem of the adiabatic invariance (or, as Bohr calls it, of the mechanical transformability) of the action variables was carried out by Burgers [1] and Krutkow,[2] who at the same time treated the case of several degrees of freedom.[3]

We think of a mechanical system of one degree of freedom subject to an external influence. This can be expressed by introducing in the equation of motion, in addition to the variables, a parameter $a(t)$ depending on the time. We consider now an adiabatic variation of the system to be such that it has firstly no relation to the period of the undisturbed system, and secondly, that it takes place sufficiently slowly for $\dot{a}$ to be regarded as indefinitely small. We assume further that, for a certain range of values of a, the motion for con-

---

[1] J. M. Burgers, *Ann. d. Physik*, vol. lii, p. 195, 1917.
[2] S. Krutkow, *Proc. Kon. Akad. Amsterdam*, vol. xxi, p. 1112, comm. 1919.
[3] Other proofs on more general assumptions have been given by M. v. Laue, *Ann. d. Physik*, vol. lxxvi, p. 619, 1925, and P. A. M. Dirac, *Proc. Roy. Soc.*, vol. cvii, p. 725, 1925.

stant a is periodic, and that we can introduce angle and action variables w and J. We then have the theorem:

The action variable J is adiabatically invariant, provided the frequency does not vanish.

The Hamiltonian function

$$H(p, q, a(t))$$

is dependent on the time; the energy therefore is not constant, but the canonical equations

$$\dot{q}=\frac{\partial H}{\partial p}, \qquad \dot{p}=\frac{\partial H}{\partial q}$$

are still valid.

We imagine now the canonical transformation carried out which transforms, for constant a, the variables q, p into the angle and action variables w, J. It is useful to write the transformation in the form (*cf.* (1), § 7, and (5), § 9)

$$p=\frac{\partial S^*}{\partial q},$$

$$J=-\frac{\partial S^*}{\partial w}.$$

The function S* depends on the parameter a in addition to the variables q and w; S* is therefore dependent on the time and, by (1), § 7, H becomes

$$\bar{H}=H+\frac{\partial S^*}{\partial t}.$$

The transformed canonical equations are therefore

$$\dot{w}=\frac{\partial H}{\partial J}+\frac{\partial}{\partial J}\left(\frac{\partial S^*}{\partial t}\right),$$

$$\dot{J}=-\frac{\partial H}{\partial w}-\frac{\partial}{\partial w}\left(\frac{\partial S^*}{\partial t}\right).$$

Since H depends on the action variables only

$$\dot{J}=-\frac{\partial}{\partial w}\left(\frac{\partial S^*}{\partial t}\right)=-\frac{\partial}{\partial w}\left(\frac{\partial S^*}{\partial a}\right)\dot{a},$$

in which the differentiation with respect to t and a is to be carried out for fixed values of q and w, and the differentiation with respect to w for fixed J and a. The change of J in a time interval (t_1, t_2) will be

$$J^{(2)}-J^{(1)}=-\int_{t_1}^{t_2}\dot{a}\frac{\partial}{\partial w}\left(\frac{\partial S^*}{\partial a}\right)dt.$$

Since the variation of a is supposed slow and not connected with the period of the system, $\dot{a}$ can be brought outside the integral sign.

We shall carry out the proof of the invariance of J by showing that

$$\frac{J^{(2)}-J^{(1)}}{\dot{a}}=-\int_{t_1}^{t_2}\frac{\partial}{\partial w}\left(\frac{\partial S^*}{\partial a}\right)dt \tag{3}$$

is of the order of magnitude $\dot{a}(t_2-t_1)$; for from this it follows that in the limit of infinitely slow variation ($\dot{a}\to 0$) and for finite $\dot{a}(t_2-t_1)$, the variation of J becomes zero.

Since (by § 9) S^* is a periodic function of w, the same is true of $\frac{\partial S^*}{\partial a}$; this remains true if we introduce the variables w, J, a. The integrand of (3) is therefore a Fourier series

$$\sum_\tau{}' A_\tau(J, a)e^{2\pi i\tau w}$$

without a constant term (this we signify by the dash on the summation sign). If we write w as a function of the time, the integral to be estimated becomes:

$$\int_{t_1}^{t_2}\sum_\tau{}' A_\tau(J, a)e^{2\pi i\tau[\nu(J, a)t+\delta(J, a)]}dt.$$

The integrand is no longer exactly periodic in t as the A_τ's, ν, and δ depend on a, which varies with t; however, in the neighbourhood of a certain instant of time, which we can take as $t=0$, the A_τ's ν, and δ can be expanded in powers of the alteration in a from its value at $t=0$; this alteration is small, as the expansion is not going to be used for values of t greater than the periodic time T, and $\dot{a}$ is to be taken so small that the variation of a in a period of the undisturbed motion is small. Indicating differentiation with respect to a by a dash, and values of the A_τ's, ν, and δ for the value of a at $t=0$ by suffixes zero, the integrand then becomes

$$\sum_\tau{}' A_{\tau 0}e^{2\pi i(\nu_0 t+\delta_0)} \tag{4}$$
$$+\dot{a}t\sum_\tau{}'[A'_{\tau 0}+2\pi i A_{\tau 0}\tau(\nu_0' t+\delta_0')]e^{2\pi i\tau(\nu_0 t+\delta_0)}+\cdots$$

If we integrate this expression over a period of the first term, we obtain expressions of the order of magnitude $\dot{a}T$ and $\dot{a}T^2$. We now imagine the expansion (4) carried out at the beginning of the interval (t_1, t_2) and the integral taken over one period of the first term. We then imagine a new expansion (4) carried out at the beginning of the remaining interval and the integral taken once more over one period of the first term. We continue this process until the interval (t_1, t_2)

is all used up. The last integral will, in general, not be taken over a full period; it has a finite magnitude even when t_2-t_1 is indefinitely great. It is seen that if T remains finite over the whole range of integration, *i.e.* if ν_0 does not vanish, the whole integral will be of the order of magnitude $\dot{a}(t_2-t_1)$.

We have proved by this the adiabatic invariance of J. On the basis of this invariance, and the special result in the case of the oscillator, we are led to the choice of J as the quantity to be quantised in general. This assumption has been confirmed by the further development of the quantum theory. We state it in the following way:

Quantum Condition.—In the stationary states of a periodic system with one degree of freedom the action variable is an integral multiple of h:

$$J=nh.$$

The energy steps, as functions of the quantum number n, are also determined by this quantum condition.[1]

The experimental method of electron impact, mentioned in the introduction, enables the energy levels of the atomic systems to be determined in a purely empirical manner. Comparison of these determinations with the theoretical values provides a test of the foundations of the quantum theory as far as they have hitherto been developed.

As mentioned in the introduction, the interaction of the atomic systems with the radiation is governed by a further independent quantum principle, Bohr's frequency condition,

$$h\tilde{\nu}=W^{(1)}-W^{(2)},$$

which determines the frequencies of the emitted and absorbed light. $W^{(1)}$ and $W^{(2)}$ denote here the energies of two stationary states and $\tilde{\nu}$ the frequency of the light, the emission or absorption of which is coupled with the transition of the system from the state 1 to the state 2. In the case of emission ($W^{(1)}>W^{(2)}$) our formula gives a positive $\tilde{\nu}$, in the case of absorption ($W^{(1)}<W^{(2)}$) a negative $\tilde{\nu}$.

A much more rigorous test of the quantum rules is made possible by applying Bohr's frequency condition to the frequencies of spectral lines.

---

[1] This quantum condition was given first in geometrical form by M. Planck, *Vorlesungen über die Theorie der Wärmestrahlung*, first edition, 1906, § 150. It is to be found also in P. Debye, *Vorträge über kinetische Theorie der Materie und der Elektrizität* (Wolfskehl Congress), p. 27, 1913.

§ 11.—The Correspondence Principle for One Degree of Freedom

The fundamental postulate of the stability of atoms referred to in the introduction is satisfied by the two principles of atomic mechanics given in § 10. We now inquire to what extent they are in agreement with the other fundamental postulate, that the classical theory shall appear as a limiting case of the quantum theory.

Planck's constant h occurs as a characteristic magnitude in both quantum principles, and is a measure of the separation of the quantum states. Our requirement signifies that the quantum laws shall tend into the classical ones as limits as $h \to 0$; the discrete energy steps then converge to the continuum of the classical theory. The frequency condition requires special examination: we have to see if the frequencies calculated by it agree in the limit with those to be expected from the classical theory.

The radiation from a system of electrically charged particles with charges e_k at the points $\mathbf{r}_k$ is determined, according to the classical theory, by the electric moment

$$\mathbf{p}=\sum_k e_k \mathbf{r}_k.$$

If the energy radiated in the course of one period is small, the damping may for the present be neglected. For a system of one degree of freedom, such as we consider here, the rectangular co-ordinates of the charged particles will be periodic functions of

$$w=\nu t+\delta$$

with the period 1. Since the same will hold for $\mathbf{p}$, each component of the electric moment may be developed in a Fourier series of the type

$$\sum_{\tau=-\infty}^{\infty} C_\tau e^{2\pi i \tau w}.$$

The C_τ's are complex numbers; since, however, the electric moment is real, the C_τ's and $C_{-\tau}$'s must be conjugate complex quantities.

On this basis the time variation of the electric moment can be considered as a superposition of harmonic oscillations with the frequency $\tau\nu$; the amplitudes of the corresponding partial oscillations of the moment are given by the values of $|C_\tau|$ and their energies are proportional to the values of $|C_\tau|^2$. According to the classical theory the τ-th oscillation component would give rise to a radiation of frequency [1]

$$\tilde{\nu}_{cl}=\tau\nu=\tau\frac{\partial W}{\partial J}=\frac{dW}{dJ/\tau}. \tag{1}$$

[1] Since $-\tau$ as well as τ always occurs in the Fourier expansion, the sign of the expression for the classical radiation frequency has no significance.

We compare with this the quantum frequency [1]

$$\tilde{\nu}_{qu} = -\frac{\Delta W}{h}.$$

If the quantum number n decreases by τ in the quantum transition under consideration, then

$$\Delta J = J_2 - J_1 = (n_2 - n_1)h = -\tau h,$$

so that we can write

$$\tilde{\nu}_{qu} = \frac{\Delta W}{\Delta J/\tau}. \tag{2}$$

If we proceed to the limit $h \to 0$, or $\Delta J/\tau \to 0$, then (2) and (1) become identical.

For the case of a finite h we can state the relation between the two frequencies (1) and (2) as follows :

The quantum theory replaces the classical differential coefficient by a difference quotient. We do not proceed to the limit of infinitely small variations of the independent variables, but stop at finite intervals of magnitude h.

The transition between two neighbouring quantum states for which $\tau = 1$ is associated with, or " corresponds " to, the classical fundamental vibration ; a transition in which n changes by τ corresponds to the classical τth overtone $\tilde{\nu} = \tau\nu$.

This relation between classical and quantum frequencies forms the substance of Bohr's correspondence principle.

According to this correspondence the quantum frequency $\tilde{\nu}$ is, in general, different from the classical frequency $\tau\nu$. If, instead of proceeding to the limit $h \to 0$, we go to the limiting case of large quantum numbers n, and consider only such changes of n as are small compared with the value of n itself, then, on account of the monotonic character [2] (§ 9) of the function W(J), the difference quotient will very nearly coincide with the differential coefficient and we obtain the approximately correct equation

$$\tilde{\nu} = \tau\nu = (n_1 - n_2)\nu, \qquad (n_1 \text{ large, } n_1 - n_2 \text{ small compared to } n_1).$$

If $n_1 - n_2$ is no longer small in comparison with n_1, then the agreement between the classical and quantum frequencies will not be so good. For a given n_1 the correspondence between the frequencies in the case of emission ($n_1 > n_2$) has a limit, inasmuch as $\tau = n_1 - n_2$ cannot be greater than n_1.

---

[1] Positive $\tilde{\nu}$ in the expression for the frequency given by the quantum theory denotes emission, negative $\tilde{\nu}$ absorption.

[2] A function of one variable is said to be monotonic when its differential coefficient has the same sign for all relevant values of the independent variable.

The two quantum principles hitherto given do not, however, provide a complete description of the radiation processes. A light wave is characterised not only by a frequency, but also by intensity, phase, and state of polarisation. The quantum theory is at present unable to give exact information with regard to these features. Bohr has, however, shown that it is possible, by extending the correspondence principle from frequencies to amplitudes, to make at any rate approximate estimates regarding the intensity and polarisation.

In order that, in spite of the totally different mechanism of radiation, quantum theory and classical theory may give, in the limiting case of large quantum numbers (or in limit $h \to 0$), radiations with the same distribution of intensity among the component oscillations, it must be assumed that in this limiting case the Fourier coefficients C_τ represent the amplitudes of the emission governed by the quantum theory. Thus the values of C_τ must be related to the probabilities of the transitions necessary in order that the energy principle may remain valid. By considering the different components of the electric moment $\mathbf{p}$ a determination of the polarisation properties can be made at the same time as that of the intensities.

The case $C_\tau=0$ is of especial importance, for here in the classical case there is no emission of the corresponding frequency, so the corresponding quantum transition should not occur. Since, however, the correspondence principle only gives a relation between *radiation* phenomena on the classical and quantum theories the results deduced from it concerning the possibility of quantum transitions hold only in those cases where the atomic system is interacting with radiation. They need not hold for impacts between atomic systems.

On the basis of the correspondence principle we can deal effectively with the difficulties which we have met with in the introduction (§ 1, 2) in the case of the resonator. The expression for the displacement q as a function of the angle variables is by (9), § 9 :

$$=\left(\frac{J}{2\pi^2 \nu m}\right)^{\frac{1}{2}} \sin 2\pi w ;$$

this is clearly a Fourier series with only the one term $\tau = \pm 1$, according as we take the positive or negative root. According to the correspondence principle, therefore, the quantum number can, in the case of the resonator, change by 1 only, giving

$$\tilde{\nu} = \nu .$$

The correspondence principle leads then to the result that a resonator behaves on the quantum theory, as far as the frequency of its radiation is concerned, exactly as it would do according to the classical theory. In the case of other atomic systems, however, we shall see that this is by no means the case.

§ 12.—Application to the Rotator and to the Non-harmonic Oscillator

1. The Rotator.—By (1), § 6, the Hamiltonian function is

$$H=\frac{1}{2A}p^2,$$

where p is the momentum conjugated to the angle of rotation ϕ, and signifies angular momentum. In this case

$$J=\oint p d\phi=2\pi p$$

since the system assumes the same aspect each time ϕ increases by 2π. The energy, as a function of the action variable, and then of the quantum number m, becomes

$$W=H=\frac{1}{8\pi^2 A}J^2=\frac{h^2}{8\pi^2 A}\cdot m^2 \tag{1}$$

and the angle variable is

$$w=\frac{\phi}{2\pi}=\nu t+\delta,$$

where

$$\nu=\frac{\partial W}{\partial J}=\frac{J}{4\pi^2 A}=\frac{h}{4\pi^2 A}\cdot m.$$

This calculation can be applied to the motion of diatomic molecules and concerns two classes of phenomena: the theory of the rotation band spectra of polar molecules and the theory of the specific heats of gases. The simplest model of a diatomic molecule is that known as the dumb-bell model; the two atoms are regarded as massive particles at a fixed distance l apart, and it is assumed that the structure rotates, with moment of inertia A, about an axis perpendicular to the line joining the atoms. A rigorous foundation for these assumptions (*i.e.* the neglect of the rotation about the axis joining the atoms and the assumption of a rigid separation) and their replacement by more general assumptions will be given later.

(*a*) Theory of Rotation Band Spectra.—We assume that the molecule has an electric moment (*e.g.* we regard HCl as a combination of the H^+ and Cl^- ions), in which case it would, according to the classical theory, radiate light of frequency

$$\nu=\frac{\partial W}{\partial J}=\frac{J}{4\pi^2 A}.$$

Overtones do not occur. If the particles have the charges e and $-e$, the components of the electric moment $\mathbf{p}$ in the plane of the rotation are :

$$\mathbf{p}_x=e(x_2-x_1)=el\cos 2\pi w$$
$$\mathbf{p}_y=e(y_2-y_1)=el\sin(\pm 2\pi w),$$

in which the two signs correspond to the two possible directions of rotation. The expressions for the components of $\mathbf{p}$ in terms of w contain therefore only one Fourier term each, $\tau=1$ or $\tau=-1$.

We should expect that such a molecule, possessing an electric moment, would radiate according to the quantum theory ; the quantum frequencies will, however, differ from the classical ones. The energies of the stationary states are given by (1). Since only one Fourier term occurs, in the motion the quantum number can change by $+1$ or -1 only, and the Bohr frequency condition gives therefore for the emission $(m+1)\rightarrow m$:

$$(2)\qquad \tilde{\nu}=\frac{h}{8\pi^2 A}[(m+1)^2-m^2]=\frac{h}{8\pi^2 A}(2m+1).$$

If this formula be compared with that for the classical frequency

$$\nu=\frac{h}{8\pi^2 A}\,.\,2m,$$

it will be seen from the relation

$$\tilde{\nu}=\nu\left(1+\frac{1}{2m}\right)$$

that the relative difference between the two frequencies will be the smaller the greater the value of m.

Except for a small additive constant difference in the frequencies, the classical theory and the quantum theory both lead to essentially the same results in this case ; each gives a system of equidistant lines in the emission and absorption spectrum. This is the simplest case of the empirical band formula first found by Deslandres. It is easy to see that these lines are to be sought for in the infra-red. In the case of HCl, for instance, the light H atom of mass $1{\cdot}65\times 10^{-24}$ gm. essentially rotates about the much heavier Cl atom at a distance of the order of magnitude of all molecular separations, say a Ångström units or $a\,.\,10^{-8}$ cm., a being of the order of 1. The moment of inertia will then be

$$A=a^2\,.\,1{\cdot}65\times 10^{-40}\text{ gm. cm.}^2,$$

the frequency of the first line

$$\tilde{\nu}=\frac{5\times 10^{11}}{a^2}\text{ sec}^{-1}$$

and the wave-length

$$\lambda = \frac{c}{\tilde{\nu}} = 0{\cdot}06a^2 \text{ cm.}$$

Since a is of the order 1, we have to deal with lines on the farther side of the optically attainable infra-red. These pure rotation bands have been observed in the case of water vapour (for example). In the case of a large number of gases, bands have been found which are due to the combined action of the nuclear oscillations and rotation; these exhibit the same type of equidistant lines, but are situated in the region of much shorter wave-lengths. We shall deal with the theory of them further on (§§ 19, 20).

(*b*) Heats of Rotation of Diatomic Gases.—The dumb-bell molecular model leads also, as is well known, to the correct result in the theory of specific heats at high temperatures. Three translational and two rotational degrees of freedom are ascribed to such a model; the rotation about the line joining the atoms is not counted. According to the theorem of equipartition of energy, which is deduced by applying statistical mechanics to classical systems, the mean energy $\frac{1}{2}k\mathrm{T}$ is associated with every degree of freedom without potential energy, and consequently the total energy $\frac{5}{2}k\mathrm{T}$ would be associated with the five degrees of freedom mentioned; the molecular heat is therefore $\frac{5}{2}\mathrm{R}$. Now Eucken [1] has shown experimentally that the molecular heat of hydrogen decreases with decreasing temperature; for $\mathrm{T}=40°$ abs. it reaches the value $\frac{3}{2}\mathrm{R}$ and subsequently remains constant. Hydrogen changes then, in a sense, from a diatomic to a monatomic gas; its rotational energy disappears with decreasing temperature. Ehrenfest [2] has given the elementary theory of this phenomenon. The mean energy of a rotator, which can exist only in the quantum states (1), is

$$\overline{\mathrm{W}}_r = \frac{\sum\limits_{m=0}^{\infty} \mathrm{W}_m e^{-\frac{\mathrm{W}_m}{k\mathrm{T}}}}{\sum\limits_{m=0}^{\infty} e^{-\frac{\mathrm{W}_m}{k\mathrm{T}}}} = -\frac{d}{d\beta}\log \mathrm{Z},$$

where

$$\mathrm{Z} = \sum_{m=0}^{\infty} e^{-\beta \mathrm{W}_m}, \qquad \beta = \frac{1}{k\mathrm{T}}.$$

If the values (1) be substituted for W_m we shall have

---

[1] A. Eucken, *Sitzungsber. d. Preuss. Akad. d. Wiss.*, p. 141, 1912; see also K. Scheel and W. Heuse, *Ibid.*, p. 44, 1913; *Ann. d. Physik*, vol. xl, p. 473, 1913.

[2] P. Ehrenfest, *Verhandl. d. Deutsch. Physikal. Ges.*, vol. xv, p. 451, 1913.

$$Z=\sum_{m=0}^{\infty} e^{-\sigma m^2},$$

where

$$\sigma=\frac{h^2}{8\pi^2 A}\cdot\beta.$$

Ehrenfest calculates the heats of rotation by assuming for the mean energy of a molecule twice the mean energy of one of our rotators, because the molecule has two perpendicular axes about which it can rotate. The heat of rotation per gram molecule is then

$$c_r=2N\frac{d\overline{W}_r}{dT}$$
$$=2R\sigma^2\frac{d^2}{d\sigma^2}\log Z.$$

We examine the behaviour of this expression for low and high temperatures.

For small values of T we have large σ; thus $e^{-\sigma}$ is very small, and the series for Z may therefore be broken off after the first two terms:

$$Z=1+e^{-\sigma}$$
$$\log Z=e^{-\sigma},$$

consequently

$$c_r=2R\sigma^2 e^{-\sigma},$$

and this expression tends to zero with decreasing T (increasing σ).

For large values of T, σ is small, and then the sum in the expression for Z may be replaced by an integral

$$Z=\int_0^{\infty} e^{-\sigma m^2}dm=\tfrac{1}{2}\sqrt{\frac{\pi}{\sigma}}$$
$$\log Z=-\tfrac{1}{2}\log\sigma+\text{constant},$$

consequently

$$c_r=R.$$

The heat of rotation gives rise therefore, with increasing temperature, to an increase of the total molecular heat from $\frac{3}{2}$R to $\frac{5}{2}$R.

Ehrenfest's theory can, of course, give only a rough approximation to the actual state of affairs, since the two rotational degrees of freedom are not independent of one another. A more rigorous investigation must take account of the motion of the molecules in space.[1]

2. The Non-harmonic Oscillator.—We shall consider the case of a linear oscillator of slightly non-harmonic character, *i.e.* with a

[1] See the detailed treatment by F. Reiche, *Ann. d. Physik*, vol. lviii, p. 657, 1919, or see C. G. Darwin and R. H. Fowler, *Phil. Mag.*, vol. xliv, p. 472, 1922.

system of one degree of freedom for which the Hamiltonian function is given by

$$H=\frac{p^2}{2m}+\frac{m}{2}\omega_0{}^2q^2+aq^3=W, \tag{3}$$

where a is small.

Our first object will be to find the relation between the action variable J and the energy W in the form of an expansion in powers of a.

We have

$$p=\sqrt{2ma}\sqrt{f(q)},$$

where

$$f(q)=-q^3-\frac{m\omega_0{}^2}{2a}q^2+\frac{W}{a}. \tag{4}$$

We write this in the form

$$f(q)=(e_1-q)(q-e_2)(q-e_3).$$

For small values of a, two roots, which we take as e_1 and e_2, lie in the neighbourhood of $\pm\sqrt{\frac{2W}{m\omega_0{}^2}}$, and the motion takes place between them; the third root, e_3, is large compared to e_1, e_2, and has the opposite sign from a ($af(q)$ must be positive for values of q lying between e_1 and e_2). We write therefore

$$f(q)=-e_3(e_1-q)(q-e_2)\left(1-\frac{q}{e_3}\right)$$

$$\sqrt{f(q)}=\sqrt{-e_3}\sqrt{(e_1-q)(q-e_2)}\left(1-\frac{q}{2e_3}-\frac{q^2}{8e_3{}^2}+\ldots\right) \tag{5}$$

and obtain the following expansion for J :

$$J=\oint pdq=\sqrt{-2mae_3}\left(J_0-\frac{1}{2e_3}J_1-\frac{1}{8e_3{}^2}J_2+\ldots\right);$$

where

$$J_0=\oint\sqrt{(e_1-q)(q-e_2)}dq$$

$$J_1=\oint q\sqrt{(e_1-q)(q-e_2)}dq$$

$$J_2=\oint q^2\sqrt{(e_1-q)(q-e_2)}dq.$$

We transform these integrals by means of the substitution (*cf.* Appendix II)

$$\frac{2q-(e_1+e_2)}{e_1-e_2}=\sin\psi. \tag{6}$$

If q oscillates from one the libration limits e_1 to the other e_2, and back, ψ increases from $\frac{\pi}{2}$ to $\frac{\pi}{2}+2\pi$. We then find :

$$J_0=\left(\frac{e_1-e_2}{2}\right)^2\int_0^{2\pi}\cos^2\psi d\psi$$

$$J_1=\left(\frac{e_1-e_2}{2}\right)^2\left[\frac{e_1+e_2}{2}\int_0^{2\pi}\cos^2\psi d\psi+\frac{e_1-e_2}{2}\int_0^{2\pi}\sin\psi\cos^2\psi d\psi\right]$$

$$J_2=\left(\frac{e_1-e_2}{2}\right)^2\left[\left(\frac{e_1+e_2}{2}\right)^2\int_0^{2\pi}\cos^2\psi d\psi\right.$$

$$\left.+\frac{e_1^2-e_2^2}{2}\int_0^{2\pi}\sin\psi\cos^2\psi d\psi+\left(\frac{e_1-e_2}{2}\right)^2\int_0^{2\pi}\sin^2\psi\cos^2\psi d\psi\right],$$

or, on inserting the values of the integrals,

$$J_0=\frac{\pi}{4}(e_1-e_2)^2$$

$$J_1=\frac{e_1+e_2}{2}\cdot J_0$$

$$J_2=\tfrac{1}{16}[5(e_1+e_2)^2-4e_1e_2]\cdot J_0.$$

To determine the roots e_1 and e_2 we write q as a power series in a and then find for what values of the coefficients the polynomial $f(q)$ vanishes. We thus find

$$(7)\qquad \begin{aligned} e_1&=q_0+aq_1+a^2q_2,\\ e_2&=-q_0+aq_1-a^2q_2,\end{aligned}$$

where

$$q_0=\sqrt{\frac{2W}{m\omega_0^2}},\qquad q_1=-\frac{q_0^2}{m\omega_0^2},\qquad q_2=\frac{5}{2}\frac{q_0^3}{m^2\omega_0^4}.$$

To obtain the third root we find for what values of the coefficients in

$$q=\frac{1}{a}(\alpha+\beta a+\gamma a^2+\ldots)$$

the function $f(q)$ vanishes. We thus find

$$(8)\qquad e_3=\frac{1}{a}\left(\alpha+\frac{W}{\alpha^2}a^2+\ldots\right),\qquad \alpha=-\frac{m\omega_0^2}{2}.$$

If we now introduce these expressions into the equations for J_0, J_1, and J_2, we obtain, after a somewhat lengthy calculation,

$$J=2\pi\frac{W}{\omega_0}\left(1+\frac{15}{4}a^2\frac{W}{m^3\omega_0^6}+\ldots\right).$$

If we further substitute the first approximation

$$W=\frac{\omega_0}{2\pi}J=\nu_0 J$$

for W within the brackets, we get finally

(9) $$\mathrm{W}=\nu_0\mathrm{J}-\frac{15a^2}{4(2\pi\nu_0)^6m^3}(\nu_0\mathrm{J})^2.$$

It will thus be seen that the frequency $\nu=\frac{d\mathrm{W}}{d\mathrm{J}}$ is not ν_0, but, to this degree of approximation,

$$\nu=\nu_0-\frac{15}{2(2\pi)^6\nu_0{}^4m^3}a^2\,.\,\mathrm{J}.$$

In the case of radiation from an atomic system which may be represented approximately by a non-harmonic oscillator it becomes of importance to determine which transitions between the energy steps given by (9) are permissible according to the correspondence principle. In order to find this, we calculate q as a function of the angle variable w. The latter is given by

$$w=\frac{\partial \mathrm{S}}{\partial \mathrm{J}}=\int\frac{\partial p}{\partial \mathrm{J}}dq=\sqrt{\frac{m}{2a}}\frac{d\mathrm{W}}{d\mathrm{J}}\int\frac{dq}{\sqrt{f(q)}},$$

and thus, from the expansion (5), we have, to the order required,

$$w=\sqrt{\frac{m}{-2ae_3}}\frac{d\mathrm{W}}{d\mathrm{J}}\int\frac{dq}{\sqrt{(e_1-q)(q-e_2)}}\left(1+\frac{q}{2e_3}\right),$$

$$=\sqrt{\frac{m}{-2ae_3}}\frac{d\mathrm{W}}{d\mathrm{J}}\left(\mathrm{K}_0+\frac{1}{2e_3}\mathrm{K}_1\right).$$

The integrals

$$\mathrm{K}_0=\int\frac{dq}{\sqrt{(e_1-q)(q-e_2)}},\qquad \mathrm{K}_1=\int\frac{qdq}{\sqrt{(e_1-q)(q-e_2)}}$$

may also be calculated by means of the substitution (6), their values being

$$\mathrm{K}_0=\psi,\qquad \mathrm{K}_1=\frac{e_1+e_2}{2}\psi-\frac{e_1-e_2}{2}\cos\psi.$$

If now we substitute the values (7) and (8) found above for e_1, e_2, e_3, we get

$$w=\frac{1}{\omega_0}\frac{d\mathrm{W}}{d\mathrm{J}}\left[\psi+\frac{a}{m\omega_0{}^2}\sqrt{\frac{2\mathrm{W}}{m\omega_0{}^2}}\cos\psi+\ldots\right].$$

If we now neglect the terms in a^2, we can put

$$\frac{d\mathrm{W}}{d\mathrm{J}}=\nu_0$$

and obtain

(10) $$w=\frac{1}{2\pi}\left[\psi+a\sqrt{\frac{2\nu_0\mathrm{J}}{(2\pi\nu_0)^6m^3}}\cos\psi\right].$$

It follows from (6) and (7) that, neglecting terms in a^2,

$$q = aq_1 + q_0 \sin\psi,$$

where $\sin\psi$ may be calculated from (10). To the same order we get

$$q = q_0 \sin 2\pi w - a\frac{q_0^2}{2m\omega_0^2}(3 + \cos 4\pi w),$$

and finally

$$(11) \qquad q = \sqrt{\frac{J}{2\pi^2\nu_0 m}} \sin 2\pi w - a\frac{\nu_0 J}{(2\pi\nu_0)^4 m^2}(3 + \cos 4\pi w).$$

The deviation of the co-ordinate q from its value in the case of the harmonic oscillator ($a=0$) is of the order a, whereas the energy difference is of the order a^2. The mean value of the co-ordinate will not be zero, but to our degree of approximation will be given by

$$(12) \qquad \bar{q} = -3a\frac{\nu_0 J}{(2\pi\nu_0)^4 m^2} = -3a\frac{W}{(2\pi\nu_0)^4 m^2}.$$

In the case of the non-harmonic oscillator, therefore, the co-ordinate oscillates about a mean position differing from the position of equilibrium. The oscillation is not harmonic, for overtones occur, the first of which has an amplitude of the order a.

On the basis of the correspondence principle, the appearance of overtones in the motion of the system implies that quantum transitions are possible for which the quantum number alters by more than one unit. The probability of an alteration in the quantum number of 2 is of the order a^2 (*i.e.* the square of the amplitude of the corresponding oscillation).

The fact that the mean value of the displacement does not vanish, but increases in proportion to the energy, has been used by Boguslawski[1] in explaining the phenomena of pyroelectricity. He imagines the (charged) atoms of a polar crystal bound non-harmonically in equilibrium positions, so that with increasing temperature (*i.e.* energy) a mean electric moment will arise. In his first calculation Boguslawski took for the mean energy the classical value kT but later introduced the quantum theory by using for the mean energy Planck's resonator formula ((5), § 1).

[1] S. Boguslawski, *Physikal. Zeitschr.*, vol. xv, pp. 283, 569, 805, 1914. The problem of the non-harmonic oscillator was first considered by Boguslawski, in an attempt to explain pyroelectricity by means of the quantum theory. The phase integral is actually a period of the elliptic function belonging to $f(q)$ and may be represented exactly by means of hypergeometric functions. In the physical application, Boguslawski restricts himself to small values of a, and arrives at the same final formula as that given in the text.

The theory of the non-harmonic oscillator finds a further application in the explanation of the increase in the specific heat of solid bodies at high temperatures above Dulong and Petit's value,[1] and also in the explanation of band spectra (see § 20).

§ 13.—Multiply Periodic Functions

Before we can proceed to apply our results to systems of several degrees of freedom we must introduce the conception of multiply periodic functions, and examine some of their properties.

Definition 1.—A function $F(x_1 \ldots x_f, y_1 \ldots)$ is periodic in the variables $x_1 \ldots x_f$, with the period $\tilde{\omega}$ having the components

$$\tilde{\omega}_1, \tilde{\omega}_2 \ldots \tilde{\omega}_f,$$

if

$$F(x_1+\tilde{\omega}_1, x_2+\tilde{\omega}_2 \ldots x_f+\tilde{\omega}_f)=F(x_1, x_2 \ldots x_f) \tag{1}$$

identically in $x_1 \ldots x_f$.

If $x_1, x_2 \ldots x_f$ be considered as co-ordinates in f-dimensional space, each period corresponds to a vector in this space.

If in (1) $(x_1, x_2 \ldots x_f)$ be replaced by $(x_1 \pm \tilde{\omega}_1, x_2 \pm \tilde{\omega}_2 \ldots x_f \pm \tilde{\omega}_f)$, and this operation be repeated indefinitely, the truth of the following theorem will be found to hold.

Theorem 1.—A function which has the period $\tilde{\omega}$ has also the period $\tau\tilde{\omega}$, *i.e.* the period with the components $\tau\tilde{\omega}_1, \tau\tilde{\omega}_2 \ldots \tau\tilde{\omega}_f$, where τ is an arbitrary integer (positive or negative).

If the function F has the period $\tilde{\omega}'$, in addition to $\tilde{\omega}$, it will be seen, by replacing $(x_1, x_2 \ldots x_f)$ in (1) by $(x_1+\tilde{\omega}_1', x_2+\tilde{\omega}_2' \ldots x_f+\tilde{\omega}_f')$, that the following also holds.

Theorem 2.—The vectorial sum $\tilde{\omega}+\tilde{\omega}'$ of two periods $\tilde{\omega}$ and $\tilde{\omega}'$, *i.e.* the vector having the components

$$\tilde{\omega}_1+\tilde{\omega}_1', \tilde{\omega}_2+\tilde{\omega}_2' \ldots \tilde{\omega}_f+\tilde{\omega}_f',$$

is likewise a period.

By combining the theorems 1 and 2 we have the general

Theorem 3.—If a function has several periods

$$\begin{aligned} \tilde{\omega}^{(1)} &= (\tilde{\omega}_1^{(1)}, \tilde{\omega}_2^{(1)} \ldots \tilde{\omega}_f^{(1)}) \\ \tilde{\omega}^{(2)} &= (\tilde{\omega}_1^{(2)}, \tilde{\omega}_2^{(2)} \ldots \tilde{\omega}_f^{(2)}) \\ &\ldots\ldots\ldots\ldots \\ \tilde{\omega}^{(g)} &= (\tilde{\omega}_1^{(g)}, \tilde{\omega}_2^{(g)} \ldots \tilde{\omega}_f^{(g)}), \end{aligned}$$

then every integral linear combination of these periods

[1] M. Born and E. Brody, *Zeitschr. f. Physik*, vol. vi, p. 132, 1921; for detailed list of literature, see M. Born, *Atomtheorie des festen Zustandes*, Leipzig, 1923, p. 698.

$$(2)\qquad \sum_k \tau_k \tilde{\omega}^{(k)} = \Big(\sum_k \tau_k \tilde{\omega}_1^{(k)}, \sum_k \tau_k \tilde{\omega}_2^{(k)} \ldots \sum_k \tau_k \tilde{\omega}_f^{(k)} \Big)$$

is likewise a period.

Definition 2.—Two points $(x_1 \ldots x_f)$ and $(x_1' \ldots x_f')$ are said to be *equivalent* if the vector joining them is of the form $\sum_k \tau_k \tilde{\omega}^{(k)}$.

In order to eliminate trivial exceptional cases we add the condition :

Condition.—The function F shall possess no infinitely small periods, *i.e.* none, for which the length of the representative vector is smaller than any arbitrary number.

We shall consider now two periods $\tilde{\omega}$ and $\lambda\tilde{\omega}$, represented by parallel vectors, in which case λ must be a rational number, otherwise the period $(\tau+\tau'\lambda) \,.\, \tilde{\omega}$ could, by a suitable choice of the integers τ and τ', be made arbitrarily small.[1]

If now q is the smallest denominator by means of which λ may be expressed in the form p/q, p and q being integers, then $\tilde{\omega}/q$ is likewise a period, for by a theorem in the theory of numbers we can always find two integers τ and τ', so that

$$q\tau + p\tau' = 1,$$

and so

$$\tau + \tau'\lambda = \tau + \tau'\frac{p}{q} = \frac{1}{q}.$$

We see now that we can express each period whose vector has a certain direction as an integral multiple of a certain minimum one.

From this theorem may be deduced a generalisation which is valid for all periods of a function F. In order to derive it we shall suppose all the periods arranged in order according to the magnitude of their vectors :

$$(3)\qquad |\tilde{\omega}| \leqq |\tilde{\omega}'| \leqq |\tilde{\omega}''| \leqq \cdots .$$

We select the first period of this series together with the next one having a vector in another direction. These two periods, which we now call $\tilde{\omega}^{(1)}$ and $\tilde{\omega}^{(2)}$, define a parallelogram mesh in the plane of the corresponding vectors, with this property, that each vector which joins two points of intersection of the net also represents a period.

In this way we can account for all periods whose vectors lie in this plane, for if there were a vector $\tilde{\omega}$, the end point of which did not coincide with a mesh point (see fig. 6), then there would be a mesh point at a distance less than $|\tilde{\omega}^{(2)}|$ from that end point. If $\tilde{\omega}$

[1] See Appendix I.

were a period, then the vector represented by this separation would likewise be a period; its magnitude would, however, be smaller than $|\tilde{\omega}^{(2)}|$, which is contrary to supposition.

To $\tilde{\omega}^{(1)}$ and $\tilde{\omega}^{(2)}$ we now add the immediately succeeding period in the series (3), whose vector does not lie in the plane defined by $\tilde{\omega}^{(1)}$ and $\tilde{\omega}^{(2)}$, and call it $\tilde{\omega}^{(3)}$. These three periods determine in this way a three-dimensional lattice, possessing the property that each vector joining two lattice points corresponds to a period. In this way all periods are accounted for, whose vectors lie in the three-dimensional space defined by $\tilde{\omega}^{(1)}, \tilde{\omega}^{(2)}, \tilde{\omega}^{(3)}$. If we continue this procedure until all the periods are exhausted, which must happen when the $\tilde{\omega}$-space becomes f-dimensional, if not before, we shall have proved the following theorem.

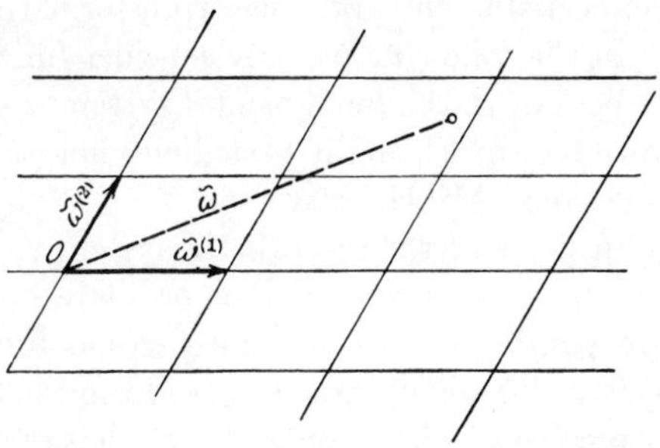

FIG 6.

Theorem 4.—For each periodic function $F(x_1 \ldots x_f, y_1 \ldots)$ of $x_1 \ldots x_f$ there is a system of periods $\tilde{\omega}^{(1)}, \tilde{\omega}^{(2)} \ldots \tilde{\omega}^{(g)}$ with the property that every period $\tilde{\omega}$ of the function F can be expressed in the form

$$\tilde{\omega}=\sum_k \tau_k \tilde{\omega}^{(k)}.$$

The highest possible value of g, the number of the periods, is equal to the number of variables f.

Definition 3.—A system of periods, possessing the property mentioned in theorem 4, is called a fundamental period system.

We have represented all periods of F by means of a g-dimensional lattice. For this, of course, only the lattice points are essential, and not the vectors joining them. If the system $\tilde{\omega}^{(1)}, \tilde{\omega}^{(2)} \ldots \omega^{(g)}$ were replaced by another system, with the same number (g) of periods

$$\begin{aligned} \tilde{\omega}^{(1)\prime} &= \sum_k \tau_{1k} \tilde{\omega}^{(k)} \\ \tilde{\omega}^{(2)\prime} &= \sum_k \tau_{2k} \tilde{\omega}^{(k)} \\ &\cdots\cdots \\ \tilde{\omega}^{(g)\prime} &= \sum_k \tau_{gk} \tilde{\omega}^{(k)} \end{aligned} \tag{4}$$

giving the same points of intersection, the new system of periods $\tilde{\omega}^{(1)\prime}, \tilde{\omega}^{(2)\prime} \ldots \tilde{\omega}^{(g)\prime}$ would be equally suitable for the representation of the periods of F. The coincidence of the lattice points in the two systems is achieved if, and only if, the determinant of the τ_{ik}'s has the value ± 1. This determinant represents the ratio of the cell volumes of the two lattices. Thus we have:

Theorem 5.—All fundamental period systems of a function are connected by integral linear transformations with determinants ± 1.

In the following we only consider functions for which the number of periods in the fundamental system is equal to the number f of the variables in which the periodicity holds. We consider therefore only functions of periodicity f.

In place of the co-ordinate system $x_1 \ldots x_f$, we introduce in our f-dimensional space a new co-ordinate system $w_1 \ldots w_f$, whose axes are parallel to the vectors corresponding to a fundamental period system for which these vectors form the units; then the function F, expressed as a function of the w's, has the fundamental period system

$$\begin{array}{c} (1, 0, 0 \ldots 0) \\ (0, 1, 0 \ldots 0) \\ (0, 0, 1 \ldots 0) \\ \cdot \quad \cdot \quad \cdot \quad \cdot \quad \cdot \\ (0, 0, 0 \ldots 1). \end{array} \tag{5}$$

In this case, F is said to have the "fundamental period 1." This leads us then to

Theorem 6.—By means of a linear transformation of the variables in which a function is periodic, it may be made to have the fundamental period 1.

We shall now see to what extent this co-ordinate system $w_1, w_2 \ldots$ is still arbitrary. First it is clear that by means of a transformation

$$\begin{array}{l} w_1 = \bar{w}_1 + \psi_1(\bar{w}_1\bar{w}_2 \ldots \bar{w}_f, y_1y_2 \ldots) \\ w_2 = \bar{w}_2 + \psi_2(\bar{w}_1\bar{w}_2 \ldots \bar{w}_f, y_1y_2 \ldots) \\ \cdot \quad \cdot \quad \cdot \quad \cdot \quad \cdot \quad \cdot \quad \cdot \quad \cdot \quad \cdot \\ w_f = \bar{w}_f + \psi_f(\bar{w}_1\bar{w}_2 \ldots \bar{w}_f, y_1y_2 \ldots), \end{array} \tag{6}$$

in which each ψ is periodic in all the $\bar{w}_k$'s with the period 1 in each, the periodic properties of $F(x_1 \ldots x_f, y_1 \ldots)$ will not be altered. The lattice points of the w-co-ordinate system pass to the lattice points of the $\bar{w}$-co-ordinate system by means of a simple displacement. Further, it is evident that the given transformation is the only one for which this transference from one set of intersections to the other is the result of a simple displacement. On passing, for example, from a point in the w-space to an equivalent one, each w_k increases by a whole number. The $\bar{w}_k$ must increase by the same whole number when we carry out the similar transition in the $\bar{w}_k$-space. The differences $w_k - \bar{w}_k$ must therefore have the same value for all equivalent points, *i.e.* they are periodic in the $\bar{w}_k$ and in the w_k.

Now there are still other transformations for which the correlation of the lattice points with values of the w_k's will be varied, but for which lattice point will still coincide with lattice point. To each of the fundamental period systems in the x_k, referred to in theorem 5, there corresponds, for example, such a transformation; these are the integral homogeneous linear transformations with the determinant ± 1.

Let us suppose that the most general transformation, which transforms the periodicity lattice into itself, be resolved into such a linear one and also another transformation. This second transformation must be of the form (6). The most general transformation is therefore

$$(7)\qquad \begin{aligned} w_1 &= \sum \tau_{1k}\bar{w}_k + \psi_1(\bar{w}_1 \ldots \bar{w}_f, y_1 \ldots) \\ w_2 &= \sum \tau_{2k}\bar{w}_k + \psi_2(\bar{w}_1 \ldots \bar{w}_f, y_1 \ldots) \\ &\cdots\cdots\cdots\cdots \\ w_f &= \sum \tau_{fk}\bar{w}_k + \psi_f(\bar{w}_1 \ldots \bar{w}_f, y_1 \ldots). \end{aligned}$$

Theorem 7.—All systems of variables, in which a function of periodicity f has the fundamental period 1, are connected by transformations of the form (7), where the τ_{ik} are whole numbers, the system of which has the determinant ± 1 and the ψ_i are periodic in the $\bar{w}_k$ with the period 1.[1]

The function F may be written very simply with the help of the variables $w_1 \ldots w_f$. It may be expressed as a Fourier series

$$(8)\qquad F(w_1 \ldots w_f) = \sum_{\tau_1 \ldots \tau_f = -\infty}^{\infty} C_{\tau_1\tau_2 \ldots \tau_f} e^{2\pi i(\tau_1 w_1 + \tau_2 w_2 + \ldots + \tau_f w_f)},$$

[1] This theorem may be proved analytically as follows: we seek a transformation

$$w_k = f_k(\bar{w}_1\bar{w}_2 \ldots \bar{w}_f, y_1 \ldots),$$

for which the periodicity of the function

$$F(w_1 w_2 \ldots w_f, y_1 \ldots) = \bar{F}(\bar{w}_1\bar{w}_2 \ldots \bar{w}_f, \bar{y}_1 \ldots)$$

is preserved in the first f variables. If we put

$$f_k(\bar{w}_1 + 1, \bar{w}_2 \ldots \bar{w}_f, y_1 \ldots) = w_k',$$

then

$$\begin{aligned} F(w_1' w_2' \ldots w_f', y_1 \ldots) &= \bar{F}(\bar{w}_1 + 1, \bar{w}_2 \ldots \bar{w}_f, \bar{y}_1 \ldots) \\ &= \bar{F}(\bar{w}_1, \bar{w}_2 \ldots \bar{w}_f, \bar{y}_1 \ldots) = F(w_1 w_2 \ldots w_f, y_1 \ldots). \end{aligned}$$

This means, however, that w_k' and w_k differ by a whole number:

$$f_k(\bar{w}_1 + 1, \bar{w}_2 \ldots \bar{w}_f, y_1 \ldots) = f_k(\bar{w}_1, \bar{w}_2 \ldots \bar{w}_f, y_1 \ldots) + \tau_{k1}.$$

We likewise conclude that

$$f_k(\bar{w}_1 \ldots \bar{w}_l + 1 \ldots \bar{w}_f, y_1 \ldots) = f_k(\bar{w}_1, \bar{w}_2 \ldots \bar{w}_f, y_1 \ldots) + \tau_{kl}.$$

This, however, is possible only if f_k is of the form:

$$f_k(\bar{w}_1 \ldots \bar{w}_f, y_1 \ldots) = \Sigma\tau_{kl}\bar{w}_l + \psi_k(\bar{w}_1 \ldots \bar{w}_f, y_1 \ldots),$$

where ψ_k is periodic in the $\bar{w}$ with the period 1.

which, for conciseness, we write

(8′) $$F(w)=\sum_\tau C_\tau e^{2\pi i(\tau w)}.$$

If the function F be multiplied by $e^{-2\pi i(\tau' w)}$ and integrated over a unit cube of the w-space, we get

$$\int F(w)e^{-2\pi i(\tau' w)}dw=\sum_\tau C_\tau \cdot \int e^{2\pi i[(\tau w)-(\tau' w)]}dw=C_{\tau'}.$$

The coefficients of the Fourier expansion may therefore be obtained in the form

(9) $$C_\tau=\int F(w)e^{-2\pi i(\tau w)}dw$$

from the function F.

If the function $F(w)$ is real, $C_{\tau_1 \ldots \tau_f}$ and $C_{-\tau_1 \ldots -\tau_f}$ are conjugate complex quantities.

§ 14.—Separable Multiply Periodic Systems

Our next problem is to extend the results found for a system with one degree of freedom to systems with several degrees of freedom.

In the case of absolutely general systems there is no object in introducing angle and action variables, since these are associated with the existence of periodic properties.

We consider first the simple case in which the Hamiltonian function of the system resolves into a sum of terms, each of which contains only one pair of variables q_k, p_k:

(1) $$H=H_1(q_1, p_1)+\ldots+H_f(q_f, p_f).$$

The Hamilton-Jacobi equation is solved by separation of the variables on putting

$$H_k\left(q_k \frac{\partial S_k}{\partial q_k}\right)=W_k,$$

where the relation

$$W_1+\ldots+W_f=W$$

holds between the W_k. It is seen that the motion corresponds completely with that of f independent systems, each of which has one degree of freedom. We consider now the case where the variation of each of the co-ordinates q_k is periodic in time. The correct generalisation of the earlier considerations is to define the action variables by

(1′) $$J_k=\oint p_k dq_k,$$

to express the function S_k in terms of q_k and J_k, and to put

(2) $$w_k=\frac{\partial S_k}{\partial J_k}.$$

Example : Spatial Oscillator.—A massive particle is restrained by any set of forces in a position of stable equilibrium (*e.g.* a light atom in a molecule otherwise consisting of heavy, and therefore relatively immovable atoms). The potential energy is then, for small displacement, a positive definite quadratic function of the displacement components. The axes of the co-ordinate system (x, y, z) can always be chosen to lie along the principal axes of the ellipsoid corresponding to this quadratic form. The Hamiltonian function is then

$$\text{(3)} \qquad H=\frac{1}{2m}(p_x{}^2+p_y{}^2+p_z{}^2)+\frac{m}{2}(\omega_x{}^2x^2+\omega_y{}^2y^2+\omega_z{}^2z^2).$$

It has therefore the form of (1) above, so the motion may be considered as the resultant of the vibrations of three linear oscillators along the co-ordinate axes. We have then, by (9) and (10), § 9 :

$$\text{(4)} \qquad \begin{aligned} x&=\sqrt{\frac{J_x}{2\pi^2\nu_x m}}\sin 2\pi w_x \qquad & p_x&=\sqrt{2\nu_x m J_x}\cos 2\pi w_x \\ y&=\sqrt{\frac{J_y}{2\pi^2\nu_y m}}\sin 2\pi w_y \qquad & p_y&=\sqrt{2\nu_y m J_y}\cos 2\pi w_y \\ z&=\sqrt{\frac{J_z}{2\pi^2\nu_z m}}\sin 2\pi w_z \qquad & p_z&=\sqrt{2\nu_z m J_z}\cos 2\pi w_z, \end{aligned}$$

where

$$w_x=\nu_x t+\delta_x, \qquad \nu_x=\frac{\omega_x}{2\pi}.$$

The energy has the value

$$\text{(5)} \qquad W=\nu_x J_x+\nu_y J_y+\nu_z J_z.$$

The motion is of an altogether different type according to whether integral linear relations

$$\tau_x\nu_x+\tau_y\nu_y+\tau_z\nu_z=0$$

exist between the ν or not. We assume first that such relations do not exist. We can prove quite generally (see Appendix I) that in such cases the path traverses a region of as many dimensions as there are degrees of freedom ; it approaches indefinitely close to every point in this region. In the case of the spatial oscillator this region is a rectangular prism parallel to the axes having sides of lengths

$$\sqrt{\frac{2}{\pi^2 m\nu_x}}\,.\,\sqrt{J_x}, \qquad \sqrt{\frac{2}{\pi^2 m\nu_y}}\,.\,\sqrt{J_y}, \qquad \sqrt{\frac{2}{\pi^2 m\nu_z}}\,.\,\sqrt{J_z}$$

(spatial Lissajous-figure).

In order to see what special cases may arise when the ν's are commensurable with one another, we consider the simple case where $\nu_x=\nu_y$. This occurs when the ellipsoid corresponding to the potential energy possesses rotational symmetry about the z-axis. The curve representing the path is situated then on an elliptic cylinder enclosing the z-axis. Corresponding to a given motion we no longer have uniquely determined values of J_x and J_y, for we can rotate the co-ordinate system arbitrarily about the z-axis, whereby the sides perpendicular to the z-axis of the rectangular prism touching the path will be varied. J_z, on the other hand, remains uniquely determined as the height of the elliptic cylinder on which the path is situated (if no other fresh commensurability exists). Since the energy is

(6) $$W=\nu(J_x+J_y)+\nu_z J_z, \qquad (\nu_x=\nu_y=\nu)$$

only the sum J_x+J_y is determined by the motion.

If, finally, all three frequencies are equal, the motion is confined to an ellipse and none of the three J's are now uniquely determined, since the co-ordinate system may still be arbitrarily rotated. The energy is

(7) $$W=\nu(J_x+J_y+J_z),$$

the sum of the J's will therefore remain unaltered by such a rotation.

If now we ask what are the quantum conditions for such a system of several degrees of freedom, the obvious suggestion is to put

(8) $$J_k=n_k h.$$

In the case of the oscillator with two equal frequencies $\nu_x=\nu_y$ the conditions

$$J_x=n_x h, \qquad J_y=n_y h$$

are clearly meaningless. If, for instance, we have a motion, for which J_x and J_y are integral multiples of h for any position of the x- and y-axes, we can always rotate the co-ordinate system so that this property is destroyed. The sum J_x+J_y, on the other hand, remains integral, so that the condition

(9) $$J_x+J_y=nh$$

would still be significant. Since in the expression for the energy J_x and J_y occur in this combination only, this quantum condition would not define the path uniquely, but would fix the energy. The condition

(10) $$J_z=n_z h$$

retains its significance. The example shows, therefore, that only so many quantum conditions may be prescribed as there are different periods.

If all three frequencies coincide there remains only the one condition

(11) $$J_x+J_y+J_z=nh$$

left. This again fixes the energy uniquely.

We shall now examine more closely the manner in which the action variables alter when, in the case of $\nu_x=\nu_y$, the co-ordinate system is rotated. Let the action variables J_x, J_y correspond to the rectangular co-ordinates x, y, and the action variables $J_{\bar{x}}$, $J_{\bar{y}}$ to the co-ordinates

$$\bar{x}=x\cos a-y\sin a$$
$$\bar{y}=x\sin a+y\cos a.$$

If we express the barred co-ordinates and momenta occurring in

$$\nu J_{\bar{x}}=\frac{1}{2m}p_{\bar{x}}^2+\frac{m}{2}\omega^2\bar{x}^2$$

$$\nu J_{\bar{y}}=\frac{1}{2m}p_{\bar{y}}^2+\frac{m}{2}\omega^2\bar{y}^2$$

in terms of those not barred (the momenta transform just like the co-ordinates) we get

$$\nu J_{\bar{x}}=\left(\frac{1}{2m}p_x^2+\frac{m}{2}\omega^2x^2\right)\cos^2 a+\left(\frac{1}{2m}p_y^2+\frac{m}{2}\omega^2y^2\right)\sin^2 a$$
$$-\left(\frac{1}{m}p_xp_y+m\omega^2xy\right)\sin a\cos a,$$

$$\nu J_{\bar{y}}=\left(\frac{1}{2m}p_x{}^2+\frac{m}{2}\omega^2x^2\right)\sin^2 a+\left(\frac{1}{2m}p_y{}^2+\frac{m}{2}\omega^2y^2\right)\cos^2 a$$
$$+\left(\frac{1}{m}p_xp_y+m\omega^2xy\right)\sin a\cos a.$$

The coefficients of $\cos^2 a$ and $\sin^2 a$ are clearly the magnitudes νJ_x and νJ_y. The coefficients of $\sin a\cos a$ we determine from the transformation equations (4) and obtain

$$J_{\bar{x}}=J_x\cos^2 a+J_y\sin^2 a-2\sqrt{J_xJ_y}\cos(w_x-w_y)\sin a\cos a,$$
$$J_{\bar{y}}=J_x\sin^2 a+J_y\cos^2 a+2\sqrt{J_xJ_y}\cos(w_x-w_y)\sin a\cos a;$$

where, in our case w_x-w_y is a constant since $\nu_x=\nu_y$. The constants J_x, J_y are thus transformed into $J_{\bar{x}}$, $J_{\bar{y}}$, which are also constants.

The transformation which transforms the angle and action variables, corresponding to a rectangular co-ordinate system, into those associated with another rectangular co-ordinate system, is not one which transforms the angle and action variables among themselves. In fact, the constant difference of the angle variables appears in the transformation equations for the J. We shall meet with a similar state of affairs in the case of a second example, and later quite generally in the case of degeneration.

It may happen that the Hamiltonian function does not consist of a sum of terms depending on only one pair of variables q_kp_k, but that the Hamilton-Jacobi equation may be solved by separation of the variables, *i.e.* on the assumption that

$$\text{(11')}\qquad S=S_1(q_1)+S_2(q_2)+\ldots S_f(q_f).$$

Then

$$p_k=\frac{\partial S_k}{\partial q_k}$$

is a function of q_k alone. We now suppose that each of the co-ordinates q_k behaves in the same way as we assumed above (§ 9) in the case of systems of one degree of freedom, *i.e.* either that q_k oscillates to and fro periodically in time, between two fixed limits (case of libration), or that the corresponding p_k is a periodic function of q_k (case of rotation). Since each integral

$$\text{(12)}\qquad J_k=\oint p_kdq_k$$

taken over a period q_k is constant, we can introduce the J_k here as constant momenta in place of $\alpha_1\alpha_2\ldots.$ The function H depends then only on the J_k's; S may be expressed as a function of the q_k's and of the J_k's. Instead of the q_k's, the quantities w_k, conjugate to the J_k's, will now be introduced; they are related to the q_k's by means of the equations

$$\text{(13)}\qquad w_k=\frac{\partial S}{\partial J_k}=\sum_l\frac{\partial S_l}{\partial J_k}.$$

We will now prove that the variables w_k, J_k, introduced in this way, have similar properties to w and J for one degree of freedom, namely, that the q_k's are multiply periodic functions of the w_k's with the fundamental period system

$$\begin{matrix}(1, 0, 0 \dots 0)\\(0, 1, 0 \dots 0)\\(0, 0, 1 \dots 0)\\ \cdot \quad \cdot \quad \cdot \quad \cdot \quad \cdot \\(0, 0, 0 \dots 1).\end{matrix}$$

We wish to find the change in w_k during a to-and-fro motion, or in the course of one revolution, of the co-ordinate q_h, when the other co-ordinates remain unaltered. This change will be :

$$\Delta_h w_k = \oint \frac{\partial w_k}{\partial q_h} dq_h.$$

Now, by partial differentiation of equation (13)

$$\frac{\partial w_k}{\partial q_h} = \sum_l \frac{\partial^2 S_l}{\partial J_k \partial q_h} = \frac{\partial}{\partial J_k} \sum_l \frac{\partial S_l}{\partial q_h} = \frac{\partial}{\partial J_k} \frac{\partial S_h}{\partial q_h}$$

so by integration

$$\Delta_h w_k = \frac{\partial}{\partial J_k} \oint \frac{\partial S_h}{\partial q_h} dq_h = \frac{\partial J_h}{\partial J_k} = \begin{cases} 1 (h = k) \\ 0 (h \neq k). \end{cases}$$

If we fix our attention on the functions $q_l(w_1 \dots w_f)$, and increase w_k by 1, while the other w's remain unaltered, q_k goes through one period ; the remaining q's may also depend on w_k, but they return to the initial values without going through a complete period (if, for example, q_l went through a complete period w_l would increase by 1). This proves the theorem stated above, concerning the periodic properties of the q_k's in the w_k's.

It may happen that a particular q does not depend on all the w_k's, that is, it may not have the full periodicity f, but the system of all the q's taken together depends of course on all the w_k's.

In our treatment of the spatial oscillator, for example, each co-ordinate depended on one w only.

In every case q_k may be expressed as a Fourier series in the form

(14) $$q_k = \sum_\tau C_\tau^{(k)} \cdot e^{2\pi i (\tau w)}$$

(see (8) and (8′), § 13, for the abbreviated notation adopted). We obtain the w's as functions of the time from the canonical equations

(15) $$w_k = \nu_k t + \delta_k, \qquad \nu_k = \frac{\partial H}{\partial J_k}.$$

Written as a function of t:

$$q_k = \sum_\tau C_\tau^{(k)} \cdot e^{2\pi i[(\tau\nu)t+(\tau\delta)]},$$

where

$$(\tau\nu)=\tau_1\nu_1+\tau_2\nu_2+\ldots+\tau_f\nu_f$$
$$(\tau\delta)=\tau_1\delta_1+\tau_2\delta_2+\ldots+\tau_f\delta_f,$$

so that q_k is not in general periodic; it is only periodic when, and only when, $(f-1)$ rational relations exist between the ν's (for example when all the ν's are equal). Periodicity of the motion signifies, therefore, that all individual periods $(1/\nu_k)$ have a common multiple $(1/\nu$, say), *i.e.* that a relation

$$\frac{\nu_1}{\tau_1'}=\frac{\nu_2}{\tau_2'}=\ldots=\frac{\nu_f}{\tau_f'}=\nu,$$

with integral τ_k''s, exists. This is equivalent, however, to $(f-1)$ rational relations between the ν_k's. Conversely $(f-1)$ independent linear homogeneous equations with integral coefficients

$$\tau_{11}\nu_1+\tau_{12}\nu_2+\ldots+\tau_{1f}\nu_f=0$$
$$\tau_{21}\nu_1+\tau_{22}\nu_2+\ldots+\tau_{2f}\nu_f=0$$
$$\ldots\ldots\ldots\ldots\ldots\ldots$$
$$\tau_{f-1,1}\nu_1+\tau_{f-1,2}\nu_2+\ldots+\tau_{f-1,f}\nu_f=0$$

determine the ratios of the ν_k's; these ratios are rational, it is therefore possible to choose ν so that

$$\nu_k=\tau_k'\nu,$$

the τ_k''s being integers. The Fourier representation of the co-ordinates q_k assumes in this case the form

$$q_k=\sum_\tau C^{(k)}_{\tau_1\ldots\tau_f} e^{2\pi i[(\tau_1\tau_1'+\tau_2\tau_2'+\ldots+\tau_f\tau_f')\nu t+(\tau\delta)]}.$$

Here again the periodicity will at once be recognised.

In the non-periodic case the motion is analogous to that which in two dimensions is called a Lissajous-motion, the path being closed only in the event of a rational relation between the ν_k's. We consider the path in the w-space, confined to a standard unit cell of the period lattice (see § 13) by replacing every point on the actual path by the equivalent point in the standard cell. If there are no linear integral relations between the ν_k's, this path in the w-space approaches indefinitely near to each point in the standard cell (as proved in Appendix I). The representation of the q-space in the w-space is continuous; so in this case the path in the q-space approaches indefinitely close to every point of an f-dimensional region.

Astronomers call such motions conditionally periodic.

Since the function S increases by J_k each time the co-ordinate q_k traverses a period while the other q's remain unaltered, it follows that the function

$$S^* = S - \sum_k w_k J_k \tag{16}$$

is a multiply periodic function of the w's with the fundamental period 1. For, if w_k alters by 1, and the other w's remain the same, q_k traverses one period and the remaining q's return to their original values, without having completed a period, *i.e.* S increases by J_k and S^* remains unaltered.

S^* may be regarded as the generator of a canonical transformation instead of S. The equation

$$\sum p_k \dot{q}_k = -\sum w_k \dot{J}_k + \frac{dS}{dt}$$

is in fact equivalent to

$$\sum p_k \dot{q}_k = \sum J_k \dot{w}_k + \frac{dS^*}{dt},$$

and this gives the transformation

$$\begin{aligned} J_k &= -\frac{\partial}{\partial w_k} S^*(q, w), \\ p_k &= \frac{\partial}{\partial q_k} S^*(q, w). \end{aligned} \tag{17}$$

From this we can deduce a simple expression for the mean kinetic energy in the case of non-relativistic mechanics. We have (*cf.* (8), § 5)

$$\begin{aligned} 2\overline{T} &= \frac{1}{t_2 - t_1}\int_{t_1}^{t_2} \sum p_k \dot{q}_k dt = \frac{1}{t_2 - t_1}\int_{t_1}^{t_2} \sum p_k dq_k \\ &= \frac{1}{t_2 - t_1}\int_{t_1}^{t_2} \sum J_k dw_k + \frac{1}{t_2 - t_1}\int_{t_1}^{t_2} dS^*. \end{aligned}$$

If we choose the time interval (t_1, t_2) sufficiently long, it follows that

$$\begin{aligned} 2\overline{T} &= \frac{1}{t_2 - t_1}\int_{t_1}^{t_2} \sum J_k \nu_k dt \\ 2\overline{T} &= \sum J_k \nu_k. \end{aligned} \tag{18}$$

The integrals J_k (12) introduced here appear to be suitable for the formulation of quantum conditions in the form $J_k = n_k h$. By definition, however, they are associated with a co-ordinate system (q, p) in which the Hamilton-Jacobi equation is separable; it is therefore essential that we should next examine the conditions under which this co-ordinate system is uniquely determined by the condition of separability. We shall therefore see if there are point transformations (*i.e.* transformations of the co-ordinates among themselves) which transform the set of variables in which the Hamilton-Jacobi equation is separable into another such set.

Let us suppose that there is a co-ordinate system, in which the Hamilton-Jacobi equation of the motion under consideration is separable. We suppose further, that no commensurabilities independent of the initial conditions, or, as we say, " identical " commensurabilities, exist between the periods. We can then choose the initial conditions so that the path does not close. If one variable q_k performs a libration, the motion is confined between two $(f-1)$-dimensional planes q_k=const., which are touched successively. If, however, q_k performs a rotation, it may be confined to the region 0 to $\tilde{\omega}_k$, where $\tilde{\omega}_k$ is the corresponding period, by displacing the parts of the path in the intervals

$$(\tau\tilde{\omega}_k, (\tau+1)\tilde{\omega}_k)$$

back to the interval $(0, \tilde{\omega}_k)$. The whole path is confined then to the interior of an f-dimensional " parallelepiped " orientated in the direction of the co-ordinate axes. The $(f-1)$-dimensional planes bounding the parallelepiped have a significance independent of the co-ordinate system.

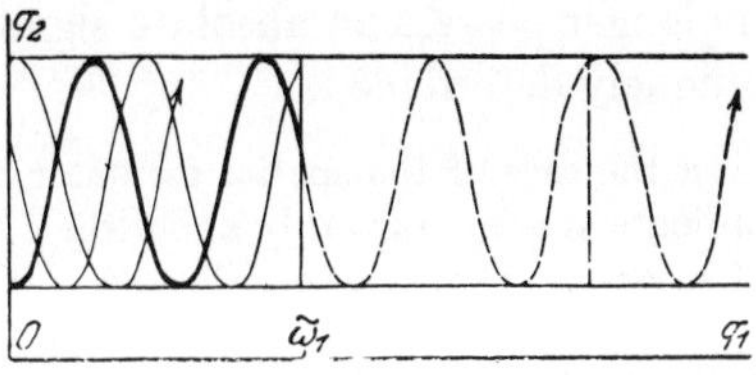

FIG. 7.

By varying the initial conditions we can alter the dimensions of the parallelepiped and so displace the invariable planes. It follows that in this case (*i.e.* no identical commensurabilities) the directions in the f-dimensional q-space which are the axes of the co-ordinates in which the Hamilton-Jacobi equation is separable have an absolute significance, and that only the scale of each individual variable can be altered.

Hence in the absence of identical commensurabilities all systems of co-ordinates, in which separation of the variables is possible, are connected by a transformation of the form

$$\bar{q}_k = f_k(q_k).$$

The associated momenta transform, by (10), § 7, according to the equation

$$p_k = \bar{p}_k \frac{df_k}{dq_k} + g_k(q_1 \ldots q_f).$$

We thus have

$$\oint p_k dq_k = \oint \bar{p}_k \frac{df_k}{dq_k} dq_k + \oint g_k dq_k.$$

The second integral on the right-hand side vanishes (on account of the closed path of integration), and the first integral becomes

$$\oint \bar{p}_k d\bar{q}_k.$$

Thus the integrals J_k are really uniquely determined.

In the case of the spatial oscillator the path fills, in the general case, a parallelepiped. In the absence, then, of identical commensurabilities, the rectangular co-ordinates, or functions of them, are the only separation variables, and the integrals J_x, J_y, and J_z have an absolute significance.

If identical commensurabilities exist, the path does not occupy all the space of the parallelepiped and the co-ordinate directions need no longer possess an absolute significance. The J_k also need not be uniquely determined.

In the case of the spatial oscillator with $\nu_x = \nu_y$, we could rotate the co-ordinate system arbitrarily about the z-axis without destroying the property of separation in x, y, z co-ordinates. We obtained, in the various co-ordinate systems, different J_x's and J_y's. Further, rectangular co-ordinates are not the only ones for which the oscillator may be treated by the separation method.

In order to show this and at the same time to give an example of the solution of the Hamilton-Jacobi equation by separation, in a case where it does not resolve additively (*i.e.* is not of the form (1)), we shall use cylindrical co-ordinates in treating the spatial oscillator for which $\nu_x = \nu_y = \nu$. The canonical transformation (12), § 7 :

$$\begin{aligned} x &= r\cos\phi \qquad & p_r &= p_x \cos\phi + p_y \sin\phi \\ y &= r\sin\phi \qquad & p_\phi &= -p_x r\sin\phi + p_y r\cos\phi \\ z &= z \qquad & p_z &= p_z \end{aligned}$$

transforms the Hamiltonian function into

$$H = \frac{1}{2m}\left(p_r^2 + p_z^2 + \frac{1}{r^2}p_\phi^2\right) + \frac{m}{2}(\omega^2 r^2 + \omega_z^2 z^2).$$

We try to solve the Hamilton-Jacobi equation

$$\left(\frac{\partial S}{\partial r}\right)^2 + \left(\frac{\partial S}{\partial z}\right)^2 + \frac{1}{r^2}\left(\frac{\partial S}{\partial \phi}\right)^2 + m^2(\omega^2 r^2 + \omega_z^2 z^2) = 2mW$$

on the assumption that

$$S = S_r(r) + S_\phi(\phi) + S_z(z).$$

Since ϕ is a cyclic co-ordinate,

$$S_\phi = \alpha_\phi \phi.$$

If now we collect together the terms dependent on z and put them equal to a constant, which we denote by $m^2\omega_z^2 a_z^2$, we get :

$$\left(\frac{dS_z}{dz}\right)^2 + m^2\omega_z^2 z^2 = m^2\omega_z^2 a_z^2,$$

and, for the terms depending on r there remains

$$\left(\frac{dS_r}{dr}\right)^2+\frac{\alpha_\phi^{\ 2}}{r^2}+m^2\omega^2r^2=2mW-m^2\omega_z^{\ 2}a_z^{\ 2}.$$

Two of the three action integrals may be evaluated at once (J_z by introducing the auxiliary variable $\psi=\sin^{-1}\frac{z}{a_z}$ as in § 9); we find:

$$(19)\qquad \begin{aligned} J_r&=m\omega\oint\left[-r^4+\frac{2W-m\omega_z^{\ 2}a_z^{\ 2}}{m\omega^2}r^2-\frac{\alpha_\phi^{\ 2}}{m^2\omega^2}\right]^{\frac{1}{2}}\frac{dr}{r}\\ J_\phi&=2\pi\alpha_\phi\\ J_z&=m\omega_z\oint(a_z^{\ 2}-z^2)^{\frac{1}{2}}dz=\pi m\omega_z a_z^{\ 2}. \end{aligned}$$

On substituting $r^2=x$, the first integral takes the form

$$J_r=\frac{m\omega}{2}\oint[-a+2bx-x^2]^{\frac{1}{2}}dx/x,$$

where

$$a=\frac{\alpha_\phi^{\ 2}}{m^2\omega^2},\qquad b=\frac{W-\frac{1}{2}m\omega_z^{\ 2}a_z^{\ 2}}{m\omega^2}.$$

This integral may be evaluated by the method given in the Appendix. We get (*cf.* (5) in Appendix II)

$$J_r=\frac{m\omega}{2}\cdot 2\pi(b-\sqrt{a})=\pi\left(\frac{W}{\omega}-\alpha_\phi-\frac{m\omega_z^{\ 2}a_z^{\ 2}}{2\omega}\right).$$

By expressing α_ϕ and a_z here in terms of J_ϕ and J_z, we get for the energy

$$(20)\qquad W=\nu(2J_r+J_\phi)+\nu_zJ_z,\qquad \nu=\frac{\omega}{2\pi},\qquad \nu_z=\frac{\omega_z}{2\pi}.$$

It will be seen from the equations (19) that J_r and J_ϕ have a completely different meaning from the quantities J_x and J_y, derived by separation in rectangular co-ordinates; J_ϕ, for example, is now 2π times the angular momentum about the z-axis. J_z, however, has the same meaning as before; also, the factor of ν, namely $2J_r+J_\phi$, has the same significance as the former J_x+J_y (it is $1/\nu$ times the energy of an oscillator for which J_z is zero). In this case, therefore, a meaning could be attached to the quantum conditions

$$2J_r+J_\phi=nh$$
$$J_z=n_zh.$$

The restriction of J_r and J_ϕ individually by such conditions would, on the other hand, lead to quantum motions altogether different from those arising from the corresponding restriction of J_x and J_y in the case of a certain rectangular co-ordinate system.

We now consider more closely the connection between the w_x, w_y, J_x, J_y and the w_r, w_ϕ, J_r, J_ϕ.

We have

$$J_\phi=2\pi p_\phi,$$

where

$$p_\phi=m(x\dot{y}-y\dot{x})$$

is the component of angular momentum about the z-axis. If x and y are expressed here in terms of the angle and action variables by (9), § 9, we find

$$J_\phi = \frac{2}{\nu}\sqrt{J_x J_y}\sin 2\pi(w_x - w_y). \tag{21}$$

Here $w_x - w_y = \delta_x - \delta_y$ is a constant. On the other hand

$$\frac{w_x + w_y}{2} = \nu t + \frac{\delta_x + \delta_y}{2}$$

is equal to the variable $w_\phi = \frac{\phi}{2\pi}$, conjugated with J_ϕ. The value of J_r is found from the equation

$$2J_r + J_\phi = J_x + J_y,$$

and is given by

$$J_r = \frac{1}{2}(J_x + J_y) - \frac{1}{\nu}\sqrt{J_x J_y}\sin 2\pi(w_x - w_y).$$

Finally, the equation for w_r may be obtained by calculating w_r from J_r and J_ϕ with the help of the equations of motion and substituting for these quantities the values found above.

The transformation which connects the system of variables $w_r w_\phi\ J_r J_\phi$ with the system $w_x w_y\ J_x J_y$ is not one which transforms the w's and the J's among themselves. In fact, the constant difference $w_x - w_y$ enters into the relations between $J_\phi J_r$ and $J_x J_y$. We shall see that this is a characteristic of every degenerate system (see § 15 for definition of degenerate system).

§ 15.—General Multiply Periodic Systems. Uniqueness of the Action Variables

Hitherto we have applied the quantum theory only to mechanical systems whose motion may be calculated by separation of the variables. We proceed now to deal in a general manner with the question of when it is possible to introduce the angle and action variables w_k and J_k so admirably suited to the application of the quantum theory. For this purpose it is necessary, in the first place, to fix the J's by suitable postulates so that only integral linear transformations with the determinant ± 1 are possible; for it is only in such cases that the quantum conditions

$$J_k = n_k h \tag{1}$$

can have a meaning attached to them.

Generalising our former considerations, we fix our attention on mechanical systems[1] whose Hamiltonian functions $H(q_1, p_1 \ldots)$ do not involve the time explicitly. We assume further that it is possible to find new variables w_k, J_k derived from the q_k, p_k by means

[1] The following conditions according to J. M. Burgers, *Het Atoommodel van Rutherford-Bohr* (Diss. Leyden), Haarlem, 1918, § 10.

of a canonical transformation with the generator S $(q_1, J_1 \ldots q_f, J_f)$ so that

$$p_k = \frac{\partial S}{\partial q_k} \tag{2}$$
$$w_k = \frac{\partial S}{\partial J_k}$$

in such a way as to fulfil the following conditions :—

(A) The configuration of the system shall be periodic in the w_k's with the fundamental period 1. The q_k's, which are uniquely determined by the configuration state of the system, shall be periodic functions of the w_k's with the fundamental period 1 ; if for a given configuration of the system q_k is indeterminate to the extent of an integral multiple of some constant (2π, say), it is only the residue of q_k to the modulus of this constant which is periodic. In the latter case there are also functions (*e.g.* $\sin q_k$) which are periodic in the w_k, in the strict sense of the word (§ 13).

(B) The Hamiltonian function transforms into a function W, depending only on the J_k's.

It follows from this that the w_k's are linear functions of the time, and that the J_k's are constant. The functions $q_k(w_1 \ldots w_f)$ possess a periodicity lattice in the w-space, the cells of the lattice being cubes with sides 1.

Now it may be easily shown that the quantities J_k (apart from being indeterminate to the extent of a linear integral transformation with the determinant ± 1) are not yet uniquely determined by the two conditions (A) and (B).

A simple canonical transformation, which does not violate the conditions (A) and (B), is as follows :—

$$\bar{w}_k = w_k + f_k(J_1 \ldots J_f) \tag{3}$$
$$\bar{J}_k = J_k + c_k,$$

where the c_k's are constants. The arbitrariness in the choice of the c_k's prevents the application of the quantum conditions (1) for, if the J_k's are determined as integral multiples of h, this will not in general be the case for the $\bar{J}_k$'s. We must therefore do away with this remaining arbitrariness in the choice of the variables. This may be accomplished by postulating generally a property of the w's and J's found previously to hold in the case of separable systems.

(C) The function

$$S^* = S - \sum_k w_k J_k,$$

which is the generator of our transformation ($q_k p_k \rightarrow w_k J_k$) in the form

$$p_k = \frac{\partial}{\partial q_k} S^*(q_1 w_1 \ldots)$$

(5)

$$J_k = -\frac{\partial}{\partial w_k} S^*(q_1 w_1 \ldots),$$

shall be a periodic function of the w_k's with the period 1.

It is all the same here whether we regard S^* as a function of q_k and w_k or of J_k and w_k, since the q_k's are also periodic in the w_k's.

If it be required in (C) that 1 shall be a fundamental period, (A) will be superfluous. For, if the q_k's are calculated as functions of the w_k's and J_k's from the second system of equations, they will be periodic in the w_k's with the period 1. Apart from this, it will be seen from the first system of equations that the same is true of the p_k's.

We must now prove that the conditions (A), (B), and (C) really suffice for the logical applications of quantum conditions in the form (1); we carry out the proof by finding the most general canonical transformation

$$w_k J_k \rightarrow \bar{w}_k \bar{J}_k$$

which satisfies the conditions (A), (B), and (C).

We seek the first group of the transformation equations, viz. those for $\bar{w}_k$'s in terms of the w's and J's. According to (A) the transformation must transform into itself the system of lattice points corresponding to the fundamental period 1. By (7), § 13, the w_k's must transform as follows :—

(6) $$w_k = \tau_{k1}\bar{w}_1 + \ldots + \tau_{kf}\bar{w}_f + \psi_k(\bar{w}_1, J_1, \bar{w}_2, J_2, \ldots).$$

Here the system of integers τ_{kl} has the determinant ± 1. The ψ's are periodic in the $\bar{w}_k$'s with the period 1, and, written as functions of the w_k's, periodic in these also; they may therefore be expressed in the form

$$\psi = \sum_\sigma C_\sigma e^{2\pi i(\sigma_1 w_1 + \ldots + \sigma_f w_f)}.$$

The condition (B) introduces a fresh restriction. Considered as functions of the time, the w_k's, as well as the $\bar{w}_k$'s, must be linear; from (6) it follows that ψ_k's are likewise linear functions of the time, but if they vary at all with the time they must be multiply periodic, as has just be shown; they must therefore be constant. This means, however, that, in the exponent of the Fourier series, the only combinations of the w_k which can occur are such as make

$$\sigma_1 w_1 + \ldots + \sigma_f w_f = (\sigma_1 \nu_1 + \ldots + \sigma_f \nu_f)t + (\sigma_1 \delta_1 + \ldots + \sigma_f \delta_f)$$

independent of t and therefore

$$\sigma_1\nu_1+\ldots+\sigma_f\nu_f=0$$

(identically in the J_k). ν_k denotes here the derivative $\frac{\partial W}{\partial J_k}$.

The case where identical relations

$$(\tau\nu)=\tau_1\nu_1+\ldots+\tau_f\nu_f=0$$

exist between the frequencies will enter largely into our considerations; systems for which such relations exist we shall call degenerate systems, while the others we shall refer to as non-degenerate.

We shall deal also with the case in which such relations exist only for certain values of the J_k; the mechanical system is then non-degenerate; the particular motions in question, for which $(\tau\nu)=0$, we shall call accidentally degenerate, whilst the motions of a degenerate system [$(\tau\nu)=0$ identically] are spoken of as intrinsically degenerate.

We consider first non-degenerate systems. For these the transformation (6) takes the form

$$w_k=\sum_l \tau_{kl}\bar{w}_l+\psi_k(J_1\ldots J_f). \tag{7}$$

In order now to find the second group of transformation equations of a non-degenerate system (*i.e.* those for the $\bar{J}$'s in terms of the w's and J's), we write down the generator of the transformation (7), viz.:

$$V(\bar{w}_1, J_1\ldots\bar{w}_f, J_f)=\sum_{kl}\tau_{kl}J_k\bar{w}_l+\Psi(J_1\ldots J_f)+F(\bar{w}_1\ldots\bar{w}_f),$$

where Ψ has the partial derivatives ψ_k.[1] The second group of the transformation equations now becomes

$$\bar{J}_k=\frac{\partial V}{\partial\bar{w}_k}=\sum_l \tau_{lk}J_l+f_k(\bar{w}_1\ldots\bar{w}_f). \tag{8}$$

In order to see if the transformation

$$\begin{aligned} w_k&=\sum_l \tau_{kl}\bar{w}_l+\psi_k(J_1\ldots J_f)\\ \bar{J}_k&=\sum_l \tau_{lk}J_l+f_k(\bar{w}_1\ldots\bar{w}_f)\end{aligned} \tag{9}$$

actually leaves the conditions (A), (B), and (C) unaltered, or whether we must still further restrict the number of permissible transformations, we resolve them into the three transformations

$$w_k=\mathfrak{w}_k+\psi_k(J_1\ldots J_f),\quad J_k=\mathfrak{J}_k \tag{10}$$

$$\mathfrak{w}_k=\sum_l \tau_{kl}\bar{\mathfrak{w}}_l,\qquad \bar{\mathfrak{J}}_k=\sum_l \tau_{lk}\mathfrak{J}_l \tag{11}$$

$$\bar{\mathfrak{w}}_k=\bar{w}_k,\qquad \bar{J}_k=\bar{\mathfrak{J}}_k+f_k(\bar{w}_1\ldots\bar{w}_f). \tag{12}$$

[1] It will be seen from this, that the ψ_k's in (7) must fulfil certain differential relations in order that the transformation may be canonical.

All three are canonical; to each may be assigned a generator in the sense of § 7.

The first transformation (10) does not conflict with (A) and (B). That (C) likewise remains satisfied can be seen as follows: If S(q, J) and $\mathfrak{S}$(q, $\mathfrak{J}$) are the generators of transformations of the form (2), transforming the q, p into w, J and into $\mathfrak{w}$, $\mathfrak{J}$ respectively, then

$$\frac{\partial S(q, J)}{\partial q_k} = \frac{\partial \mathfrak{S}(q, \mathfrak{J})}{\partial q_k} = p_k;$$

since the same variables are maintained constant during the differentiation, it follows that S$-\mathfrak{S}$ is independent of q_k. For S*$-\mathfrak{S}$* we have then

$$S^* - \mathfrak{S}^* = S - \mathfrak{S} - \sum_k w_k J_k + \sum_k (w_k - \psi_k) J_k = S - \mathfrak{S} - \sum_k \psi_k J_k;$$

from which it is seen that (C) is fulfilled.

It will be seen at once that (11) leaves (A) and (B) unviolated; we test as follows for the condition (C). For $\mathfrak{S}^*(q, \mathfrak{w})$ and $\overline{\mathfrak{S}^*}(q, \bar{\mathfrak{w}})$ we have on the one hand

$$\frac{\partial \mathfrak{S}^*}{\partial q_k} = \frac{\partial \overline{\mathfrak{S}^*}}{\partial q_k} = p_k;$$

since the same variables are kept constant during the differentiation (the $\mathfrak{w}$'s are transformed into the $\bar{\mathfrak{w}}$'s by a linear transformation with a non-zero determinant) it follows that $\mathfrak{S}^* - \overline{\mathfrak{S}^*}$ does not depend on q. On the other hand

$$\frac{\partial \overline{\mathfrak{S}^*}}{\partial \bar{\mathfrak{w}}_k} = \bar{\mathfrak{J}}_k = \sum_l \tau_{lk} \mathfrak{J}_l = \sum_l \tau_{lk} \frac{\partial \mathfrak{S}^*}{\partial \mathfrak{w}_l} = \sum_l \frac{\partial \mathfrak{S}^*}{\partial \mathfrak{w}_l} \frac{\partial \mathfrak{w}_l}{\partial \bar{\mathfrak{w}}_k} = \frac{\partial \mathfrak{S}^*}{\partial \bar{\mathfrak{w}}_k},$$

and it follows from this that $\mathfrak{S}^* - \overline{\mathfrak{S}^*}$ is also independent of $\bar{\mathfrak{w}}$ and $\mathfrak{w}$.

In order that the complete transformation (9) may fulfil all three conditions it is necessary and sufficient that this shall be the case for (12).

For $\overline{\mathfrak{S}^*}(q, \bar{\mathfrak{w}})$ and $\overline{S^*}(q, \bar{w})$ we have:

$$\frac{\partial \overline{\mathfrak{S}^*}}{\partial q_k} = \frac{\partial \overline{S^*}}{\partial q_k} = p_k,$$

thus

$$\overline{\mathfrak{S}^*} - \overline{S^*} = R(\bar{w}_1 \ldots \bar{w}_f).$$

Further, from (12)

$$\frac{\partial \overline{\mathfrak{S}^*}}{\partial \bar{\mathfrak{w}}_k} = \frac{\partial \overline{S^*}}{\partial \bar{w}_k} - f_k(\bar{w}_1 \ldots \bar{w}_f),$$

thus

$$\frac{\partial R}{\partial \bar{w}_k} = -f_k(\bar{w}_1 \ldots \bar{w}_f).$$

If (C) is to remain valid for the transformation (12), R must be periodic in the $\bar{w}_k$, f_k may therefore be represented by a Fourier series without a constant term. If (B) is to remain valid, f_k must not depend on the time. From these two conditions it follows that f_k must vanish. Hence if $f_k=0$, (A), (B), and (C) remain unviolated.

We have proved by this that the most general transformation for the action variables is

$$\bar{J}_k = \sum_l \tau_{lk} J_l. \tag{13}$$

If the J_k's are now determined as integral multiples of h, the same will be true of the $\bar{J}_k$'s and conversely.

Although we have been guided in our considerations by the idea that J_k/h must take integral values, we can state the mechanical theorem proved in a form independent of any quantum theory :

Uniqueness theorem for non-degenerate systems : If we can introduce in a mechanical system variables w_k and J_k so that the conditions (A), (B), and (C) are satisfied, and if between the quantities

$$\nu_k = \frac{\partial W}{\partial J_k}$$

no commensurability exists, then the J_k's are determined uniquely, apart from a homogeneous linear integral transformation with the determinant ± 1.

We proceed now to the treatment of degenerate systems.

If between the ν_k's there exist $(f-s)$ commensurability relations

$$\sum_k \tau_k \nu_k = 0 \tag{14}$$

we can arrange, by means of a canonical transformation satisfying the conditions (A), (B), and (C), that $f-s$ of the frequencies $\bar{\nu}_k = \frac{\partial W}{\partial \bar{J}_k}$ shall vanish and that between the remaining s no relation of the type (14) shall exist. If we call the new variables w_k and J_k once more, we have

$$\begin{aligned} &\nu_\alpha\text{'s incommensurable}, && \alpha = 1, 2 \ldots s, \\ &\nu_\rho = 0 && \rho = s+1, s+2 \ldots f, \end{aligned} \tag{14'}$$

and the Hamiltonian function has the form

$$W(J_\alpha).$$

The w_α's and J_α's we call proper angle and action variables, the w_ρ's and J_ρ's improper or degenerate variables ; the w_ρ's remain constant during the motion. The number s of the independent frequencies ν_α is called the degree of periodicity of the system.

In the case of accidental degeneration, the number of independent frequencies is less for certain motions than for the number of the whole system. We call the former number the degree of periodicity of the motion under consideration.

We must now seek the most general transformation which violates neither this division of the variables nor the conditions (A), (B), and (C). The first group of transformation equations (*i.e.* that for the w_k's) is now :

$$w_k=\sum_l \tau_{kl}\bar{w}_l+\psi_k(\bar{w}_{s+1}\ldots\bar{w}_f,\ J_1\ldots J_f).$$

The generator is therefore

$$\text{(15)}\qquad \begin{aligned} &V(\bar{w}_1\ldots\bar{w}_f,\ J_1\ldots J_f)\\ &\quad=\sum_{kl}\tau_{kl}J_k\bar{w}_l+\Psi(\bar{w}_{s+1}\ldots\bar{w}_f,\ J_1\ldots J_f)+F(\bar{w}_1\ldots\bar{w}_f),\end{aligned}$$

where Ψ is periodic in the $\bar{w}_\rho$. The second group of transformation equations then becomes :

$$\bar{J}_k=\sum_l \tau_{lk}J_l+\frac{\partial\Psi}{\partial\bar{w}_k}+f_k(\bar{w}_1\ldots\bar{w}_f)\ ;$$

the derivative of Ψ is non-zero only if k is one of the numbers $s+1\ldots f$.

In order that the division into non-degenerate and degenerate variables may persist, the w_ρ's must not depend on the $\bar{w}_\alpha$'s or the $\bar{w}_\rho$'s on the w_α's. This means, however, that the $\tau_{\rho\alpha}$'s vanish. The transformation equations can then be written as follows :—

$$\text{(16)}\qquad \left.\begin{aligned} w_\alpha&=\sum_l \tau_{\alpha l}\bar{w}_l+\psi_\alpha(\bar{w}_\sigma,\ J)\\ w_\rho&=\sum_\sigma \tau_{\rho\sigma}\bar{w}_\sigma+\psi_\rho(\bar{w}_\sigma,\ J)\\ \bar{J}_\alpha&=\sum_\beta \tau_{\beta\alpha}J_\beta+f_\alpha(\bar{w})\\ \bar{J}_\rho&=\sum_l \tau_{l\rho}J_l+\phi_\rho(\bar{w}_\sigma,\ J)+f_\rho(\bar{w}),\end{aligned}\right\}\begin{aligned}&\alpha,\ \beta=1\ldots s\\ &\rho,\ \sigma=s+1\ldots f\\ &l=1\ldots f\end{aligned}$$

where $\dfrac{\partial\Psi}{\partial\bar{w}_\rho}$ is put equal to ϕ_ρ. Since the τ_{kl} are whole numbers and the $\tau_{\rho\alpha}$ vanish, it follows, from the value of the determinant, that

$$|\tau_{kl}|=\pm1,$$

also

$$|\tau_{\alpha\beta}|=\pm1.$$

We now divide the transformation (16) in two parts :

$$(17)\qquad \begin{aligned} w_\alpha &= \sum_l \tau_{\alpha l}\mathfrak{w}_l + \psi_\alpha(\mathfrak{w}_\sigma, \mathrm{J}) & \mathfrak{J}_\alpha &= \sum_\beta \tau_{\beta\alpha}\mathrm{J}_\beta \\ w_\rho &= \sum_\sigma \tau_{\rho\sigma}\mathfrak{w}_\sigma + \psi_\rho(\mathfrak{w}_\sigma, \mathrm{J}) & \mathfrak{J}_\rho &= \sum_l \tau_{l\rho}\mathrm{J}_l + \phi_\rho(\mathfrak{w}_\sigma, \mathrm{J}) \end{aligned}$$

and

$$(18)\qquad \mathfrak{w}_k = \bar{w}_k, \qquad \bar{\mathrm{J}}_k = \mathfrak{J}_k + f_k(\bar{w}),$$

and show that the first satisfies the condition (C) and that the second does this only for $f_\alpha = 0$.

As before, let $\mathrm{S}(q, \mathrm{J})$ and $\mathfrak{S}(q, \mathfrak{J})$ be the generators of the transformations $q, p \to w, \mathrm{J}$ and $q, p \to \mathfrak{w}, \mathfrak{J}$. We consider the function $\mathrm{S} - \mathfrak{S}$ from the point of view of its dependence on $\mathfrak{w}$ and J, *i.e.* we write

$$\mathrm{S} = \mathrm{S}(q(\mathfrak{w}, \mathrm{J}), \mathrm{J}), \qquad \mathfrak{S} = \mathfrak{S}(q(\mathfrak{w}, \mathrm{J}), \mathfrak{J}(\mathfrak{w}, \mathrm{J}))$$

and form

$$\begin{aligned} \frac{\partial}{\partial \mathfrak{w}_k}(\mathrm{S} - \mathfrak{S}) &= \sum_l \frac{\partial \mathrm{S}}{\partial q_l}\frac{\partial q_l}{\partial \mathfrak{w}_k} - \sum_l \frac{\partial \mathfrak{S}}{\partial q_l}\frac{\partial q_l}{\partial \mathfrak{w}_k} - \sum_l \frac{\partial \mathfrak{S}}{\partial \mathfrak{J}_l}\frac{\partial \mathfrak{J}_l}{\partial \mathfrak{w}_k} \\ &= -\sum_\sigma \mathfrak{w}_\sigma \frac{\partial \phi_\sigma}{\partial \mathfrak{w}_k} \end{aligned}$$

from (17), the first two terms cancelling. We have therefore

$$(19)\qquad \frac{\partial}{\partial \mathfrak{w}_\alpha}(\mathrm{S} - \mathfrak{S}) = 0, \qquad \frac{\partial}{\partial \mathfrak{w}_\rho}(\mathrm{S} - \mathfrak{S}) = -\sum_\sigma \mathfrak{w}_\sigma \frac{\partial \phi_\sigma}{\partial \mathfrak{w}_\rho}.$$

We derive further :

$$(20)\qquad \begin{aligned} \frac{\partial}{\partial \mathrm{J}_k}(\mathrm{S} - \mathfrak{S}) &= \sum_l \frac{\partial \mathrm{S}}{\partial q_l}\frac{\partial q_l}{\partial \mathrm{J}_k} + \frac{\partial \mathrm{S}}{\partial \mathrm{J}_k} - \sum_l \frac{\partial \mathfrak{S}}{\partial q_l}\frac{\partial q_l}{\partial \mathrm{J}_k} - \sum_l \frac{\partial \mathfrak{S}}{\partial \mathfrak{J}_l}\frac{\partial \mathfrak{J}_l}{\partial \mathrm{J}_k} \\ &= w_k - \sum_l \mathfrak{w}_l \frac{\partial \mathfrak{J}_l}{\partial \mathrm{J}_k} = \psi_k - \sum_\sigma \mathfrak{w}_\sigma \frac{\partial \phi_\sigma}{\partial \mathrm{J}_k}. \end{aligned}$$

It follows from (19) and (20) that

$$\mathrm{S} - \mathfrak{S} = \Psi(\mathfrak{w}_\sigma, \mathrm{J}) - \sum_\sigma \mathfrak{w}_\sigma \phi_\sigma,$$

where Ψ has the same meaning as in (15). We shall have therefore

$$\begin{aligned} \mathrm{S}^* - \mathfrak{S}^* &= \mathrm{S} - \mathfrak{S} - \sum_k \Big(\sum_l \tau_{kl}\mathfrak{w}_l + \psi_k\Big)\mathrm{J}_k \\ &\quad + \sum_k \mathfrak{w}_k\Big(\sum_l \tau_{lk}\mathrm{J}_l + \phi_k\Big) \\ &= \Psi(\mathfrak{w}_\sigma, \mathrm{J}) - \sum_k \mathrm{J}_k \psi_k(\mathfrak{w}_\sigma, \mathrm{J})\,; \end{aligned}$$

this denotes, however, that (C) remains valid.

The condition that (C) should be satisfied by the transformation (18) is found as in the non-degenerate case, viz, :

$$f_k(\bar{w}) = -\frac{\partial}{\partial w_k} R(\bar{w}).$$

If (C) and (B) are satisfied, $f_k(\bar{w})$ is a periodic function of the form

$$f_k(\bar{w}) = \sum_\tau C_\tau \tau_k e^{2\pi i(\tau \bar{w})},$$

in which only exponents containing $\bar{w}_\rho$ alone may occur; consequently $\tau_\alpha = 0$ always. It follows from this, however, that

$$f_\alpha(\bar{w}) = 0.$$

The most general permissible transformation of the non-degenerate action variables is therefore

$$\bar{J}_\alpha = \sum_\beta \tau_{\beta\alpha} J_\beta. \tag{21}$$

The J_ρ's, on the other hand, need not transform integrally. Since the condition (C) does not forbid the occurrence here of $\bar{w}_l$ in the transformation equations of the J_ρ's, it follows that from a system J_ρ, in which all the J_ρ's are integral multiples of h, a system $\bar{J}_\rho$ may always be derived which does not possess this property (*cf.* examples of § 14).

We can state the result of our investigations independently of the quantum theory as follows:—

If we can introduce in a mechanical system variables $w_k J_k$ which satisfy the conditions (A), (B), and (C), we can always arrange so that certain of the partial derivatives

$$\nu_k = \frac{\partial W}{\partial J_k},$$

namely, the ν_α's ($\alpha = 1 \ldots s$), are incommensurable while the remaining ones ν_ρ ($\rho = s+1 \ldots f$) vanish. The J_α's are then uniquely determined, apart from a homogeneous integral linear transformation with the determinant ± 1.[1]

We deduce still another consequence from the periodicity of S^* as a function of q and w or J and w; the function

$$S = S^* + \sum w_k J_k$$

increases by J_k when w_k increases by 1 and the other w's and J's remain constant. We can write this in the form:

$$J_k = \int_0^1 dw_k \left(\frac{\partial S}{\partial w_k}\right)_J = \int_0^1 dw_k \sum_l \frac{\partial S}{\partial q_l} \frac{\partial q_l}{\partial w_k},$$

or:

[1] J. M. Burgers, who refers to this theorem in his dissertation, does not give a complete proof.

$$J_k = \int_0^1 dw_k \sum_l p_l \frac{\partial q_l}{\partial w_k}. \tag{22}$$

This integral may be employed to ascertain if a given motion fulfils the quantum conditions or not, since all that is necessary is a knowledge of the p and q as functions of the w_α's.

§ 16.—The Adiabatic Invariance of the Action Variables and the Quantum Conditions for Several Degrees of Freedom

As in the case of one degree of freedom, the uniqueness of the action variables is only one of the conditions necessary if the quantum conditions in the form

$$J_\alpha = n_\alpha h$$

are to have a definite meaning attached to them.

As a second condition we must require that the J_α's shall be constant not only for an isolated system but also in the case of a system subject to slowly varying influences, in accordance with the principles of classical mechanics.

In fact the following principle applies in this case also :—

The action variables J_α are adiabatically invariant so long as they remain in a region free from new degenerations.

We carry out the proof (after J. M. Burgers) exactly as we did in the case of one degree of freedom.[1] We imagine the canonical transformation

$$p_k = \frac{\partial S^*}{\partial q_k},$$

$$J_k = -\frac{\partial S^*}{\partial w_k}$$

applied to the variables q_k, p_k, satisfying the canonical equations

$$\dot{q}_k = \frac{\partial H}{\partial p_k}, \qquad \dot{p}_k = -\frac{\partial H}{\partial q_k},$$

so that, for constant a, the variables q_k, p_k are transformed into the angle and action variables w_k, J_k. By (1), § 7, H is transformed to

$$\bar{H} = H + \frac{\partial S^*}{\partial t}.$$

Thus the transformed canonical equations can be written

---

[1] The proof of the adiabatic invariance of the J's given here is not altogether free from objection on account of difficulties due to the appearance of accidentally degenerate motions in the course of the adiabatic change. A strict proof has been given by M. v. Laue, *Ann. d. Physik*, vol. lxxi, p. 619, 1925.

$$\dot{w}_k = \frac{\partial H}{\partial J_k} + \frac{\partial}{\partial J_k}\left(\frac{\partial S^*}{\partial t}\right),$$

$$\dot{J}_k = -\frac{\partial H}{\partial w_k} - \frac{\partial}{\partial w_k}\left(\frac{\partial S^*}{\partial t}\right).$$

Since H depends only on the J_k's, it follows that

$$\dot{J}_k = -\frac{\partial}{\partial w_k}\left(\frac{\partial S^*}{\partial t}\right) = -\frac{\partial}{\partial w_k}\left(\frac{\partial S^*}{\partial a}\right)\dot{a}.$$

In the differentiation with respect to t and a, S^* is to be regarded as a function of q_k, w_k, and t or a. Now the variation of J_k in the time interval (t_1, t_2) is

$$J_k^{(2)} - J_k^{(1)} = -\int_{t_1}^{t_2} \dot{a}\frac{\partial}{\partial w_k}\left(\frac{\partial S^*}{\partial a}\right)dt\ ;$$

and on account of the supposed slow alteration of a, independently of the period of the system, $\dot{a}$ can be put before the integral sign. We will now show that

(1) $$\frac{J_k^{(2)} - J_k^{(1)}}{\dot{a}} = -\int_{t_1}^{t_2} \frac{\partial}{\partial w_k}\left(\frac{\partial S^*}{\partial a}\right)dt$$

is of the order of magnitude $\dot{a}(t_2 - t_1)$ (*cf.* § 10).

S^* is a periodic function of the w_k, so also is $\frac{\partial S^*}{\partial a}$, and the integrand of (1) is a Fourier series

$$\sum_\tau{}' A_\tau(J, a)e^{2\pi i(\tau w)},$$

without a constant term, so that the integral to be evaluated takes the form

$$\int_{t_1}^{t_2} \sum_\tau{}' A_\tau e^{2\pi i[(\tau\nu)t + (\tau\delta)]}dt\ ;$$

where A_τ, ν, and δ are functions of the J's and of a. We develop the integrand in the neighbourhood of a certain value of t, which we denote by $t=0$ as in § 10, and obtain

(2) $$\sum_\tau{}' A_{\tau 0}e^{2\pi i[(\tau\nu_0)t + (\tau\delta_0)]}$$
$$+\dot{a}t\sum_\tau{}'[A'_{\tau 0} + 2\pi i A_{\tau 0}\{(\tau\nu_0)t + (\tau\delta_0)\}]e^{2\pi i[(\tau\nu_0)t + (\delta_0)]} + \ldots,$$

the notation being similar to that used in (4), § 10. Consider this expansion carried out at the beginning of the interval (t_1, t_2) and the integral taken from t_1 to such a point that the integral of the first term vanishes. This is always possible, since the indefinite integral of the first term is a multiply periodic function, and in intervals of the order of magnitude $1/(\tau\nu_0)$ passes continually through zero. The integral of the second term is of the order of magnitude $\dot{a}$T or $\dot{a}$T^2. We imagine now a new expansion (2) carried out at the beginning of the remaining interval and the integral again taken so far that the first term vanishes. This process we suppose continued until finally there remains an interval over which the integral of the first term has a non-zero value. It will be seen that, if none of the $(\tau\nu)$'s vanish on the path of integration, the complete integral is of the order of magnitude $\dot{a}(t_2-t_1)$.

In the case where an identical relation (*i.e.* a relation valid for all J's) $(\nu\tau)=0$ exists for a certain value of a, the w's and J's may be chosen so that the ν_α's are incommensurable and the ν_ρ's equal to 0 (*cf.* (14), § 15). Constant exponents ($(\tau\nu)=0$) then appear in S*, but they involve the w_ρ's only ; the terms in question disappear, therefore, on differentiating with respect to w_α, consequently the J_α's remain invariant at such places of degeneration ; this cannot be said generally to hold for the J_ρ's.

In addition to those cases where $(\tau\nu)$ is identically zero, it may happen that $(\tau\nu)$ is zero only for the particular values of J_k under consideration ; in the latter case we speak of " accidental degeneration," and under such circumstances the J's need not be invariant unless, in the expansion (2) of the integrand of (1) for the different J_k's, the term $A_{\tau 0}$ with the corresponding exponent (τw) occurs in S with zero amplitude.

It follows then that if the J_k's are to be adiabatically invariant we must exclude all cases for which an accidental commensurability exists (*i.e.* one which holds only for the values of J under consideration) between frequencies which occur conjointly in the form $(\tau\nu)$ in the exponent of a term of the Fourier series for S*.

As an example of the adiabatic invariance of an action variable we consider the case where the mechanical system is invariant with respect to a rotation about an axis fixed in space. If (r, ϕ, z) are cylindrical co-ordinates, the angle of rotation ϕ_1 and the differences $\phi_k-\phi_1$ may be introduced as co-ordinates instead of the individual ϕ; ϕ_1 is then a cyclic variable, and (*cf.* § 6) the momentum conjugated with it is the angular momentum of the system about the z-axis. The principle of the conservation of angular momentum about an axis is also valid when the expression for the potential energy contains the time explicitly, provided only that the invariance with respect to a rotation about the axis persists identically in time. If the field of force of rotational symmetry be strengthened or weakened, the angular momentum about the z-axis remains invariant, and we have a special case of the principle of the adiabatic invariance of the action variables.

In order to see what may happen in the case of a passage of the system through a degenerate state, we consider once again the spatial oscillator. We suppose that the directions of the principal axes of the potential energy ellipsoid as well as the magnitudes of the three frequencies are functions of a parameter a, which can be varied arbitrarily in time. If now for a certain value of a no commensurability exists between the frequencies, the J's will be adiabatic invariants. If, however, for a certain value of a we have degeneration, *e.g.* $\nu_x = \nu_y$, this will no longer be the case, though certainly there are special variations for which the J's do remain invariant. If, for instance, the directions of the principal axes are left unaltered and only the frequencies varied, the co-ordinates behave as independent linear oscillators, and the J's are adiabatic invariants for each individually. As an example of an adiabatic variation in which the J's do not remain invariant in the case of degeneration, we consider the following. We allow the original potential energy ellipsoid with three unequal axes to pass over into an ellipsoid of rotation, keeping the axes fixed; without varying the axis of rotation we now allow the axes of the ellipsoid again to become all unequal, but with the other two axes turned through a finite angle with respect to the original ones. In the instant of degeneration the projection of the motion in a plane perpendicular to the axis of rotation is an ellipse. The limiting values of the J's which are correlated with the J values before and after the degeneration are determined by the amplitudes of this elliptic motion in the directions of the principal axes of the potential energy ellipsoid; it will be seen at once that these values are different for different directions of the axes.

The uniqueness of the J_α's (in the sense of § 15), together with their adiabatic invariance, strongly suggests the following generalisation of the quantum condition for one degree of freedom:

In a mechanical system which satisfies the conditions (A), (B), and (C) of § 15, let the w_k's and J_k's be chosen so that the ν_α's ($\alpha = 1, 2 \ldots s$) are incommensurable and the ν_ρ's ($\rho = s+1 \ldots f$) are zero (it may be that $s = f$). The stationary states of this system will be defined by the conditions[1]

$$J_\alpha = n_\alpha h. \qquad (\alpha = 1, 2 \ldots s).$$

Since the Hamiltonian function depends only on the J_α's its value is determined uniquely by the quantum numbers n_α.

To this is added, as the second quantum principle, Bohr's frequency condition

$$h\tilde{\nu} = W^{(1)} - W^{(2)}.$$

[1] The first generalisation of the quantum conditions for systems of more than one degree of freedom was given by M. Planck (*Verh. d. Dtsch. Phys. Ges.*, vol. xvii, pp. 407 and 438, 1915), W. Wilson (*Phil. Mag.*, vol. xxix, p. 795, 1915), and A. Sommerfeld (*Sitzungsber. d. K. Bay. Akad.*, p. 425, 1915). All three start out by equating the action variables to integral multiples of h. The general case of multiply periodic systems was dealt with by K. Schwarzschild (*Sitzungsber. d. Preuss. Akad.*, p. 548, 1916), and the conception of degeneration together with the restriction of the quantum conditions to the non-degenerate J's was first made clear by him. The unique determination of the J's through our conditions (§ 15) is given by J. M. Burgers, *Het Atoommodel van Rutherford-Bohr* (Diss. Leyden, 1918).

We will now collect together once more the fundamental ideas underlying the quantum mechanics as hitherto developed: the totality of the motions (supposed multiply periodic) of a given model are to be calculated according to the principles of classical mechanics (neglecting the radiation damping) ; a discrete number of motions will be selected from this continuum by means of the quantum conditions. The energies of these selected states of motion will be the actual energy values of the system, measurable by electron impact, and the energy differences will be connected with the actual light frequencies emitted by Bohr's frequency condition. Apart from the frequency the observable qualities of the emitted light comprise the intensity, phase, and state of polarisation ; with regard to these the theory gives approximate results only (§ 17). This completes the properties of the motion of atomic systems which are capable of observation. Our calculation prescribes still other properties, however, namely, frequencies of rotation and distances of separation ; in short, the progress of the motion in time. It appears that these quantities are not in general amenable to observation.[1] This leads us, then, to the conclusion that our method is, for the time being, only a formal scheme of calculation, enabling us, in certain cases, to replace true quantum principles, which are as yet unknown, by calculations on a classical basis. We must require of these true principles that they shall contain relations between observable quantities only, *i.e.* energies, light frequencies, intensities, and phases.[2] So long as these principles are unknown we must always be prepared for the failure of our present quantum rules ; one of our main problems will be to determine, by comparison with observation, the limits within which these rules are valid.

§ 17.—The Correspondence Principle for Several Degrees of Freedom

As in § 11, we must now investigate to what extent the classical theory may be regarded as a limiting case of the quantum theory. In this limiting case the discrete energy steps run together into the continuum of the classical theory. We show further that a relation similar to that holding in the case of one degree of freedom exists between the classical and quantum frequencies.

When the classical radiation damping is neglected, the electric

---

[1] Measurements of the radii of atoms and the like do not give a closer approximation to reality than, say, the agreement between rotation frequencies and light frequencies.

[2] This idea forms the starting-point of the new quantum mechanics. See W. Heisenberg, *Zeit. f. Phys.*, vol. xxxiii, p. 879, 1925.

moment of the atomic system may be represented by a Fourier series of the form

$$\mathbf{p}=\sum_{\tau}\mathbf{C}_{\tau}e^{2\pi i(\tau w)}=\sum_{\tau}\mathbf{C}_{\tau}e^{2\pi i[(\tau\nu)t+(\tau\delta)]}. \tag{1}$$

The components of the vectors $\mathbf{C}_{\tau}$ are complex quantities; since the components of $\mathbf{p}$ are real, the components of $\mathbf{C}_{\tau}$ turn into the conjugate complex quantities when the signs of all the τ_k's are reversed. By including in the constant the terms in w_{ρ}, it may be arranged that only the non-vanishing (and incommensurable) frequencies ν_{α} occur in the exponent (see (14′), § 15, for significance of suffixes α and ρ).

Now the quantum frequency associated with a transition in which the quantum numbers alter by $\tau_1 \ldots \tau_s$ corresponds, in an analogous way to the case of one degree of freedom, to the overtone of frequency

$$(\tau\nu)=\tau_1\nu_1+\ldots+\tau_s\nu_s.$$

The relation between this classical frequency and the quantum frequency is in this case also that between a differential coefficient and a difference quotient.

We consider a fixed point J_{α}^{0} in the J_{α}-space and all the straight lines

$$J_{\alpha}=J_{\alpha}^{0}-\tau_{\alpha}\lambda,$$

going out from this point, the directions of which may be pictured as lines joining J_{α}^{0} with the angular points of a cubic lattice (of arbitrary mesh magnitude) surrounding this point. The classical frequency may then be written in the form[1]

$$\tilde{\nu}_{cl}=\sum_{\alpha}\tau_{\alpha}\nu_{\alpha}=-\sum_{\alpha}\frac{\partial W}{\partial J_{\alpha}}\cdot\frac{dJ_{\alpha}}{d\lambda}=-\frac{dW}{d\lambda}. \tag{2}$$

The quantum frequency may be written in the form

$$\tilde{\nu}_{qu}=-\frac{\Delta W}{h}. \tag{3}$$

In order to describe the relation between (2) and (3) we imagine the above-defined grating chosen so that the side of the cube is equal to h, $\tilde{\nu}_{qu}$ is then the decrease in the energy in going from the grating point J_{α}^{0} to the grating point $J_{\alpha}^{0}-\tau_{\alpha}h$, expressed as a multiple of the mesh magnitude h. The classical frequency is obtained when the mesh magnitude h is made infinitely small.

The quantum frequency may also be looked upon as a mean value of the classical frequency between the grating points J_{α}^{0} and $J_{\alpha}^{0}-\tau_{\alpha}h$

[1] The signs are chosen so that emission occurs when all the τ_{α}'s are positive.

for a finite h, *i.e.* as a certain mean value between the initial and final orbits of the quantum transition, associated with radiation of that frequency. We have in fact [1]

$$(4) \qquad \tilde{\nu}_{qu} = -\frac{1}{h}\int dW = -\frac{1}{h}\int_0^h \frac{dW}{d\lambda} d\lambda = \frac{1}{h}\int_0^h \tilde{\nu}_{kl} d\lambda.$$

If the alterations τ_k of the quantum numbers are small in comparison with the numbers themselves, the expressions (3) and (2) differ very little from one another.

As in the case of one degree of freedom, the correspondence principle may be employed for the approximate determination of the intensities and states of polarisation.

If the alterations τ_k of the quantum numbers are small in comparison with the numbers themselves, the Fourier coefficients $\mathbf{C}_\tau$ for the initial and final states differ by a relatively small amount. On the basis of the correspondence principle we must now lay down the following requirement: For large values and small variations of the quantum numbers, the light wave corresponding to the quantum transition $\tau_1 \ldots \tau_s$ is approximately the same as that which would be sent out by a classical radiator with electric moment

$$\mathbf{C}_\tau e^{2\pi i(\tau w)}.$$

This determines approximately the intensity and state of polarisation of the wave. The same quantities $\mathbf{C}_\tau$ determine also the probabilities of transitions between the stationary states.

If the alterations of the quantum numbers are of the same order of magnitude as the numbers themselves, it seems likely that the amplitudes are determined by a mean value of $\mathbf{C}_\tau$ between the initial and final states. How this mean value is to be determined is still an open question.[2] It can be answered only when certain components of the classical $\mathbf{C}_\tau$ are identically zero; it may be assumed that the corresponding oscillation is also absent in the quantum theory.

These considerations can be applied in practice to the determination of the polarisation only if, during the process, at least one direction in space is kept fixed for all atoms by external conditions, *e.g.* an external field. In other cases the orientations of the atoms would be irregular and no polarisation could be established. If, for example, a certain $\mathbf{C}_\tau$ had the same direction for all atoms, then to this would correspond a linearly polarised light wave with the

[1] Comp. H. A. Kramers, *Intensities of Spectral Lines* (Diss. Leyden), Copenhagen, 1919.

[2] This question is now answered by the new quantum mechanics founded by Heisenberg (*loc. cit.*) and developed by Born, Jordan, Dirac, Schrödinger, and others.

distribution of intensity given by the classical theory for different directions in space.

Of special importance for the application of the quantum conditions and of the correspondence principle is the case in which the Hamiltonian function is not changed by the rotation as a whole of an atomic system about a fixed direction in space. If we introduce as co-ordinates the azimuth $\phi=q_f$ of one of the particles of the system together with the differences of the azimuths of the other particles from ϕ, and other magnitudes depending only on the relative position of the particles of the system with respect to the fixed direction in space, ϕ will be a cyclic variable and the momentum p_ϕ conjugated to it is, by § 6, the angular momentum of the system parallel to the fixed direction. On account of the constancy of $\frac{\partial S}{\partial \phi}$, the function S, which transforms the q_k and their momentum p_k into angle and action variables, has the form

$$S=\frac{1}{2\pi}F(J_1, J_2 \ldots J_f)\phi+\bar{S}(q_1, q_2 \ldots q_{f-1}, J_1, J_2 \ldots J_f).$$

It follows from this that

$$\begin{aligned} w_1&=\frac{1}{2\pi}\frac{\partial F}{\partial J_1}\phi+\frac{\partial \bar{S}}{\partial J_1} \\ w_2&=\frac{1}{2\pi}\frac{\partial F}{\partial J_2}\phi+\frac{\partial \bar{S}}{\partial J_2} \\ &\cdot\quad\cdot\quad\cdot\quad\cdot\quad\cdot\quad\cdot\quad\cdot \\ w_f&=\frac{1}{2\pi}\frac{\partial F}{\partial J_f}\phi+\frac{\partial \bar{S}}{\partial J_f}. \end{aligned}$$

If now $q_1 q_2 \ldots q_{f-1}$ be kept fixed and ϕ allowed to increase by 2π (*i.e.* if the whole system be rotated through 2π), the w_k's must change by whole numbers (for the q_k's are periodic in the w_k's with the period 1); for this to be the case the derivatives of F must be whole numbers and F has the form

$$F=\tau_1 J_1+\ldots+\tau_f J_f+c.$$

By means of a suitable integral transformation with the determinant ± 1 this may always be brought to the form

$$F=J_\phi+c,$$

so that

$$S=\frac{1}{2\pi}J_\phi\phi+\frac{1}{2\pi}c\,.\,\phi+\bar{S}(q_1 \ldots q_{f-1}, J_1 \ldots J_{f-1}, J_\phi).$$

It follows from this that

$$(5)\qquad \begin{aligned} w_k &= \Phi_k(q_1 \ldots q_{f-1}, J_1 \ldots J_{f-1}, J_\phi) \qquad (k=1\ldots f-1)\\ w_\phi = w_f &= \frac{1}{2\pi}\phi + \Phi_f(q_1 \ldots q_{f-1}, J_1 \ldots J_{f-1}, J_\phi), \end{aligned}$$

and by solving for the q_k

$$(6)\qquad \begin{aligned} q_k &= \Psi_k(w_1 \ldots w_{f-1}, J_1 \ldots J_{f-1}, J_\phi) \qquad (k=1\ldots f-1)\\ \phi = q_f &= 2\pi w_f + \Psi_f(w_1 \ldots w_{f-1}, J_1 \ldots J_{f-1}, J_\phi), \end{aligned}$$

so that we can write also

$$S = w_\phi(J_\phi + c) + \frac{\Psi_f}{2\pi}(J_\phi + c) + \Psi(w_1 \ldots w_{f-1}, J_1 \ldots J_{f-1}, J_\phi).$$

Since $S - w_\phi J_\phi$ must be periodic in w_ϕ, it follows that $c=0$ and so

$$(7)\qquad S = \frac{1}{2\pi}J_\phi \phi + \bar{S}(q_1 \ldots q_{f-1}, J_1 \ldots J_{f-1}, J_\phi).$$

The angular momentum in the direction of our fixed axis is consequently

$$p_\phi = \frac{\partial S}{\partial \phi} = \frac{1}{2\pi}J_\phi.$$

If there is no degeneration then we must put

$$J_\phi = mh.$$

In words :—In every system for which the potential energy is invariant with respect to a rotation about an axis fixed in space, the component of the angular momentum about the axis multiplied by 2π is an action variable. If the energy depends essentially on this quantity, it is to be quantised.

Since the functions Φ_k in (5) depend only on the relative positions of the particles of the system with respect to one another and to the fixed axis, these relative positions will be determined also by $w_1 \ldots w_{f-1}$, while w_ϕ fixes the absolute position of the system. According to (6), $2\pi w_f$ can be regarded as the mean value of the azimuth ϕ of the arbitrarily selected particle of the system over the motions of the " relative " angle variables $w_1 \ldots w_{f-1}$. The motions can therefore be considered as a multiply periodic relative one on which is superposed a uniform precession about the fixed axis. If H, regarded as a function of the J_k, does not depend on J_ϕ, this precession is zero ; the system is then degenerate.

We consider first the case where the system moves under the action of internal forces only. Every fixed direction in space can then be regarded as the axis of a cyclic azimuth. The energy does not depend on the individual components of the resultant angular momentum, but only on the sum of their squares, *i.e.* on the magnitude of the resultant angular momentum. If the direction of the angular momentum be chosen as axis, the corresponding azimuth ψ is cyclic and w_ψ non-degenerate. The resultant angular momentum p is therefore determined by a quantum condition of the form

$$(8) \qquad 2\pi p = J_\psi = jh.$$

If we fix our attention on a second arbitrary axis fixed in space, there will be a cyclic azimuth ϕ about this; the associated action variable $J_\phi = 2\pi p_\phi$ does not occur, however, in the energy function in addition to J_ψ, because the energy of the system cannot depend on a component of momentum in an arbitrary direction. The angle variable w_ϕ conjugated to J_ϕ is therefore degenerate, and J_ϕ may not be quantised. The significance of w_ϕ will be recognised from the general property of a cyclic angle variable, that it is equal to the mean value of the azimuth of an arbitrary point of the system taken over the motions relative to the axis. w_ϕ is thus a constant angle which can be chosen equal to the azimuth of the axis of the resultant angular momentum about a plane through the fixed ϕ-axis.

We now consider the case where the mechanical system is subjected to a homogeneous external (electric or magnetic) field. The azimuth ϕ of a particle of the system about an axis parallel to the field is then a cyclic variable; in general H will depend on J_ϕ, and we have the quantum condition

$$(9) \qquad 2\pi p_\phi = J_\phi = mh.$$

For an arbitrary external field, on the other hand, the resultant angular momentum p is not in general an integral of the equations of motion and cannot therefore be quantised, but it may happen, in special cases, that p is constant and is an action variable. The relations (8) and (9) will then be true at the same time; but p_ϕ is the projection of p in the direction of the field and, if α denotes the angle between the angular momentum and the direction of the field, we have

$$(10) \qquad \cos\alpha = \frac{p_\phi}{p} = \frac{J_\phi}{J_\psi} = \frac{m}{j}.$$

This angle is therefore not only constant (regular precession of the resultant angular momentum about the direction of the field), but is also restricted by the quantum condition to discrete values. One speaks, in this case, of "spatial quantisation." [1] Since by (10) m can take only the values $-j, -j+1, \ldots j$, it follows that for every j there are in all $2j+1$ possible orientations of the angular momentum. This describes a cone of constant angle α about the direction of the field with the precessional velocity

$$\nu_\phi = \frac{\partial H}{\partial J_\phi}.$$

This regular precession is, in general, possible only for certain initial conditions. We shall show later (by the method of secular perturbations, § 18) that, for weak fields, the spatial quantisation holds in general for every motion; the only exceptions to this are certain cases of double degeneration (*e.g.* hydrogen atom in an electric field, *cf.* § 35).

Certain predictions regarding the polarisation of the emitted light and the transition possibilities may now be made with the help of the correspondence principle.

If z is an axis of symmetry fixed in space, we combine the components of the electric moment $\mathbf{p}_x$, $\mathbf{p}_y$, perpendicular to this, in the form of a complex quantity and write:

$$\begin{aligned} \mathbf{p}_x + i\mathbf{p}_y &= \sum_k e_k(x_k + iy_k) \\ \mathbf{p}_z &= \sum_k e_k z_k \end{aligned} \qquad (k=1, 2, \ldots n).$$

If r_k's are the distances from the axis and ϕ_k's the azimuths (one of them being ϕ), then

$$x_k + iy_k = r_k e^{i\phi_k} = e^{i\phi}(r_k e^{i(\phi_k - \phi)}).$$

Now the bracketed expression $(r_k e^{i(\phi_k - \phi)})$, like the z_k, depends only on the $q_1, \ldots q_{f-1}$; substituting for these the values (6) we have

$$\begin{aligned} \mathbf{p}_x + i\mathbf{p}_y &= e^{2\pi i w_\phi} \sum P_{\tau_1 \ldots \tau_{f-1}} e^{2\pi i(\tau_1 w_1 + \ldots + \tau_{f-1} w_{f-1})} \\ \mathbf{p}_z &= \sum Q_{\tau_1 \ldots \tau_{f-1}} e^{2\pi i(\tau_1 w_1 + \ldots + \tau_{f-1} w_{f-1})}. \end{aligned}$$

The integer τ_ϕ can therefore assume only the value 1 in the x- and y-components of the electric moment and the value 0 in the case of the z-component.[2] According to the correspondence principle, the corresponding quantum number can alter only by 1 or 0. (This holds, of course, only if J_ϕ is to be quantised at all, *i.e.* provided there is no degeneration.) The change of ± 1 corresponds to a right- or left-

[1] A. Sommerfeld, *Phys. Zeitschr.*, vol. xvii, p. 491, 1916; *Ann. d. Physik*, vol. li, p. 1, 1916.

[2] The sign of τ is meaningless, since in the Fourier expansion $-\tau$ always occurs as well as τ.

handed rotation of the electric moment about the axis of symmetry, and, therefore, to right- or left-handed circularly polarised light. Since the angular momentum of the system increases when the quantum number changes by +1, that of the light therefore decreases, so that for this transition of +1 in J_ϕ the light is negatively circularly polarised for emission and positively circularly polarised for absorption; for the transition −1 in J_ϕ the reverse holds.[1] Corresponding to the transition without change of angular momentum, we have light polarised parallel to the axis of symmetry.[2] If the motion of each point of the system is confined to a plane perpendicular to the axis of symmetry then (except for $\tau_1 = \ldots \tau_{f-1} = 0$)

$$Q_{\tau_1 \ldots \tau_{f-1}} = 0,$$

a transition without change of angular momentum does not then occur.

We consider now the case of a system which is subject to internal forces only. The above considerations are then applicable to the axis of the resultant angular momentum, where, in place of ϕ, the angle denoted above by ψ appears and the quantum condition (8) applies. The polarisation of the light cannot be observed, however, since the atoms or molecules of a gas have all possible orientations. The case mentioned above, where all the particles of the system move in planes perpendicular to the axis, is of frequent occurrence, *e.g.* in the case of the two-body problem (atom with one electron) and in that of the rigid rotator (dumb-bell model of the molecule); the transition $j \rightarrow j$ is then impossible.

We consider further the case in which the system is subject to the action of an external homogeneous field and spatial quantisation exists (which is approximately true for weak fields). The alterations of m and the polarisation of the light are then subject to the rules derived above. It is easy to see that the transition possibilities $\Delta j = -1, 0, +1$, which are valid for a free system, remain true for j.

We imagine a co-ordinate system ξ, η, ζ introduced so that the ζ-axis is in the direction of the angular momentum, and the η-axis perpendicular to the direction of the field. In this system of co-ordinates the electric moment may be expressed in the form

---

[1] Rubinowicz (*Physikal. Zeitschr.*, vol. xix, pp. 441 and 456, 1918) used the relation between polarisation and angular momentum (about the same time as the general correspondence principle was given by Bohr) in order to arrive at the selection principle for the alteration of quantum numbers.

[2] In optics, such light would be said to be polarised perpendicular to the z-direction, since the plane of polarisation is taken conventionally as the plane of oscillation of the magnetic vector.

$$\text{(11)} \quad \begin{aligned} \mathbf{p}_\xi + i\mathbf{p}_\eta &= e^{2\pi i w_\psi} \sum_\tau P_\tau e^{2\pi i(\tau w)} \\ \mathbf{p}_\zeta &= \sum_\tau Q_\tau e^{2\pi i(\tau w)}, \end{aligned}$$

in which only the angle variables of the relative motion $w_1 \ldots w_{f-1}$ (not w_ϕ and w_ψ) occur in the summations. The co-ordinates ξ, η, ζ are connected with those of the fixed system x, y, z by the relations

$$\begin{aligned} x+iy &= e^{2\pi i w_\phi}(\xi \cos \alpha - \zeta \sin \alpha + i\eta) \\ z &= \xi \sin \alpha + \zeta \cos \alpha ; \end{aligned}$$

which express the fact that the ζ-axis makes a constant angle α with the z-axis, and describes a regular precession $w_\phi = \nu_\phi t$ about it. The same transformation formulæ hold also for the components of the vector $\mathbf{p}$ in the two co-ordinate systems. If the Fourier series (11) be substituted for $\mathbf{p}_\xi$, $\mathbf{p}_\eta$, $\mathbf{p}_\zeta$, it will be seen at once that the angle variables w_ϕ and w_ψ occur only with the factors $\tau_\phi = \pm 1$; $\tau_\psi = 0, \pm 1$, in the exponents of the Fourier series for $\mathbf{p}_x$ and $\mathbf{p}_y$, and in $\mathbf{p}_z$ with the factors $\tau_\phi = 0$; $\tau_\psi = 0, \pm 1$ only. The quantum number j can therefore change only by 0 or ± 1.

§ 18.—Method of Secular Perturbations

A multiply periodic degenerate system may frequently be changed into a non-degenerate one by means of slight influences or variation of the conditions. We shall consider, in particular, the simple case where the Hamiltonian function involves a parameter λ and the system is degenerate for $\lambda = 0$. We imagine the energy function H expanded in powers of λ ; for sufficiently small values of λ we can break off this series after the term linear in λ and write

$$\text{(1)} \qquad H = H_0 + \lambda H_1.$$

To this approximation then each perturbation of the unperturbed system, whose Hamiltonian function is H_0, may be taken account of by the addition of an appropriate " perturbation function " λH_1. The effect of the perturbation function on the motion, when the system whose Hamiltonian function is H_0 is not degenerate, will be examined later ; here we shall consider only the case where H_0 is degenerate. We suppose the problem of the unperturbed system solved and angle and action variables w_k^0, J_k^0 introduced by a canonical substitution ; on account of the degeneration, H_0 will depend only on the proper action variables $J_\alpha^0 (\alpha = 1, 2 \ldots s)$ (see (14′), § 15, for the significance of suffixes α, ρ). H_1 will be a function of all the w_k^0's and J_k^0's, thus :

$$\text{(2)} \qquad H = H_0(J_\alpha^0) + \lambda H_1(J_k^0, w_k^0).$$

We obtain an approximate solution of the " perturbation problem " by a method which will here be based on an intuitive line of argument; it will be established mathematically later in a more general context (Ch. 4, § 43).

In the undisturbed motion the w_ρ^0's are constant and the w_α^0's variable with the time. The effect of a small perturbation will be that the w_ρ^0's will also be variable in time, but in such a manner that their rates of change will be small, *i.e.* that they vanish with λ. Since now the co-ordinates q_k, p_k are periodic functions of all the w_k^0's with the period 1, it follows that, during the time in which the w_ρ^0's vary by a given amount, the system will have traversed a large number of periods (rotations or librations) of the w_α^0's. The coupling between the motions of the w_α's and the w_ρ's may therefore be represented approximately by taking the mean value of the energy function over the unperturbed motion of the w_α^0; (2) then becomes

$$\overline{H}=H_0(J_\alpha^0)+\lambda\overline{H}_1(J_\alpha^0;\ w_\rho^0,\ J_\rho^0). \tag{3}$$

In this expression the w_α's do not appear; the J_α^0's are therefore constant during the perturbed motion, and appear as parameters only; the only variables are the w_ρ^0's and J_ρ^0's. These satisfy the canonical equations:

$$\begin{aligned}\dot{w}_\rho^0&=\lambda\frac{\partial\overline{H}_1}{\partial J_\rho^0}\\ \dot{J}_\rho^0&=-\lambda\frac{\partial\overline{H}_1}{\partial w_\rho^0}.\end{aligned} \tag{4}$$

The only solutions which are of importance from the point of view of the quantum theory are those of a multiply periodic nature. We assume, therefore, that the perturbed motion has a principal function of the form

$$S=\sum_{k=1}^{f}w_k^0J_k+F(w_\rho^0,\ J_\rho), \tag{5}$$

where F is a periodic function of the w_ρ^0's with the fundamental period 1, and such that the canonical transformation with the generator S, viz.

$$\begin{aligned}w_\alpha&=w_\alpha^0 & J_\alpha^0&=J_\alpha\\ w_\rho&=w_\rho^0+\frac{\partial F}{\partial J_\rho} & J_\rho^0&=J_\rho+\frac{\partial F}{\partial w_\rho^0},\end{aligned} \tag{6}$$

transforms the function $\overline{H}_1$ into a function of the J_k's alone:

$$\overline{H}_1(J_\alpha^0;\ w_\rho^0,\ J_\rho^0)=W_1(J_\alpha,\ J_\rho). \tag{7}$$

The portion of S depending on w_ρ^0, J_ρ, viz.

$$S_1 = S - \sum_{\alpha=1}^{s} w_\alpha^0 J_\alpha,$$

satisfies the Hamilton-Jacobi partial differential equation

$$\bar{H}_1\left(J_\alpha\,;\ w_\rho^0,\ \frac{\partial S_1}{\partial w_\rho^0}\right) = W_1. \tag{8}$$

The variations of $w_\rho^0 J_\rho^0$ are determined, therefore, from the mean of the perturbation function just as the original co-ordinates of a system are from the total energy function.

To this approximation the solution takes the form

$$J_\alpha = \text{const.} \qquad w_\alpha = \nu_\alpha t + \delta_\alpha$$
$$J_\rho = \text{const.} \qquad w_\rho = \nu_\rho t + \delta_\rho,$$

where

$$\nu_\alpha = \frac{\partial H_0}{\partial J_\alpha} + \lambda \frac{\partial \bar{H}_1}{\partial J_\alpha}$$
$$\nu_\rho = \lambda \frac{\partial \bar{H}_1}{\partial J_\rho}.$$

We see, therefore, that the rates of variation of the w_ρ's are in fact small compared with those of the w_α's and vanish for $\lambda=0$. In celestial mechanics the name " secular perturbations " has been introduced for such slow motions.

It will be seen from (6) that the original co-ordinates q and p of the system are now periodic functions of the new angle variables w_ρ as well as of the old angle variables w_α.

For the motions represented by equation (8) also, cases of libration, rotation, or limitation may occur. This problem is soluble practically only if the differential equation (8) is separable in the variables w_ρ^0, or if it is possible to find other separation variables. That is the case, for example, if all the variables w_ρ^0, or all with the exception of one, are cyclic ; the simplest case is that in which only one variable w_ρ^0 appears, *i.e.* when the unperturbed system is simply degenerate.

Further, it may happen that the problem defined by $\bar{H}$ is also degenerate in respect to certain w_ρ's, in which case these w_ρ's remain constant during the motion. By the addition of a further perturbation function these w_ρ's can, of course, become secularly variable.

The calculation of the mean value of the perturbation function H_1 is frequently simplified by employing the original variables q, p instead of the angle variables, and averaging with respect to the time. The orbital constants of the unperturbed motion, which occur in the mean value $\overline{H}_1$, have then to be replaced subsequently by the degenerate angle variables w_ρ^0 and by the action variables J_k^0.

In the case of a system subject to internal forces only, the azimuth, about any straight line fixed in space, of a plane passing through the axis of the resultant angular momentum and this straight line is a degenerate co-ordinate and is constant. If now a weak external homogeneous field, having the direction of this straight line, acts on this system, the mean value of the perturbation function λH_1 cannot depend on this azimuth. If now there is no other degenerate variable of the unperturbed system which could be secularly varied by means of the perturbation function (as is, for example, the case for a hydrogen atom in an electric field, *cf.* § 37), then the only secular motion induced by the external field is a precession of the resultant angular momentum about the direction of the field with the frequency

$$\nu_\phi=\lambda\frac{\partial\overline{H}_1}{\partial J_\phi}.$$

We have then an approximate realisation of the case of spatial quantisation, dealt with in the foregoing paragraph. The exact motion differs from that described by small superimposed oscillations ; it is a " pseudo-regular precession."

§ 19.—Quantum Theory of the Top and Application to Molecular Models

We have already examined (in § 12) the motion of diatomic molecules, which we considered as " rotators." We shall deal now with the general case of molecules containing several atoms, regarded, to a first approximation, as rigid bodies. The case of diatomic molecules, mentioned above (and generally of molecules for which all the atoms lie on a straight line), will then appear as a limiting case, and we shall obtain, at the same time, a more rigorous foundation for our previous results.

The conception of molecules as rigid bodies must, of course, be founded on the electron theory ; for, actually, the molecule is a complicated system made up of several nuclei and a large number of electrons. It can in fact be shown [1] that the nuclei move, to a close approximation, like a rigid system, but the resultant angular momentum of the molecules will not be identical with the angular momentum of the nuclear motion, because the electron system itself possesses, relatively to the nuclei, an angular momentum of the same

[1] M. Born and W. Heisenberg, *Ann. d. Physik*, vol. lxxiv, p. 1, 1924.

order of magnitude. We arrive, therefore, following Kramers and Pauli,[1] at the conclusion that the adequate molecular model is not simply a top, but a rigid body, in which is situated a fly-wheel with fixed bearings. We shall consider then, in this paragraph, the theory of this top provided with a fly-wheel.

Let the top, including the mass of the fly-wheel (which we take as symmetrical about an axis, so that the mass distribution is not altered by its rotation), have the principal moments of inertia A_x, A_y, A_z, the axes of which shall be, at the same time, the axes of a co-ordinate system (x, y, z) fixed in the top; let A be the moment of inertia of the fly-wheel. Let **a** be the unit vector in the direction of the axis of the fly-wheel, ζ the angle of rotation of the fly-wheel about its axis, and $\dot{\zeta}=\omega$ its angular velocity. As before, we note by **d** the vector of the angular velocity of the whole top, and to define the position of the top relative to axes fixed in space, we again employ the Eulerian angles θ, ϕ, ψ (θ and ψ pole distance and azimuth of the A_z-axis, ϕ the angle between nodal line and the A_x-axis). The relations between the derivatives of θ, ϕ, ψ and the components of **d** have been given previously (in (2), § 6). Let **D** be the vector of the resultant angular momentum of the body.

The components of the total angular momentum are made up of the components due to the top alone and those of the fly-wheel:

$$(1) \qquad \begin{aligned} \mathbf{D}_x &= A_x \mathbf{d}_x + A \cdot \mathbf{a}_x \omega \\ \mathbf{D}_y &= A_y \mathbf{d}_y + A \cdot \mathbf{a}_y \omega \\ \mathbf{D}_z &= A_z \mathbf{d}_z + A \cdot \mathbf{a}_z \omega. \end{aligned}$$

The angular momentum of the fly-wheel about its axis is

$$(2) \qquad \Omega = A(\omega + (\mathbf{da})).$$

The four equations of motion are obtained by applying the principle of the conservation of angular momentum. In the first place, the total angular momentum must remain constant in magnitude, and in a direction fixed in space; this gives the Eulerian equations

$$\dot{\mathbf{D}} = [\mathbf{D}, \mathbf{d}].$$

Secondly, the angular momentum of the fly-wheel can be changed only through interaction with the body of the top resulting in a change in direction of the axis; its alteration is therefore perpendicular to the axis, so that its component in the direction of the axis is constant; *i.e.*

[1] H. A. Kramers, *Zeitschr. f. Physik*, vol. xiii, p. 343, 1923; H. A. Kramers and W. Pauli, jr., *Zeitschr. f. Physik*, vol. xiii, p. 351, 1923.

(3) $$\Omega=\text{const.}$$

The kinetic energy is

(4) $$T=\tfrac{1}{2}[(\mathbf{dD})+\omega\Omega];$$

on substituting the expressions (1) this becomes

(5) $$T=\tfrac{1}{2}[A_x\mathbf{d}_x^2+A_y\mathbf{d}_y^2+A_z\mathbf{d}_z^2+A\omega(\mathbf{ad})+\omega\Omega].$$

In order to obtain the energy as a function of the components of the angular momentum we substitute in (5) the values of $\mathbf{d}_x$, $\mathbf{d}_y$, $\mathbf{d}_z$ calculated from (1):

$$T=\tfrac{1}{2}\left[\frac{\mathbf{D}_x^2}{A_x}+\frac{\mathbf{D}_y^2}{A_y}+\frac{\mathbf{D}_z^2}{A_z}-A\omega\left(\frac{\mathbf{a}_x\mathbf{D}_x}{A_x}+\frac{\mathbf{a}_y\mathbf{D}_y}{A_y}+\frac{\mathbf{a}_z\mathbf{D}_z}{A_z}\right)+\omega\Omega\right].$$

We calculate ω by deducing a relation between ω and $(\mathbf{da})$ by multiplying the equations (1) by $\frac{\mathbf{a}_x}{A_x}, \frac{\mathbf{a}_y}{A_y}, \frac{\mathbf{a}_z}{A_z}$ respectively, and adding; from this and (2) we get

$$\omega=\frac{\dfrac{\Omega}{A}-\dfrac{\mathbf{a}_x\mathbf{D}_x}{A_x}-\dfrac{\mathbf{a}_y\mathbf{D}_y}{A_y}-\dfrac{\mathbf{a}_z\mathbf{D}_z}{A_z}}{1-A\left(\dfrac{\mathbf{a}_x^2}{A_x}+\dfrac{\mathbf{a}_y^2}{A_y}+\dfrac{\mathbf{a}_z^2}{A_z}\right)},$$

and obtain therefore

(6) $$T=\frac{1}{2}\left[\frac{\mathbf{D}_x^2}{A_x}+\frac{\mathbf{D}_y^2}{A_y}+\frac{\mathbf{D}_z^2}{A_z}+\frac{\left(\dfrac{\Omega}{A}-\dfrac{\mathbf{a}_x\mathbf{D}_x}{A_x}-\dfrac{\mathbf{a}_y\mathbf{D}_y}{A_y}-\dfrac{\mathbf{a}_z\mathbf{D}_z}{A_z}\right)^2}{\dfrac{1}{A}-\dfrac{\mathbf{a}_x^2}{A_x}-\dfrac{\mathbf{a}_y^2}{A_y}-\dfrac{\mathbf{a}_z^2}{A_z}}\right].$$

Besides this integral, we have the principle of the conservation of the angular momentum which gives:

(7) $$\mathbf{D}^2=\mathbf{D}_x^2+\mathbf{D}_y^2+\mathbf{D}_z^2=\text{const.}$$

The general character of the motion can be summarised as follows: The components of $\mathbf{D}$ are the co-ordinates (relative to the axes (x, y, z) fixed in the top) of the point in which the invariable axis of the system (*i.e.* the axis of resultant angular momentum, which is fixed in space) penetrates the sphere (7). This point traverses the curve of intersection of the sphere with the ellipsoid (6), which is rigidly connected to the top. In the fixed co-ordinate system, therefore, the x, y, z system of axes, fixed in the top, executes a periodic nutation superposed on a precession about the axis of resultant angular momentum. In the case where the sphere touches the ellipsoid the motion becomes a rotation about a permanent axis.

In order to formulate the quantum conditions for the motion we must return to the co-ordinates θ, ϕ, ψ and calculate the corresponding momenta. If we suppose the kinetic energy T expressed as a function of θ, ϕ, ψ and their derivatives, by means of the relations (2), § 6,

$$\begin{aligned}\mathbf{d}_x&=\dot\theta\cos\phi+\dot\psi\sin\theta\sin\phi\\ \mathbf{d}_y&=\dot\theta\sin\phi-\dot\psi\sin\theta\cos\phi\\ \mathbf{d}_z&=\dot\phi+\dot\psi\cos\theta,\end{aligned}$$

we obtain :

$$\begin{aligned}p_\theta&=\frac{\partial T}{\partial\dot\theta}=\frac{\partial T}{\partial \mathbf{d}_x}\frac{\partial \mathbf{d}_x}{\partial\dot\theta}+\frac{\partial T}{\partial \mathbf{d}_y}\frac{\partial \mathbf{d}_y}{\partial\dot\theta}+\frac{\partial T}{\partial \mathbf{d}_z}\frac{\partial \mathbf{d}_z}{\partial\dot\theta}\\ p_\phi&=\frac{\partial T}{\partial\dot\phi}=\frac{\partial T}{\partial \mathbf{d}_x}\frac{\partial \mathbf{d}_x}{\partial\dot\phi}+\frac{\partial T}{\partial \mathbf{d}_y}\frac{\partial \mathbf{d}_y}{\partial\dot\phi}+\frac{\partial T}{\partial \mathbf{d}_z}\frac{\partial \mathbf{d}_z}{\partial\dot\phi}\\ p_\psi&=\frac{\partial T}{\partial\dot\psi}=\frac{\partial T}{\partial \mathbf{d}_x}\frac{\partial \mathbf{d}_x}{\partial\dot\psi}+\frac{\partial T}{\partial \mathbf{d}_y}\frac{\partial \mathbf{d}_y}{\partial\dot\psi}+\frac{\partial T}{\partial \mathbf{d}_z}\frac{\partial \mathbf{d}_z}{\partial\dot\psi}\\ p_\zeta&=\frac{\partial T}{\partial\omega}.\end{aligned}$$

Since, by (5), the derivatives of T with respect to $\mathbf{d}_x$, $\mathbf{d}_y$, $\mathbf{d}_z$ are the components $\mathbf{D}_x$, $\mathbf{D}_y$, $\mathbf{D}_z$ of the angular momentum (1), it follows that

$$\begin{aligned}p_\theta&=\mathbf{D}_x\cos\phi+\mathbf{D}_y\sin\phi\\ p_\psi&=\mathbf{D}_x\sin\theta\sin\phi-\mathbf{D}_y\sin\theta\cos\phi+\mathbf{D}_z\cos\theta\\ p_\phi&=\mathbf{D}_z\\ p_\zeta&=\Omega.\end{aligned}$$

Since the constant angular momentum can have an arbitrary direction in space, the motion is degenerate and we can reduce the number of degrees of freedom by 1. We can, for example, without loss of generality, choose the fixed polar axis $\theta=0$ of the Eulerian co-ordinate system in the direction of the resultant angular momentum **D**, in which case we get :

$$\begin{aligned}\mathbf{D}_x&=D\sin\theta\sin\phi\\ \mathbf{D}_y&=-D\sin\theta\cos\phi\\ \mathbf{D}_z&=D\cos\theta\end{aligned}\tag{8}$$

($D=|\mathbf{D}|$), and the momenta become :

$$\begin{aligned}p_\theta&=0\\ p_\psi&=D\\ p_\phi&=D\cos\theta\\ p_\zeta&=\Omega.\end{aligned}\tag{9}$$

Cos θ is determined as a single valued function of ϕ, owing to the fact that a curve on the ellipsoid (6) is prescribed for the end point of **D**, and that this curve will be traversed just once during one revolution of ϕ. It will be seen then that the motion is separable in the co-ordinates θ, ψ, ϕ, ζ, and leads to the action integrals

$$\oint p\, d\psi = 2\pi \mathrm{D}\,; \qquad \oint p_\phi d\phi = \mathrm{D}\oint \cos\theta d\phi\,; \qquad \oint p_\zeta d\zeta = 2\pi\Omega$$

and to the quantum conditions :[1]

$$\mathrm{D} = \frac{mh}{2\pi}$$

$$\mathrm{D}\oint \cos\theta d\phi = n^* h \tag{10}$$

$$\Omega = \frac{n_\zeta h}{2\pi}.$$

The second quantum condition admits of a simple interpretation. The surface on the sphere (7), which the point of the vector **D** passes round in a negative direction of rotation, is given by

$$\mathrm{F} = -\mathbf{D}^2 \iint \sin\theta d\theta d\phi = \mathbf{D}^2 \iint d(\cos\theta) d\phi.$$

If we carry out the integration with respect to θ, we obtain, if the boundary of the surface does not enclose the polar axis :

$$\mathrm{F} = \mathbf{D}^2 \oint \cos\theta d\phi = 2\pi \mathrm{D}^2 \frac{n^*}{m}\,;$$

if it encloses the positive polar axis :

$$\mathrm{F} = \mathbf{D}^2 \oint (1 - \cos\theta) d\phi = 2\pi \mathrm{D}^2 \frac{m - n^*}{m}\,;$$

if it encloses the negative polar axis :

$$\mathrm{F} = \mathbf{D}^2 \oint (1 + \cos\theta) d\phi = 2\pi \mathrm{D}^2 \frac{m + n^*}{m}\,;$$

and if it encloses both ends of the polar axis :

$$\mathrm{F} = \mathbf{D}^2 \oint (2 - \cos\theta) d\phi = 2\pi \mathrm{D}^2 \frac{2m - n^*}{m}.$$

In all cases the ratio to the hemisphere is

$$\frac{\mathrm{F}}{2\pi \mathrm{D}^2} = \frac{n}{m}, \tag{11}$$

where n is a whole number, and the second quantum condition can be formulated as follows : the ratio of the surface cut out from the sphere (7) by the vector **D** to the hemisphere is equal to n/m ; n can take the values 0, 1 . . . $2m$.

[1] In the case of the top we do not denote the quantum number of the resultant angular momentum by j, as in the general theory, but by m, because this letter is used to denote the terms of a molecular rotation spectrum (see Rotator, § 12).

We shall now apply our considerations to the case of an ordinary top without an enclosed fly-wheel.[1] For the components of the angular momentum we obtain, in place of (1):

$$\mathbf{D}_x = A_x \mathbf{d}_x, \quad \mathbf{D}_y = A_y \mathbf{d}_y, \quad \mathbf{D}_z = A_z \mathbf{d}_z;$$

the equation (5) for the energy becomes

$$T = \tfrac{1}{2}[A_x \mathbf{d}_x^2 + A_y \mathbf{d}_y^2 + A_z \mathbf{d}_z^2].$$

On introducing the components of angular momentum,

$$T = \frac{1}{2}\left[\frac{\mathbf{D}_x^2}{A_x} + \frac{\mathbf{D}_y^2}{A_y} + \frac{\mathbf{D}_z^2}{A_z}\right]. \tag{12}$$

If in this case also we take the fixed polar axis in the direction of the resultant angular momentum, the relations (8) are again valid and we have

$$T = \frac{1}{2}D^2\left[\sin^2\theta\left(\frac{\sin^2\phi}{A_x} + \frac{\cos^2\phi}{A_y}\right) + \frac{\cos^2\theta}{A_z}\right]. \tag{13}$$

We get two quantum conditions:

$$\begin{aligned} \oint p_\psi d\psi &= 2\pi D = mh \\ \oint p_\phi d\phi &= D\oint \cos\theta d\phi = nh. \end{aligned} \tag{14}$$

In the second condition we have to write $\cos\theta$ as a function of ϕ with the help of the energy W, which is equal to T since there are no external forces. It follows from (13) that

$$\cos^2\theta = \frac{\dfrac{2W}{D^2} - \left(\dfrac{\sin^2\phi}{A_x} + \dfrac{\cos^2\phi}{A_y}\right)}{\dfrac{1}{A_z} - \left(\dfrac{\sin^2\phi}{A_x} + \dfrac{\cos^2\phi}{A_y}\right)},$$

and the second quantum condition becomes

$$\oint \sqrt{\frac{2W - D^2\left(\dfrac{\sin^2\phi}{A_x} + \dfrac{\cos^2\phi}{A_y}\right)}{\dfrac{1}{A_z} - \left(\dfrac{\sin^2\phi}{A_x} + \dfrac{\cos^2\phi}{A_y}\right)}}\, d\phi = nh. \tag{15}$$

It leads to an elliptic integral, containing the energy W as parameter. The calculation of W as a function of the quantum numbers m and n cannot be carried out explicitly, except in the case of rotational symmetry ($A_x = A_y$) which we have already dealt with (§ 6).

---

[1] See F. Reiche, *Physikal. Zeitschr.*, vol. xix, p. 394, 1918; P. S. Epstein, *Verh. d. Dtsch. phys. Ges.*, vol. xviii, p. 398, 1916; *Physikal. Zeitschr.*, vol. xx, p. 289, 1919.

In this case, $A_x = A_y$, the energy (13) becomes

$$T = \frac{1}{2} D^2 \left(\frac{\sin^2 \theta}{A_x} + \frac{\cos^2 \theta}{A_z} \right);$$

ϕ will likewise be a cyclic variable and θ is constant. From (14), the quantum conditions are:

$$D = \frac{mh}{2\pi}$$

$$D \cos \theta = \frac{nh}{2\pi};$$

therefore

$$\cos \theta = \frac{n}{m},$$

i.e. we have a kind of space quantisation, for which the angular momentum precesses not about an axis fixed in space but, relative to axes fixed in the top, about the axis of figure. As a function of the quantum numbers the energy becomes

$$W = \frac{h^2}{8\pi^2} \left[\frac{m^2}{A_x} + n^2 \left(\frac{1}{A_z} - \frac{1}{A_x} \right) \right]. \tag{16}$$

If one considers how the co-ordinates of a point of the top are expressed in terms of the cyclic co-ordinates ψ and ϕ (by finite Fourier series), it will be seen that, in the series for the electric moment, the frequencies ν_ϕ and ν_ψ occur in general with the coefficients 0 and ± 1. The quantum numbers n and m can therefore change by 0 and ± 1. When the electric moment has no component parallel to the axis of figure the transition $\Delta n = 0$ is excluded.

An application of the energy equation (16) to multiply atomic molecules would give several systems of rotation bands, displaced from one another by fixed amounts, with the arrangement of lines in any one band satisfying a formula of the simple Deslandres type (*cf.* § 12).

At this stage we raise the question how it is possible to derive from the top formula (16), by a limiting process, the formula (1), § 12, for the rotator, and we shall show to what extent the application of the rotator formula to a diatomic molecule is justified. If we have the ideal case of a system consisting of two rigidly connected particles, then we have to put $A_z = 0$ in the top formula (16), and, in order that the energy may remain finite, n can take the value 0 only. We obtain then for the energy the previous rotator formula (1), § 12:

$$W=\frac{h^2}{8\pi^2 A_x}m^2.$$

Actually, however, in the case of diatomic molecules, we have to deal with systems where, in addition to the nuclei which are practically points of large mass, a number of electrons are present, which move around the nuclei and may, under certain circumstances, possess angular momentum about the line joining the nuclei. This system may be roughly compared to a top, whose moment of inertia A_z about the nuclear axis is small in comparison with the moment of inertia A_x about a perpendicular direction. For an invariable electron configuration, the quantum number n, and consequently the second term in the energy (16), is a constant. For the dependence of the energy on the state of rotation we have therefore

$$W=W_e+\frac{h^2}{8\pi^2 A_x}m^2. \tag{17}$$

In general, in a quantum transition n, and consequently the contribution W_e to the energy from the motion of the electrons, varies, and apart from this m varies by 0 or ± 1. If we leave undetermined the dependence of W_e on the quantum numbers, since the conception of the electrons as a rigid top is naturally very doubtful, we obtain for the frequency radiated in a transition (neglecting the frequency $\tilde{\nu}=\tilde{\nu}_e$ corresponding to $\Delta m=0$)

$$\begin{aligned}\tilde{\nu}&=\tilde{\nu}_e+\frac{h}{8\pi^2 A_x}[(m\pm 1)^2-m^2]\\ &=\tilde{\nu}_e+\frac{h}{4\pi^2 A_x}(\pm m+\tfrac{1}{2}).\end{aligned} \tag{18}$$

W_e, and so $\tilde{\nu}_e$, is very large in comparison with the term originating from the rotation, on account of the smallness of A_z in (16). Since the rotation term alone gives rise, as already shown, to lines in the infra-red, the spectrum represented by (18) is displaced towards higher frequencies, and so may lie in the visible or ultra-violet regions. We have in this the simplest band formula which represents to the roughest approximation the observed bands. From the observed separation of the lines the moment of inertia A_x of the molecule may be calculated.

In passing from the energy equation (17) to the frequency equation (18), the assumption is made that the moment of inertia A_x does not vary with a change in the electron configuration. If this assumption be dropped and we assume that A_x changes from $A_x^{(1)}$ to $A_x^{(2)}$, we get, for $\Delta m=\pm 1$, the frequencies

$$\tilde{\nu}=\tilde{\nu}_e+\frac{h}{8\pi^2 A_x^{(1)}}(m\pm1)^2-\frac{h}{8\pi^2 A_x^{(2)}}m^2, \tag{19}$$
$$=a\pm bm+cm^2,$$

where

$$a=\tilde{\nu}_e+\frac{h}{8\pi^2 A_x^{(1)}}$$
$$b=\frac{h}{4\pi^2 A_x^{(1)}} \tag{20}$$
$$c=\frac{h}{8\pi^2}\left(\frac{1}{A_x^{(1)}}-\frac{1}{A_x^{(2)}}\right).$$

The frequencies (19) constitute the " positive and negative branches " of the band. For $\Delta m=0$, the " null branch " is obtained :

$$\tilde{\nu}=\tilde{\nu}_e+\frac{h}{8\pi^2}\left(\frac{1}{A_x^{(1)}}-\frac{1}{A_x^{(2)}}\right)m^2=\tilde{\nu}_e+cm^2. \tag{21}$$

It is absent if the electric moment of the molecule is perpendicular to the axis of rotation.

We obtain the distribution of the lines in the three branches by drawing the three parabolas (19) (with + and − signs) and (21), and dropping perpendiculars on the $\tilde{\nu}$-axis [1] from the points corresponding to positive integral values of m (see fig. 8). One of the two branches (19) covers part of the $\tilde{\nu}$-scale twice, the lines are concentrated (with finite density) at the reversal point, the " band-head." The line in which the positive and negative branch intersect ($m=0$) is called the " null line." To calculate the moment of inertia from an observed band, the constant b must be known, and for this one must know the position of the null line of the band. If a null branch is present its position serves to indicate the null line. If, however, the null branch is absent, the properties of the band given here do not suffice. It appears, however, that the intensities on the two sides of the null line are symmetrically distributed, and the null line itself has the intensity 0 ; we shall return to this point again shortly.

Kramers and Pauli have endeavoured to treat the band spectra of molecules whose electronic angular momentum has a direction fixed in the molecule but is otherwise unrestricted, and to explain the absence of the null line, by applying to molecules the model of the top with an enclosed fly-wheel.

The top represents here the nuclear system (considered rigid) and the fly-wheel represents the angular momentum of the electrons. Since the dimensions of the electron orbits in a molecule are of the

[1] Comp. A. Sommerfeld, *Atomic Structure and Spectral Lines* (Methuen), p. 427.

same order of magnitude as the nuclear separations, and the mass of the electron is small in comparison with that of the nucleus, A is a magnitude small in comparison with A_x, A_y, A_z; the quantum conditions require, moreover, that the angular momentum Ω of the

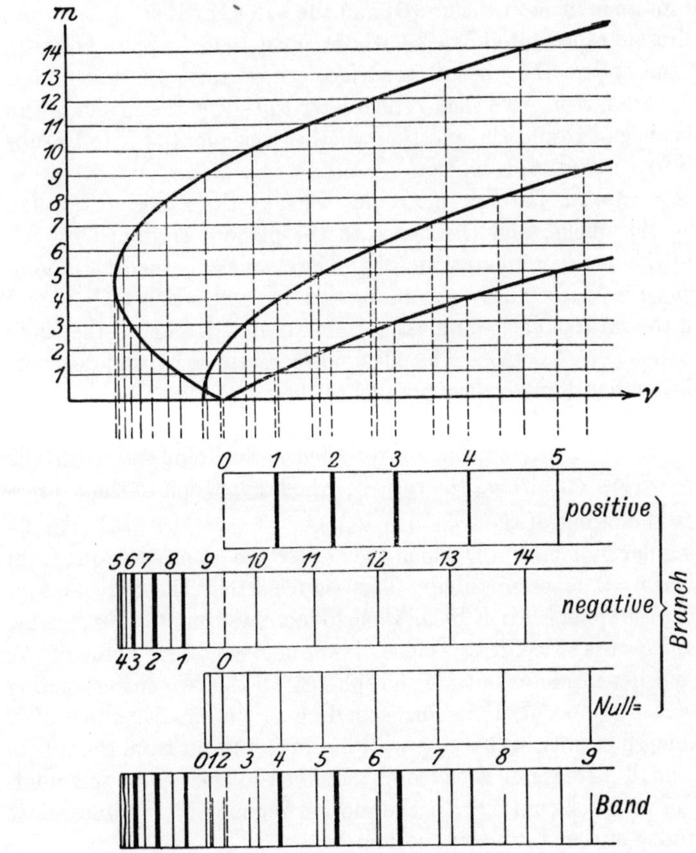

FIG. 8.

electrons shall be of the same order of magnitude as the resultant angular momentum D.

We now develop T in powers of A and break off the series after the second term:

$$T=\frac{\Omega^2}{2A}+\frac{1}{2}\left[\frac{1}{A_x}(\mathbf{D}_x-\Omega\mathbf{a}_x)^2+\frac{1}{A_y}(\mathbf{D}_y-\Omega\mathbf{a}_y)^2+\frac{1}{A_z}(\mathbf{D}_z-\Omega\mathbf{a}_z)^2\right].$$

The first term of this expression is a constant (the energy of the electron motion), the second term

(22) $$E=\frac{1}{2}\left[\frac{1}{A_x}(\mathbf{D}_x-\Omega\mathbf{a}_x)^2+\ldots\right]$$

is the energy of the gyroscopic motion of the molecule.

The stationary motions are obtained when $mh/2\pi$ is put for the resultant angular momentum $|\mathbf{D}|$ and the values of E so chosen that the ellipsoid represented by (22), whose centre is at the point $\Omega\mathbf{a}$, cuts from the sphere $|\mathbf{D}|$=const. a surface whose ratio to that of the hemisphere is n/m; we shall return later to the consideration of the significance of Ω and the question whether this quantity is to be subjected to a quantum condition.

In the case of diatomic molecules we take the z-axis in the line joining the nuclei, and the x-axis in the plane determined by the axis of the angular momentum of the electrons and the line joining the nuclei. We then have $\mathbf{a}_y=0$, A_z small in comparison with A_x and A_y (in the ratio of electron mass to nuclear mass), and (to the same approximation) $A_x=A_y$. The ellipsoid represented by (22) degenerates into a flat circular disc, parallel to the (x, y)-plane, having $\Omega\mathbf{a}_x$, 0, $\Omega\mathbf{a}_z$ as the co-ordinates of its central point.

The curve of intersection of this degenerate ellipsoid with the sphere encloses a surface the ratio of whose extension in the z direction to the radius of the sphere is $\sqrt{A_z/A_x}$. For values of the resultant angular momentum D which are not too great, only the quantum number $n=0$ is permissible. This signifies that the flat ellipsoid touches the sphere. If E be allowed to increase from 0 to ∞, such a contact occurs twice, irrespective of whether the centre point of the ellipsoid lies inside or outside the sphere. Of the two corresponding types of motion only that corresponding to the smaller value of E is stable, since only in this case will the curve cut out from the sphere for a small increase of E be closely confined to the region surrounding the point of contact, *i.e.* the motion remains in the immediate proximity of the stationary motion.

The point of contact must lie in the plane passing through the middle point of the ellipsoid and the nuclear axis; from this it follows that $\mathbf{D}_y=0$. We conclude from the relation

$$\mathbf{D}_x : \mathbf{D}_z = \frac{\mathbf{D}_x-\mathbf{a}_x\Omega}{A_x} : \frac{\mathbf{D}_z-\mathbf{a}_z\Omega}{A_z},$$

which implies that the normal to the sphere coincides with that of the ellipsoid at the point of contact, that

$$\frac{\mathbf{D}_z-\mathbf{a}_z\Omega}{\mathbf{D}_x-\mathbf{a}_x\Omega}$$

is of the order of magnitude A_z/A_x. We can therefore neglect the third term in the energy formula (22) and write

$$E=\frac{1}{2A_x}(\mathbf{D}_x-\mathbf{a}_x\Omega)^2.$$

It will be seen from fig. 9 that for this we can write also

$$E=\frac{1}{2A_x}(\sqrt{\mathbf{D}^2-\mathbf{a}_z{}^2\Omega^2}-\mathbf{a}_x\Omega)^2.$$

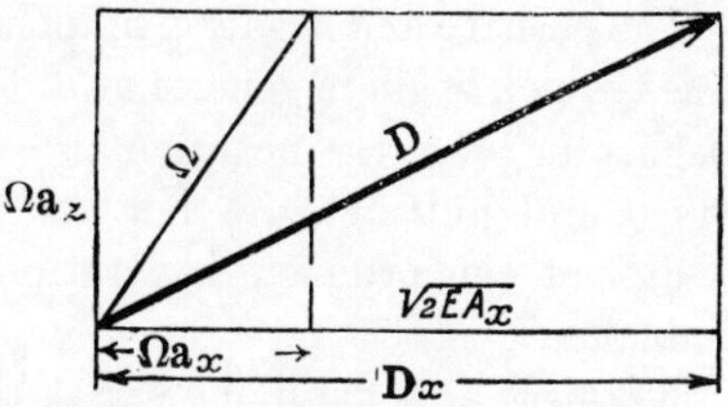

FIG. 9.

If the quantum number m be introduced together with the quantities ξ and ζ, defined by

$$\Omega\mathbf{a}_x=\frac{\xi h}{2\pi},\qquad \Omega\mathbf{a}_z=\frac{\zeta h}{2\pi}$$

it allows that

$$E=\frac{h^2}{8\pi^2A_x}(\sqrt{m^2-\zeta^2}-\xi)^2. \tag{23}$$

This is a generalisation of the formula for the energy of a simple rotator, which is obtained by putting

$$\xi=\zeta=0.$$

If the angular momentum of the electrons is directed along the nuclear axis ($\xi=0$), then

$$E=\frac{h^2}{8\pi^2A_x}(m^2-\zeta^2).$$

This formula agrees with that for the symmetrical top (16), if the term there proportional to $\frac{1}{A_z}$ (as electron energy) be removed and ζ put equal to n.

The general formula (23) has been used in different ways by Kratzer,[1] and Kramers and Pauli,[2] to explain the observed phenomena, that, in a system of equidistant band lines, one line is missing.

Kratzer uses the formula (23) for the case where $\zeta=0$, *i.e.* the angular momentum of the electrons is perpendicular to the nuclear axis. From

$$E=\frac{h^2}{8\pi^2A_x}(m-\xi)^2$$

---

[1] A. Kratzer, *Sitz.-Ber. Bayr. Akad. Math.-phys. Kl.*, p. 107, § 3, 1922.
[2] H. A. Kramers and W. Pauli, jr., *Zeitschr. f. Physik*, vol. xiii, p. 351, 1923.

he obtains for the frequency radiated in the transition $m+1 \rightarrow m$ (keeping the electron configuration constant)

$$\tilde{\nu}=\tilde{\nu}_e+\frac{h}{4\pi^2 A_x}(m-\xi+\tfrac{1}{2}), \tag{24}$$

and for the frequency radiated in the transition $m \rightarrow m+1$

$$\tilde{\nu}=\tilde{\nu}_e-\frac{h}{4\pi^2 A_x}(m-\xi+\tfrac{1}{2}). \tag{25}$$

The positive and negative branches consist therefore of equidistant lines, which begin in general at different places; the positive branch begins at $\frac{1}{2}-\xi$, the negative at $-(\frac{1}{2}-\xi)$. By forbidding the state $m=0$ and putting $\xi=\frac{1}{2}$ Kratzer thus deduces a gap, of twice the width of the ordinary separation of the lines, between the two branches.

Kramers and Pauli show that this remains essentially valid if ζ does not vanish. In this case m must be $\geqq \zeta$ and the expansion of E in terms of $1/m$,

$$E=\frac{h^2}{8\pi^2 A_x}\left[(m-\xi)^2+\zeta^2+\frac{\zeta^2\xi}{m}+\ldots\right],$$

remains approximately valid even for small values of m (except for $m=0$, which cannot occur if $\zeta \neq 0$). If we neglect the term $\frac{\zeta^2\xi}{m}$, we obtain the same frequencies (24) and (25) as above, thus also the correct size of the gap in the case $\xi=\frac{1}{2}$.

The value $\xi=\frac{1}{2}$ can arise by the angular momentum of the electrons being $h/2\pi$ and making an angle of 30° with the nuclear axis. This assumption leads, however, to difficulties in connection with the intensities given by the correspondence principle.[1] For this reason Kramers and Pauli return to the assumption $\xi=\frac{1}{2}$, $\zeta=0$, in other words to an electron momentum (with a " half " quantum number) perpendicular to the nuclear axis.

§ 20.—Coupling of Rotation and Oscillation in the Case of Diatomic Molecules

The bonds between the atoms which are combined to form a molecule have hitherto been regarded as rigid; this is only approximately

[1] There are other difficulties, inasmuch as an electron angular momentum which is not parallel to the nuclear axis is only possible for certain degenerations of the electron motion (M. Born and W. Heisenberg, *Ann. d. Physik*, vol. lxxiv, p. 1, 1924). Prof. W. Pauli informs us that the rigorous treatment of these degenerations leads to parallel and perpendicular orientations only for the angular momentum of the electrons.

true, however, for the atoms will in fact execute small oscillations with respect to one another. The problem now is to find what influence these oscillations have on the energy and on the frequency of the radiated or absorbed light.

The actual nature of the forces which bind the molecule together will be determined in an extremely complicated manner by their electronic and nuclear structure. Here we shall make the simplest possible assumption, viz. that the atoms may be regarded as centres of force which act on one another with a force depending only on the distance; it can be shown that the results so obtained represent a correct approximation to the actual behaviour.[1]

As regards the angular momentum of the electrons in diatomic molecules, we have seen in the previous paragraph that it has no influence on the rotational motion of the nuclei, and gives rise only to an additive term in the energy if its axis is parallel to the line joining the nuclei. The same must be true when the nuclei perform oscillations in this direction; we shall therefore restrict ourselves here to this case.

We consider, therefore, a diatomic molecule, consisting of two massive particles m_1 and m_2, separated by a distance r, between which there exists a potential energy $U(r)$.

It may be shown quite generally, that such a two-body problem may be reduced to a one-body problem. We choose the centre of gravity of the two particles as the origin of co-ordinates O and determine the direction of the line joining m_2 and m_1 by the polar co-ordinates θ, ϕ. If then r_1 and r_2 are the distances of the particles from O, their polar co-ordinates will be r_1, θ, ϕ and $r_2, \pi-\theta, \pi+\phi$; and further, $r_1+r_2=r$. The Hamiltonian function becomes

$$H=\frac{m_1}{2}(\dot{r}_1^2+r_1^2\dot{\theta}^2+r_1^2\dot{\phi}^2\sin^2\theta)+\frac{m_2}{2}(\dot{r}_2^2+r_2^2\dot{\theta}^2+r_2^2\dot{\phi}^2\sin^2\theta)+U(r)$$

$$=\tfrac{1}{2}(m_1\dot{r}_1^2+m_2\dot{r}_2^2)+\tfrac{1}{2}(m_1r_1^2+m_2r_2^2)(\dot{\theta}^2+\dot{\phi}^2\sin^2\theta)+U(r).$$

Since r_1 and r_2 are measured from the centre of gravity,

$$m_1r_1=m_2r_2,$$

and therefore

$$r_1=\frac{m_2r}{m_1+m_2}$$

$$r_2=\frac{m_1r}{m_1+m_2}.$$

If this be substituted in H, we get

---

[1] M. Born and W. Heisenberg, *Ann. d. Physik*, vol. lxxiv, p. 1, 1924.

(1) $$H=\frac{\mu}{2}(\dot{r}^2+r^2\dot{\theta}^2+r^2\dot{\phi}^2\sin^2\theta)+U(r),$$

on writing

(2) $$\frac{1}{\mu}=\frac{1}{m_1}+\frac{1}{m_2}.$$

Now the expression (1) is the Hamiltonian function of the motion of a particle of mass μ under the action of a centre of force from which it is separated by the distance r.

In the following chapter we shall investigate this problem quite generally ; here we shall consider only the case where a position of stable equilibrium exists, this being the only case of importance in connection with molecules.[1] There will then be a distance r_0, for which $U(r)$ is a minimum, *i.e.*

(3) $$U_0'=0, \qquad U_0''>0,$$

where the index 0 denotes here, and in what follows, the value of a quantity at $r=r_0$.

A possible state of motion of the system is a rotation with a constant nuclear separation $\bar{r}$ and a uniform angular velocity $\dot{\phi}_0$ about a fixed axis, passing through the centre of gravity O of the masses and perpendicular to the line joining them (nuclear axis). We take the axis of rotation as the line $\theta=0$, and have :

(4) $$\mu\bar{r}\dot{\phi}_0^2=\overline{U}',$$

where the bar denotes here, and in the following, the value of a quality at $r=\bar{r}$.

We take this motion as the starting-point for an approximate method of dealing with small oscillations. We suppose the separation $\bar{r}$ increased by a small amount x so that $r=\bar{r}+x$, and develop the Hamiltonian function, regarded as a function of x, ϕ and the corresponding momenta, in powers of x. The Hamiltonian function is

$$H=\frac{\mu}{2}[\dot{x}^2+(\bar{r}+x)^2\dot{\phi}^2]+U(\bar{r}+x).$$

The momentum

$$p=\mu(\bar{r}+x)^2\dot{\phi},$$

associated with ϕ is constant, because ϕ is cyclic ; moreover, p is the angular momentum ; for $x=0$, therefore

(5) $$p=\mu\bar{r}^2\dot{\phi}_0.$$

The momentum corresponding to x is

---

[1] M. Born and E. Hückel, *Physikal. Zeitschr.*, vol. xxiv, p. 1, 1923 ; see also A. Kratzer, *Zeitschr. f. Physik*, vol. iii, pp. 289 and 460, 1920.

$$p_x = \mu \dot{x}.$$

Consequently

$$\text{(6)} \qquad H = \frac{p^2}{2\mu(\bar{r}+x)^2} + \frac{p_x{}^2}{2\mu} + U(\bar{r}+x).$$

On expanding in powers of x we get

$$H = \left[\frac{p^2}{2\mu\bar{r}^2} + \overline{U}\right] + \frac{p_x{}^2}{2\mu} + \left[-\frac{p^2}{\mu\bar{r}^3} + \overline{U'}\right]x + \left[3\frac{p^2}{2\mu\bar{r}^4} + \frac{1}{2!}\overline{U''}\right]x^2$$
$$+\left[-4\frac{p^2}{2\mu\bar{r}^5} + \frac{1}{3!}\overline{U'''}\right]x^3 + \left[5\frac{p^2}{2\mu\bar{r}^6} + \frac{1}{4!}\overline{U^{(4)}}\right]x^4 + \dots$$

The coefficient of x vanishes since by (4) and (5)

$$\text{(7)} \qquad \frac{p^2}{\mu\bar{r}^3} = \overline{U'};$$

the Hamiltonian function has therefore the following form :

$$\text{(8)} \qquad H = W_0 + \frac{p_x{}^2}{2\mu} + \frac{\mu}{2}\omega^2 x^2 + ax^3 + bx^4 + \dots,$$

where

$$W_0 = \frac{p^2}{2\mu\bar{r}^2} + \overline{U}$$

$$\text{(9)} \qquad \omega^2 = (2\pi\nu)^2 = \frac{1}{\mu}\left[3\frac{p^2}{\mu\bar{r}^4} + \overline{U''}\right]$$

$$a = -4\frac{p^2}{2\mu\bar{r}^5} + \frac{1}{3!}\overline{U'''}$$

. . . .

This reduces the problem to that of the non-harmonic oscillator, which we have discussed in § 12.

If we now introduce angle and action variables we have to put

$$J = 2\pi p,$$

and then to introduce w_x and J_x in place of x and p_x, in the manner explained for the non-harmonic oscillator. If we take into consideration the terms in x^3 in (8), we find (*cf.* (9), § 12)

$$\text{(10)} \qquad H = W_0(J) + J_x\nu(J) + J_x{}^2\alpha(J),$$

where for shortness we write

$$-\frac{15a^2\nu^2}{4(2\pi\nu)^6\mu^3} = \alpha.$$

Similarly, if we take into account the term bx^4, H assumes to the same approximation the same form, only α depends also on b. The functions $W_0(J)$ and $\nu(J)$ are found by calculating $\bar{r}$ as a function of p

or J from (7) and substituting in (9). Actually in order to calculate them the function $U(r)$ must be known exactly. If we restrict ourselves, however, to such small velocities of rotation that the deviation $\bar{r}-r_0=r_1$, caused by the centrifugal force, is small in comparison with r_0, our objective may be attained by means of an expansion in terms of r_1. Since $U_0'=0$, equation (7) may be written, to a first approximation

$$\frac{J^2}{4\pi^2\mu}=\overline{r^3U'}=r_1\left(\frac{d}{dr}(r^3U')\right)_{r=r_0}=r_1r_0^3U_0'';$$

from this we obtain

$$r_1=\frac{J^2}{4\pi^2\mu}\frac{1}{r_0^3U_0''}.$$

Further

$$W_0=\frac{J^2}{8\pi^2\mu(r_0+r_1)^2}+U(r_0+r_1)=\frac{J^2}{8\pi^2\mu r_0^2}+U_0+\ldots,$$

$$\nu^2=\frac{1}{4\pi^2\mu}\left[3\frac{J^2}{4\pi^2\mu(r_0+r_1)^4}+U''(r_0+r_1)\right]$$

$$=\frac{1}{4\pi^2\mu}\left[\frac{3J}{4\pi^2\mu r_0^4}+U_0''+\frac{J^2U_0'''}{4\pi^2\mu r_0^3U_0''}+\ldots\right],$$

therefore

$$\nu=\frac{1}{2\pi}\sqrt{\frac{U_0''}{\mu}}\left[1+\frac{J^2}{8\pi^2\mu U_0''}\left(\frac{3}{r_0^4}+\frac{U_0'''}{r_0^3U''}\right)+\ldots\right]=\nu_0+\nu_1J^2+\ldots;$$

a also can be expanded in the form

$$a=a_0+a_1J^2+\cdots.$$

We have omitted here all terms of order higher than the first in J^2. The energy as a function of the action variables now becomes

$$(11)\qquad W=H=U_0+\frac{J^2}{8\pi^2A}+J_x\nu(J)+J_x^2a(J)+\ldots,$$

where $A=\mu r_0^2$ is the moment of inertia in the rotationless state, and ν and a have the meaning assigned above.

If we neglect the terms in J_x^2 and J_xJ^2, and consequently the non-harmonic character and the dependence of the ν's on J, the energy is resolved into a rotational component and an oscillation component of the well-known form. As a nearer approximation we have a dependence of the oscillation frequency on the rotation quantum number and also the non-harmonic character of the oscillation. Naturally our method admits of more accurate calculations of the energy, involving higher powers of J and J_x.

We shall apply the results obtained to the spectrum of diatomic molecules. In the stationary states they have the energy

$$W=U_0+\frac{h^2m^2}{8\pi^2A}+hn(\nu_0+\beta m^2)+h^2a_0n^2+\ldots, \tag{12}$$

where m is the rotation and n the oscillation quantum number.

The frequency corresponding to the transition

$$\begin{gathered} n_1 \to n_2 \\ m\pm 1 \to m \end{gathered}$$

is

$$\tilde{\nu}=\frac{h}{8\pi^2A}[(m\pm 1)^2-m^2]+\beta[n_1(m\pm 1)^2-n_2m^2]+\nu_0(n_1-n_2) \\ +ha_0(n_1{}^2-n_2{}^2). \tag{13}$$

For fixed values of the initial and final oscillation quantum numbers n_1 and n_2 and varying values of the rotational quantum number m, this gives a band with the branches (to which a null branch may be added):

$$\tilde{\nu}=a\pm bm+cm^2, \tag{14}$$

where a, b, and c have a somewhat different meaning from that in (20), § 19.

The frequencies

$$\tilde{\nu}=\nu_0(n_1-n_2)+ha_0(n_1{}^2-n_2{}^2), \tag{15}$$

which can be ascribed to the change of oscillation quantum number alone and so may be called " oscillation frequencies," are displaced from the null line of this band by

$$\frac{h}{8\pi^2A}+\beta n_1.$$

Thus we obtain a band system which is made up of individual bands corresponding to the series of values of n_1 and n_2. The positions of the individual bands in the system are given by (15), while (14) gives the law of arrangement of the lines in the individual bands.

The infra-red spectra of the halogen hydrides are of the type described here but without null branches.[1] These spectra consist of individual " double bands," *i.e.* an approximately equidistant succession of lines, which are symmetrically situated with respect to a gap. In this gap we have to imagine the null line mentioned in § 19. A doubling-back of the one branch is not observed in this case.

[1] Measurements, especially by E. S. Imes, *Astrophys. Journ.*, vol. l, p. 251, 1919. For the theory of A. Kratzer given here, see *Zeitschr. f. Physik*, vol. iii, p. 289, 1920. See also H. Bell, *Phil. Mag.*, vol. xlvii, p. 549, 1924.

The oscillation frequencies in the case of HCl are at $\tilde{\nu}=2877$ and $\tilde{\nu}=5657$ (in " wave numbers," *i.e.* number of waves per cm.). The corresponding bands appear in the case of absorption at the ordinary temperature. They correspond, therefore, to a change in the oscillation quantum number for which the initial state has so little energy that it is present to a considerable degree at the ordinary temperature; that, however, can only be the oscillation state $n^2=0$. We assign, therefore, to the two bands observed the two transitions

$$n=0\to 1$$
$$n=0\to 2$$

for absorption, or the values $n_1=1$ and $n_1=2$ respectively, and $n_2=0$ for emission. In accordance with the theoretical formula (15)

$$\tilde{\nu}=\nu_0 n_1+h a_0 n_1^2$$

the second band is not situated exactly at twice the frequency of the first.

An alteration of the rotation and oscillation quantum numbers may be accompanied by a simultaneous alteration in the electron configuration of the molecule. A frequency

$$\tilde{\nu}=\tilde{\nu}_{el}+\tilde{\nu}_{oscill}+\tilde{\nu}_{rot} \tag{16}$$

corresponds to a transition between two stationary states with the energies

$$W^{(1)}=W_0^{(1)}+\frac{h^2 m_1^2}{8\pi^2 A_1}+h n_1(\nu_{01}+\beta_1 m_1^2)+h^2 a_{01} n_1^2+\ldots$$

$$W^{(2)}=W_0^{(2)}+\frac{h^2 m_2^2}{8\pi^2 A_2}+h n_2(\nu_{02}+\beta_2 m_2^2)+h^2 a_{02} n_2^2+\ldots$$

where

$$\tilde{\nu}_{oscill}=\nu_{01}n_1-\nu_{02}n_2+h a_{01}n_1^2-h a_{02}n_2^2 \tag{17}$$

$$\tilde{\nu}_{rot}=a\pm bm+cm^2, \qquad \tilde{\nu}_{rot}=a'+cm^2. \tag{18}$$

Altogether we obtain a band system whose individual bands exhibit the structure described in § 19, and are arranged according to the formula (17). Written somewhat differently, it is

$$\tilde{\nu}_{oscill}=(n_1-n_2)\nu_{01}+n_2(\nu_{01}-\nu_{02})+h(a_{01}n_1^2-a_{02}n_2^2).$$

Since, in general, ν_{01} and ν_{02} are of the same order of magnitude and their difference is small compared with the values themselves, the first term is the most important. It defines the position of a " band group " in the band system; a group contains, therefore, all bands for which n changes by the same amount. The next term defines the individual bands, inside the band group, in terms of their final quantum numbers.

A beautiful example of a band system is provided by the violet cyanogen bands.[1] Fig. 10 gives the positions of the null lines and

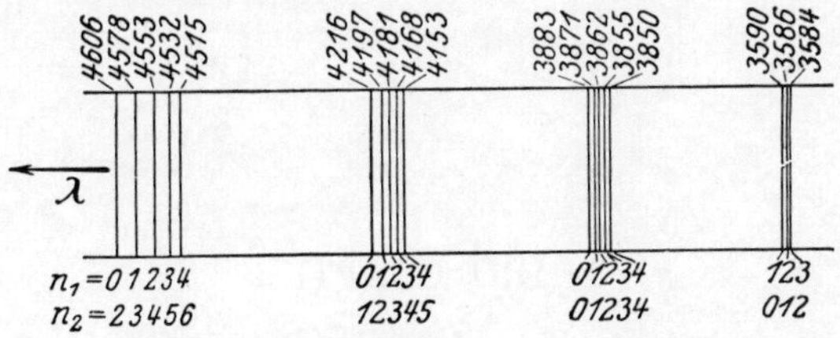

FIG. 10.

their wave-lengths: the first row underneath the oscillation quantum number in the initial state, the second row that in the final state.[2]

[1] Explained theoretically by A. Kratzer, *Physikal. Zeitschr.*, vol. xxii, p. 552, 1921; *Ann. d. Physik*, vol. lxvii, p. 127, 1922.

[2] According to A. Kratzer, *loc. cit.*

THIRD CHAPTER

SYSTEMS WITH ONE RADIATING ELECTRON

§ 21.—Motion in a Central Field of Force

THE applications of the principles of quantum mechanics, developed in the second chapter, are at present considerably restricted, owing to the fact that these principles are concerned only with multiply periodic systems. The first example dealt with by Bohr, namely, systems consisting of a nucleus and a single electron (the hydrogen atom and the similar ions He^+, Li^{++}, etc.), satisfies this condition of periodicity. In the case of other atoms the same difficulties underlie an examination of the periodic properties as in the case of the many-body problem of astronomy, and we can proceed only by a method of approximation. Bohr realised that a large number of atomic properties, especially those which exhibit themselves in the series spectra, may be explained on the hypothesis that one electron, the "radiating electron" or "series electron," plays a special rôle in the stationary states under consideration. The essential feature of these states is that this one electron is in an orbit, which, at any rate in part, is far removed from the rest of the atom, or "core,"[1] and exerts only a small reaction on the latter. We shall always speak, therefore, of the stationary orbits of the radiating electron, since we neglect the changes taking place in the core. The spectrum of the atom corresponds then to transitions of the radiating electron from one orbit to another.

This assumption implies that the motion of the outer electron is multiply periodic, and that, in traversing the core, the electron neither gives up energy to nor receives energy from it. Motions of this kind are quite special cases according to classical mechanics, for the motions of the core electrons must be such that their energy is the same after every period of the outer electron, a condition which

[1] German, *Rumpf.* The English equivalent of this word is not completely standardised: the alternatives "body," "trunk," "kernel" have been used by different writers.

is evidently fulfilled only by strictly periodic solutions of the complex many-body problem. Since, however, a large number of observations may be explained in a surprisingly simple way by such stationary orbits of the radiating electron, it appears that we are here dealing with some general process, which cannot easily be explained by such singular types of motion. We have here the same failure of the classical mechanics as was brought to light by Franck's researches on electron impact; the exchange of energy between electron and atom, or atom core, is restricted in a manner similar to that familiar to us in the energy interchange between an atom and radiation.

At present we cannot express this non-mechanical behaviour in formulæ. We endeavour to substitute for the atom a model which possesses, in common with the actual atom, this characteristic property of the absence of energy exchange between core and electron, and to which the principles of the quantum theory, developed in the second chapter, are applicable. The simplest assumption is that the action of the core on the radiating electron can be represented by a spherically symmetrical field of force. Further development has shown that this simple hypothesis suffices to provide an explanation of the main characteristics of the spectra of the first three divisions of the periodic table and their sub-groups. The conception of a single "radiating electron" is, however, no longer adequate to explain the spectra of the remaining elements, but these considerations are beyond the scope of this book.[1]

For this reason we shall now deal with the motion of a particle in a central field of force. The motion in a Coulomb field of force (such as we have in the case of the hydrogen atom) will be found from this as a special case.

So far as the calculation is concerned it is immaterial whether we consider our problem as a one-body or as a two-body problem. In the first case we have a fixed centre of force, and the potential of the field of force is a function $U(r)$ of the distance from the centre. In the second case we have two masses, whose mutual potential energy $U(r)$ depends only on their distance apart; they move about the common centre of gravity. As we have shown generally in § 20, the Hamiltonian function in polar co-ordinates is precisely the same for the two cases, if, in the one-body problem, the mass μ of the moving

---

[1] For the development of the theory of complex spectra, see H. N. Russel and F. A. Saunders, *Astroph. Journ.*, vol. lxi, p. 38, 1925; W. Pauli, jr., *Zeitsch. f. Phys.*, vol. xxxi, p. 765, 1925; W. Heisenberg, *Zeitschr. f. Phys.*, vol. xxxii, p. 841, 1925; F. Hund, *Zeitsch. f. Phys.*, vol. xxxiii, p. 345; vol. xxxiv, p. 296, 1925.

body and its distance r from the centre are used, and if in the two-body problem μ is defined by the equation (2), § 20,

$$\frac{1}{\mu}=\frac{1}{m_1}+\frac{1}{m_2},$$

and r is the distance between the two masses. The following equations admit then of both interpretations.

We work with polar co-ordinates r, θ, and ϕ. Making use of the canonical transformation (13), § 7, which transforms rectangular into polar co-ordinates, we obtain for the kinetic energy,

$$\mathrm{T}=\frac{1}{2\mu}\left(p_r^{\ 2}+\frac{p_\theta^{\ 2}}{r^2}+\frac{p_\phi^{\ 2}}{r^2 \sin^2\theta}\right),$$

where p_r, p_θ, p_ϕ are the momenta conjugate with r, θ, ϕ respectively. We arrive, of course, at the same expression when we calculate from

$$\mathrm{T}=\frac{\mu}{2}(\dot{r}^2+r^2\dot{\theta}^2+r^2\sin^2\theta\dot{\phi}^2)$$

the momenta :

$$p_r=\mu\dot{r}$$
$$p_\theta=\mu r^2\dot{\theta}$$
$$p_\phi=\mu r^2\sin^2\theta\dot{\phi}$$

and use them to replace $\dot{r}$, $\dot{\theta}$, $\dot{\phi}$. The structure of the Hamiltonian function

(1) $$\mathrm{H}=\frac{1}{2\mu}\left(p_r^{\ 2}+\frac{p_\theta^{\ 2}}{r^2}+\frac{p_\phi^{\ 2}}{r^2\sin^2\theta}\right)+\mathrm{U}(r)$$

shows that r, θ, ϕ are separation variables. If one puts

(2) $$\mathrm{S}=\mathrm{S}_r(r)+\mathrm{S}_\theta(\theta)+\mathrm{S}_\phi(\phi),$$

the Hamilton-Jacobi differential equation

$$\left(\frac{\partial\mathrm{S}}{\partial r}\right)^2+\frac{1}{r^2}\left(\frac{\partial\mathrm{S}}{\partial\theta}\right)^2+\frac{1}{r^2\sin^2\theta}\left(\frac{\partial\mathrm{S}}{\partial\phi}\right)^2+2\mu[\mathrm{U}(r)-\mathrm{W}]=0$$

splits up into three ordinary differential equations :

$$\frac{d\mathrm{S}_\phi}{d\phi}=\alpha_\phi$$

$$\left(\frac{d\mathrm{S}_\theta}{d\theta}\right)^2+\frac{\alpha_\phi^{\ 2}}{\sin^2\theta}=\alpha_\theta^{\ 2}$$

$$\left(\frac{d\mathrm{S}_r}{dr}\right)^2+\frac{\alpha_\theta^{\ 2}}{r^2}+2\mu[\mathrm{U}(r)-\mathrm{W}]=0,$$

which can be solved for the derivatives of S :

$$\frac{dS_r}{dr}=p_r=\sqrt{2\mu[W-U(r)]-\frac{\alpha_\theta^2}{r^2}}$$

(3) $$\frac{dS_\theta}{d\theta}=p_\theta=\sqrt{\alpha_\theta^2-\frac{\alpha_\phi^2}{\sin^2\theta}}$$

$$\frac{dS_\phi}{d\phi}=p_\phi=\alpha_\phi.$$

Of the three integration constants W denotes the energy ;

$$\alpha_\phi=p_\phi=\mu r^2\sin^2\theta\dot{\phi}$$

is the angular momentum about the polar axis (*i.e.* the line $\theta=0$), and

$$\alpha_\theta=\sqrt{p_\theta^2+\frac{p_\phi^2}{\sin^2\theta}}=\mu r\,.\sqrt{(r\dot{\theta})^2+(r\sin\theta\,.\,\dot{\phi})^2}$$
$$=\mu\,|[\mathbf{r}\dot{\mathbf{r}}]|$$

is the magnitude of the resultant angular momentum. Since also the direction of the angular momentum is constant (as in every system subject to internal forces only), the orbit is plane and the normal to the plane of the orbit is parallel to the vector representing the angular momentum. The inclination i of the orbital plane to the (r, ϕ)-plane is given therefore by

$$\alpha_\phi=\alpha_\theta\cos i.$$

We consider next the general character of the motion and then determine the energy as a function of the action variables for the case of a periodic motion and, finally, we consider the progress of the motion in time.

The co-ordinate ϕ is cyclic and performs a rotational motion (*cf.* § 9). The co-ordinate θ performs a libration or limitation motion in an interval, symmetrical about $\pi/2$, whose limits are given by the zero points of the radicand in the expression of p_θ, *i.e.* by

$$\sin\theta=\frac{\alpha_\phi}{\alpha_\theta}=\cos i,\qquad \theta=\frac{\pi}{2}\pm i.$$

Further, the character of the motion depends essentially on the behaviour of the radicand in the expression for p_r,

$$F(r)=2\mu[W-U(r)]-\frac{\alpha_\theta^2}{r^2}.$$

We investigate the various possible cases on the supposition that U(r) is a monotonic function of r and that the zero of potential energy is so chosen that it vanishes for $r=\infty$.

Case 1.—In a repulsive central field of force U(r) is positive. In order that positive values of F(r) shall occur at all, W must be positive. F(r) will then be positive for large values of r, decreasing continually with continuously decreasing r; for small values of r, F(r) is certainly negative; F(r) has therefore exactly one root. The motion takes place therefore between $r=\infty$ and a minimum value of r.

Case 2.—In an attractive central field, U(r) is negative, and W may be positive or negative. The sign F(r) for large values of r is determined by W. For positive W, F(r) is positive there, and there are motions which extend to infinity. There are no such orbits for a negative W. In the case of W=0 the variation of U with r, and, in certain cases, the magnitude of α_θ, is the deciding factor. The sign of F(r) for small values of r depends on the rate at which $|U(r)|$ becomes infinite. If, for small r, it increases more rapidly than $1/r^2$,[1] F(r) will be positive there, and there will be orbits which approach indefinitely close to the centre of force; if $|U(r)|$ becomes infinite more slowly than $1/r^2$ there will be no such orbits; if $|U(r)|$ approaches infinity as $1/r^2$, the magnitude of α_θ is the deciding factor. Further, there are cases where, in addition to paths extending to the centre and to infinity, orbits exist which extend between two finite and non-zero values of r, $r_{\min}$ and $r_{\max}$; this is the case when $r_{\min}$ and $r_{\max}$ are consecutive zero points of F(r), between which F is positive. In the case where $|U(r)|$ becomes infinite more slowly than $1/r^2$ it is certain that there are values of W for which such a libration sets in; for negative W there are in fact, in this case, no other motions but librations.

In many applications to atomic physics we are only concerned with those motions in which the electron remains at a finite distance from the centre and which are periodic. We consider therefore in the following only the case of attraction and take for W values such that F(r) is positive between two consecutive roots $r_{\min}$ and $r_{\max}$.

In this case we can apply the methods developed for periodic motions. We obtain the action integrals

---

[1] Mathematically expressed, this has the following significance: the order of magnitude of $|U(r)|$ is larger than that of $1/r^2$ for small values of r. The order of magnitude of a function $f(x)$ (>0) is greater than the order of magnitude of the function $g(x)$ (>0), for small values of x, if

$$\lim_{x=0}\frac{g(x)}{f(x)}=0.$$

$f(x)$ and $g(x)$ have the same order of magnitude if the limiting value of $\dfrac{g(x)}{f(x)}$ is a finite constant.

$$
(4)\qquad
\begin{aligned}
J_r &= \oint \sqrt{2\mu[W-U(r)]-\frac{\alpha_\theta^{\,2}}{r^2}}\,dr \\
J_\theta &= \oint \sqrt{\alpha_\theta^{\,2}-\frac{\alpha_\phi^{\,2}}{\sin^2\theta}}\,d\theta \\
J_\phi &= 2\pi\alpha_\phi .
\end{aligned}
$$

With the help of the substitution

$$\cos\theta = x\sin i = x\sqrt{1-\frac{\alpha_\phi^{\,2}}{\alpha_\theta^{\,2}}},$$

the second integral takes the form

$$J_\theta = -\frac{\alpha_\theta^{\,2}-\alpha_\phi^{\,2}}{\alpha_\theta}\oint\frac{\sqrt{1-x^2}\,dx}{1-x^2\dfrac{\alpha_\theta^{\,2}-\alpha_\phi^{\,2}}{\alpha_\theta^{\,2}}}.$$

The evaluation of this integral (*cf.* (3) and (8), Appendix II) gives

$$J_\theta = 2\pi(\alpha_\theta-\alpha_\phi).$$

We can now express α_θ and α_ϕ in terms of the action variables

$$
(5)\qquad
\begin{aligned}
\alpha_\theta &= \frac{J_\theta+J_\phi}{2\pi} \\
\alpha_\phi &= \frac{J_\phi}{2\pi}.
\end{aligned}
$$

In order to find the energy as a function of the J's we should have to solve the equation

$$(6)\qquad J_r = \oint\sqrt{2\mu[W-U(r)]-\frac{(J_\theta+J_\phi)^2}{4\pi^2 r^2}}\,dr$$

for W. This is impossible without a detailed knowledge of $U(r)$; it is seen, however, that W depends only on J_r and the combination $J_\theta+J_\phi$. The two frequencies

$$\nu_\theta = \frac{\partial W}{\partial J_\theta},\qquad \nu_\phi = \frac{\partial W}{\partial J_\phi}$$

are therefore equal and the system is degenerate. In accordance with the fundamental principles developed in § 15, we introduce new variables w_1, w_2, w_3, and J_1, J_2, J_3, so that w_3 is constant. We arrange at the same time that, in the case of the Coulomb field of force, where $\nu_r=\nu_\theta=\nu_\phi$, that the variable w_2 shall also be constant. We write, therefore, in accordance with (8), § 7

$$(7)\qquad \begin{aligned} w_1&=w_r & J_1&=J_r+J_\theta+J_\phi \\ w_2&=w_\theta-w_r & J_2&=J_\theta+J_\phi \\ w_3&=w_\phi-w_\theta & J_3&=J_\phi. \end{aligned}$$

The equation (6) contains then only J_1 and J_2, and we derive the energy W in the form

$$(8)\qquad W=W(J_1, J_2).$$

For the stationary motions we have, provided there is no further degeneration (*e.g.* no Coulomb field), the two quantum conditions :

$$(9)\qquad \begin{aligned} J_1&=nh \\ J_2&=kh. \end{aligned}$$

n is called the principal quantum number and k the subsidiary quantum number.[1]

The action variables have the following physical significance : J_2 is $1/2\pi$ times the total angular momentum, J_3 is $1/2\pi$ times its component in the direction of the polar axis.

It is obvious that J_1 cannot be zero. Also $J_2=0$ would signify a motion on a straight line through the centre of force, a " pendulum motion " ; in physical applications, where the centre of force is the atomic nucleus, this case must of course be excluded.

In order to find the physical significance of the angle variables, we calculate them with the help of the transformation equations

$$w_k=\frac{\partial S}{\partial J_k}.$$

If we introduce the J_k's in the equation (3) we obtain

$$p_r=\sqrt{2\mu[W(J_1, J_2)-U(r)]-\frac{J_2^{\,2}}{4\pi^2r^2}}$$

$$p_\theta=\frac{1}{2\pi}\sqrt{J_2^{\,2}-\frac{J_3^{\,2}}{\sin^2\theta}}$$

$$p_\phi=\frac{1}{2\pi}J_3,$$

and for the angle variables $\left(\text{putting } \nu_1=\dfrac{\partial W}{\partial J_1}\right)$:

---

[1] k is also called the azimuthal quantum number. This term arises from the fact that it can also be put in the form

$$\frac{1}{h}\int p_\psi\, d\psi,$$

where ψ is the azimuth of the moving point in the orbital plane.

$$w_1 = \frac{\partial S}{\partial J_1} = \int \frac{\partial p_r}{\partial J_1} dr = \int \frac{\mu \nu_1}{\sqrt{2\mu(W-U) - \frac{J_2^2}{4\pi^2 r^2}}} dr$$

$$w_2 = \frac{\partial S}{\partial J_2} = \int \frac{\partial p_r}{\partial J_2} dr + \int \frac{\partial p_\theta}{\partial J_2} d\theta$$

(10)
$$= \int \frac{\mu \nu_2 - \frac{J_2}{4\pi^2 r^2}}{\sqrt{2\mu(W-U) - \frac{J_2^2}{4\pi^2 r^2}}} dr + \frac{1}{2\pi} \int \frac{J_2 d\theta}{\sqrt{J_2^2 - \frac{J_3^2}{\sin^2\theta}}}$$

$$w_3 = \frac{\partial S}{\partial J_3} = \int \frac{\partial p_\theta}{\partial J_3} d\theta + \int \frac{\partial p_\phi}{\partial J_3} d\phi$$

$$= \frac{1}{2\pi} \left[\phi - \int \frac{J_3 d\theta}{J_2 \sin^2\theta \sqrt{1 - \frac{J_3^2}{J_2^2 \sin^2\theta}}} \right].$$

The two integrals in $d\theta$ may be evaluated. We have

(10′)
$$\int \frac{J_2 d\theta}{\sqrt{J_2^2 - \frac{J_3^2}{\sin^2\theta}}} = \int \frac{d\theta}{\sqrt{1 - \frac{\cos^2 i}{\sin^2\theta}}} = \sin^{-1}\frac{\cos\theta}{\sin i} + \text{const.}$$

and

(10″)
$$\int \frac{J_3 d\theta}{J_2 \sin^2\theta \sqrt{1 - \frac{J_3^2}{J_2^2 \sin^2\theta}}} = \int \frac{\cos i \, d\theta}{\sin^2\theta \sqrt{1 - \frac{\cos^2 i}{\sin^2\theta}}}$$
$$= \sin^{-1}(\cot i \cot\theta) + \text{const.}$$

It will be seen from fig. 11 that, apart from the arbitrary constant of integration, the integral (10′) is the angular distance ψ of the moving point from the line of nodes, measured on the orbital plane, and the integral (10″) is the projection of this angular separation on the (r, ϕ)-plane. By subtraction of this projection from ϕ we get the longitude of the line of nodes. The third of our equations (10) states, therefore, that, apart from an arbitrary additive constant, the longitude of the node is $2\pi w_3$. According to the second of the equations (10), $2\pi w_2$ is the angular distance ψ of

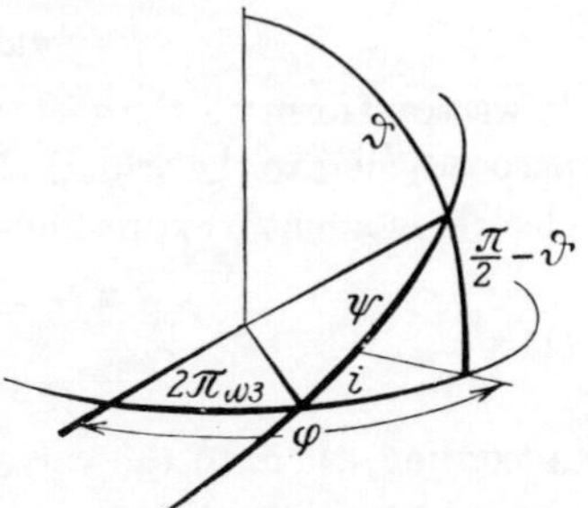

Fig. 11.

the moving point from the node, measured on the orbital plane, increased by a function of r:

$$(11)\quad \begin{aligned} 2\pi w_2 &= \psi + F_2(r, J_1, J_2) \\ F_2(r, J_1, J_2) &= \int \frac{\partial p_r}{\partial J_2} dr. \end{aligned}$$

For given J_1 and J_2, F_2 is a single-valued function of r, for, during a libration of r, $\int p_r dr$ increases by J_1; the partial derivative with respect to J_2 assumes, therefore, its old value once more. Apart from an additive constant, $2\pi w_2$ is consequently the angular distance of a point of the path with a given r from the line of nodes, measured on the orbital plane, and therefore, apart from a constant, the angular distance of the perihelion ($r_{\min}$) from the line of nodes. Finally, again apart from an additive constant, $2\pi w_1$ is what astronomers call the "mean anomaly," namely, the angular distance from perihelion of a point imagined to rotate uniformly and to pass through perihelion simultaneously with the actual moving point.

Since we have a system subjected only to internal forces, and the motion takes place in a plane, the angle variable w_2, associated with the total angular momentum, occurs in the Fourier representation of the electric moment with the factor ± 1 only (as was shown generally in § 17). We can see this also directly, from the nature of the expressions for the angle variables. These are:

$$\begin{aligned} w_1 &= f_1(r, J_1, J_2) \\ w_2 &= \frac{1}{2\pi}\psi + f_2(r, J_1, J_2) \\ w_3 &= \text{const.}, \end{aligned}$$

or, if we solve for r, ψ,

$$\begin{aligned} r &= \phi_1(w_1, J_1, J_2) \\ \psi &= 2\pi w_2 + \phi_2(w_1, J_1, J_2). \end{aligned}$$

If we transform to the rectangular co-ordinates ξ, η, ζ, where ζ is perpendicular to the orbital plane, we find for the components of the electric moment $\mathbf{p}$ expressions of the form

$$(11')\quad \begin{aligned} \mathbf{p}_\xi + i\mathbf{p}_\eta &= e^{2\pi i w_2} \sum_{\tau_1} D_{\tau_1} e^{2\pi i \tau_1 w_1} \\ \mathbf{p}_\zeta &= 0. \end{aligned}$$

According, then, to the correspondence principle, the number k, of the quantum numbers n and k introduced by (9), can alter by ± 1 only, while n can in general change by arbitrary amounts.

The orbit is best expressed in terms of the co-ordinates r and ψ. From the first equation (10) we get

$$dt = \frac{dw}{\nu_1} = \frac{\mu}{\sqrt{2\mu(W-U) - \frac{J_2^2}{4\pi^2 r^2}}} dr.$$

Also since the angular momentum is $J_2/2\pi$

$$\mu r^2 d\psi = \frac{J_2}{2\pi} dt;$$

we eliminate dt and derive the differential equation of the orbit.

$$(12) \qquad \frac{d\psi}{dr} = \frac{\frac{J_2}{2\pi}}{r^2 \sqrt{2\mu[W-U(r)] - \frac{J_2^2}{4\pi^2 r^2}}}.$$

Since the motion consists of a libration of r, combined with a uniform rotation of the perihelion, the form of the orbit is that of a rosette (*cf*. fig. 12).

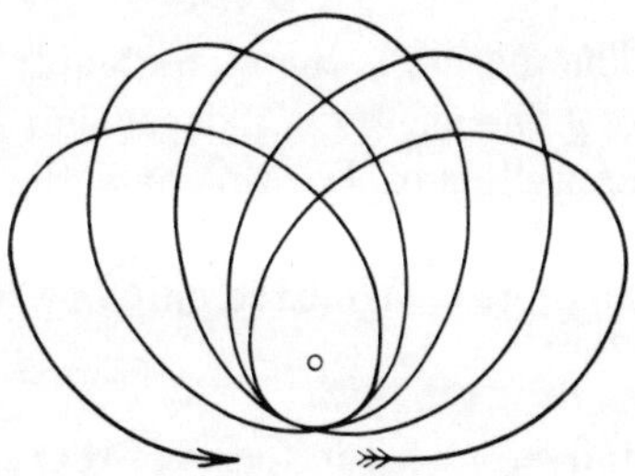

FIG. 12.

§ 22.—The Kepler Motion

The simplest application of the results of § 21 is to atoms consisting of a nucleus with a charge Ze and only one electron. In this case the motion concerned is that of two bodies under the influence of a mutual attraction giving rise to the potential energy

$$(1) \qquad U(r) = -\frac{e^2 Z}{r}.$$

This motion we shall now consider.

The action integral J_r (6), § 21, takes the form

$$(2) \qquad J_r = \oint \sqrt{-A + 2\frac{B}{r} - \frac{C}{r^2}}\, dr,$$

where

$$(2') \qquad \begin{aligned} A &= 2\mu(-W) \\ B &= \mu e^2 Z \\ C &= \left(\frac{J_\theta + J_\phi}{2\pi}\right)^2 = \left(\frac{J_2}{2\pi}\right)^2. \end{aligned}$$

It will be seen that only when W is negative can the radicand have two roots between $r=0$ and $r=\infty$ enclosing a region within which it is positive; consequently A, B, and C are all positive numbers. By the method of complex integration we obtain (*cf.* (5), Appendix II):

$$J_r=2\pi\left(-\sqrt{C}+\frac{B}{\sqrt{A}}\right)$$

$$=2\pi\frac{\sqrt{\mu}e^2Z}{\sqrt{-2W}}-J_\theta-J_\phi.$$

We can now express the energy W in terms of the action variables, the value we find being:

$$\text{(3)} \qquad W=-\frac{2\pi^2\mu e^4Z^2}{(J_r+J_\theta+J_\phi)^2}=-\frac{2\pi^2\mu e^4Z^2}{J_1^2}.$$

The motion is therefore doubly degenerate, since for a given value of J the energy is independent of J_2 (the total angular momentum) as well as of J_ϕ. Not only the longitude of the node, but also the angular distance of the perihelion from the line of nodes, remains unaltered. We have only one quantum condition,

$$J_1=nh,$$

and expressed in terms of this the energy is

$$\text{(4)} \qquad W=-\frac{2\pi^2\mu e^4Z^2}{h^2}\,\frac{1}{n^2}.$$

The motion has only one frequency different from zero; from (3) we find for this

$$\text{(5)} \qquad \nu_1=\frac{\partial W}{\partial J_1}=\frac{4\pi^2\mu e^4Z^2}{J_1^3}=\frac{4\pi^2\mu e^4Z^2}{h^3n^3};$$

the period of revolution is therefore

$$\frac{1}{\nu_1}=\frac{h^3n^3}{4\pi^2\mu e^4Z^2}.$$

We again express the orbit in terms of the co-ordinates r, ψ in the orbital plane. As differential equation of the path, we get, by (12), § 21:

$$\frac{d\psi}{dr}=\frac{\sqrt{C}}{r^2\sqrt{-A+2\frac{B}{r}-\frac{C}{r^2}}},$$

where A, B, and C have the meanings (2′). Integration gives

$$\psi-\psi_0=\cos^{-1}\frac{C-Br}{r\sqrt{B^2-AC}},$$

and, if we solve for r:

$$r=\frac{C}{B+\sqrt{B^2-AC}\cos(\psi-\psi_0)}.$$

If, for shortness, we write

$$\frac{C}{B}=l$$

(6) $$1-\frac{AC}{B^2}=\epsilon^2$$

we obtain the well-known form for the equation of an ellipse, whose focal point coincides with the origin of the co-ordinates:

(7) $$r=\frac{l}{1+\epsilon\cos(\psi-\psi_0)};$$

ϵ is the eccentricity and l the semi-latus rectum or parameter. If we express these in terms of the angle variables we have

(8) $$\epsilon^2=1-\frac{J_2^2}{J_1^2},$$

(9) $$l=\frac{J_2^2}{4\pi^2\mu e^2 Z}.$$

These two quantities fix the form of the orbital ellipse. Since an ellipse is usually determined by the semi-major axis a and the eccentricity ϵ or by means of the two semi-axes a and b, let us express a and b in terms of the action variables. We have

(10) $$a=\frac{l}{1-\epsilon^2}=\frac{J_1^2}{4\pi^2\mu e^2 Z},$$

(11) $$b=a\sqrt{1-\epsilon^2}=\frac{J_1 J_2}{4\pi^2\mu e^2 Z}.$$

Of these two quantities a alone is fixed by the quantum condition; ϵ, and with it l and b, can assume all values consistent with the corresponding a. The relation between a and the quantities W and ν_1, likewise fixed by the quantum condition, can be expressed as follows:

(12) $$W=-\frac{e^2 Z}{2a},$$

(13) $$\nu_1=\frac{e\sqrt{Z}}{2\pi\sqrt{\mu}}a^{-\frac{3}{2}}.$$

The equation (13) expresses Kepler's third law. For the case of the circular orbit, equation (12) states that the orbital energy is equal to half the potential energy. As we shall see in a moment, it is in general equal to half the time average of the potential energy.

We now consider the progress of the motion in time. By 10, § 21, we get for w_1:

$$w_1=\nu_1 t+\delta_1=\int\frac{\mu\nu_1 dr}{\sqrt{-A+2\frac{B}{r}-\frac{C}{r^2}}}.$$

If we resolve the radicand into its linear factors, we obtain

$$w_1=\int\frac{\mu r\nu_1 dr}{\sqrt{A}\sqrt{[a(1+\epsilon)-r][r-a(1-\epsilon)]}},$$

for $a(1+\epsilon)$ and $a(1-\epsilon)$ are the libration limits of r. The substitution

(14) $$r=a(1-\epsilon\cos u)$$

transforms the integral to

(15) $$w_1=\frac{\mu\nu_1 a}{\sqrt{A}}\int(1-\epsilon\cos u)du$$
$$2\pi w_1=u-\epsilon\sin u.$$

In order to make clear the geometrical significance of u, we introduce rectangular co-ordinates ξ, η such that the ξ-axis is the major axis of the orbit and the origin is the centre of force, Z (fig. 13), thus:

$$\xi=r\cos(\psi-\psi_0)$$
$$\eta=r\sin(\psi-\psi_0).$$

We obtain then from (7) and (14)

(16) $$\xi=\frac{q-r}{\epsilon}=a\cos u-\frac{a-q}{\epsilon}=a(\cos u-\epsilon)$$

(17) $$\eta^2=r^2-\xi^2=a^2(1-\epsilon^2)(1-\cos^2 u)$$
$$\eta=a\sqrt{1-\epsilon^2}\sin u.$$

In fig. 13 ON$=a$, ZQ$=\xi=a$ [cos (ZON)$-\epsilon$] and QM$=\eta=\sqrt{1-\epsilon^2}$. QN$=a\sqrt{1-\epsilon^2}\sin$(ZON). The angle ZON is therefore just the auxiliary quantity u. On account of its significance u is called the eccentric anomaly.

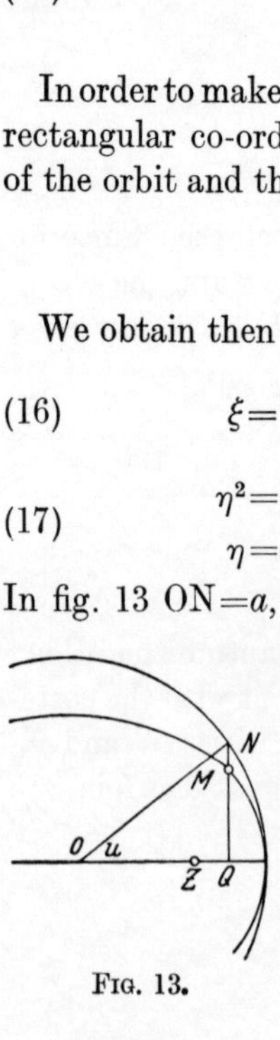

FIG. 13.

Now that we have found expressions for all the principal magnitudes of the Kepler motion we shall write them down once more in collected form. The energy of the motion is

(3) $$W=-\frac{2\pi^2\mu e^4 Z^2}{J_1^2};$$

the motion is confined to an ellipse with the semi-axes

(10) $$a=\frac{J_1^2}{4\pi^2\mu e^2 Z},$$

(11) $$b=\frac{J_1 J_2}{4\pi^2\mu e^2 Z};$$

the parameter of this ellipse is

(9) $$l=\frac{J_2^2}{4\pi^2\mu e^2 Z},$$

the eccentricity

(8a) $$\epsilon=\sqrt{1-\frac{J_2^2}{J_1^2}},$$

and the inclination i of the normal to the plane of the orbit to the polar axis of the r, θ, ϕ co-ordinate system is given by

$$\cos i=\frac{J_3}{J_2}.$$

The progress of the motion is given by

(14) $$r=a(1-\epsilon\cos u)$$

(16) $$\xi=a(\cos u-\epsilon)$$

(17) $$\eta=a\sqrt{1-\epsilon^2}\sin u.$$

Here u is defined by

(15a) $$2\pi\nu_1 t=u-\epsilon\sin u,$$

where

(5a) $$\nu_1=\frac{4\pi^2\mu e^4 Z^2}{J_1^3},$$

t being reckoned from the instant at which the perihelion is traversed.

A knowledge of the progress of the motion in time enables us to calculate certain mean values. Later we shall often require the mean values of certain powers of $1/r$ which we now proceed to evaluate. We have

$$\overline{r^{-n}}=\int\frac{\nu_1 dt}{r^n}=\int\frac{1}{r^{n-2}}\cdot\frac{\nu_1 dt}{r^2}.$$

Now the areal velocity $r^2\dot{\psi}$ is equal to $2\nu_1$ times the area of the ellipse, from which it follows that

(18) $$\frac{\nu_1 dt}{r^2}=\frac{d\psi}{2\pi ab}$$

and

$$\overline{r^{-n}}=\frac{1}{2\pi ab}\int_0^{2\pi}\frac{d\psi}{r^{n-2}}.$$

For $n \geqq 2$ we can quickly find, in this way, the mean value sought ; if we take $1/r$ from the ellipse-equation (7)

$$\frac{1}{r}=\frac{1}{l}+\frac{\epsilon}{l}\cos\psi \tag{7'}$$

we find

$$\begin{aligned}
\overline{r^{-2}}&=\frac{1}{ab}\\
\overline{r^{-3}}&=\frac{1}{b^3}\\
\overline{r^{-4}}&=\frac{1+\frac{\epsilon^2}{2}}{a^4(1-\epsilon^2)^{\frac{5}{2}}}=\frac{a\left(1+\frac{\epsilon^2}{2}\right)}{b^5}\\
\overline{r^{-5}}&=\frac{1+\frac{3}{2}\epsilon^2}{a^5(1-\epsilon^2)^{\frac{7}{2}}}=\frac{a^2(1+\frac{3}{2}\epsilon^2)}{b^7}.
\end{aligned} \tag{19}$$

The mean values $\overline{r^{-1}}$, $\bar{r}$, $\overline{r^2}$ . . . are more easily calculated by means of the eccentric anomaly. Using (14) and (15)

$$\overline{r^n}=\int r^n\nu_1 dt=a^n\cdot\frac{1}{2\pi}\int(1-\epsilon\cos u)^{n+1}du\,;$$

and we find

$$\begin{aligned}
\overline{r^{-1}}&=\frac{1}{a}\\
\bar{r}&=a\left(1+\frac{\epsilon^2}{2}\right)\\
\overline{r^2}&=a^2(1+\tfrac{3}{2}\epsilon^2).
\end{aligned} \tag{20}$$

Mean values of the form $\overline{r^n\cos^m\psi}\,(m>0)$ are best calculated for $n \leqq -2$ by the ellipse equation (7′), for $n \geqq m-1$ by the eccentric anomaly ; with the help of (18) we obtain

$$\overline{r^n\cos^m\psi}=\frac{1}{2\pi ab}\int r^{n+2}\cos^m\psi\,d\psi,$$

and from (14), (15), and (16)

$$\overline{r^n\cos^m\psi}=a^n\cdot\frac{1}{2\pi}\int(1-\epsilon\cos u)^{n-m+1}(\cos u-\epsilon)^m du,$$

so that

$$\overline{\cos\psi} = -\epsilon$$

(21) $$\bar{\xi} = \overline{r\cos\psi} = -\tfrac{3}{2}\epsilon a$$

$$\overline{r^2\cos\psi} = -(2+\tfrac{1}{2}\epsilon^2)\epsilon a^2$$

$$\overline{r^{-2}\cos\psi} = 0$$

(22) $$\overline{r^{-3}\cos\psi} = \frac{\epsilon}{2b^3}$$

$$\overline{r^{-3}\cos^2\psi} = \frac{1}{2b^3}.$$

Mean values of the form $\overline{r^n\cos^m\psi\sin^l\psi}$ vanish for odd values of l. For even values of l, $\sin^2\psi$ may be replaced by $1-\cos^2\psi$ and the mean value reduced to the form just considered. In particular

(23) $$\overline{r^{-3}\sin^2\psi} = \frac{1}{2b^3}.$$

We can now find the time average of the potential energy, it is

$$\overline{\mathrm{U}} = -e^2\mathrm{Z}\cdot\overline{r^{-1}} = -\frac{e^2\mathrm{Z}}{a} = 2\mathrm{W}$$

and is thus twice the orbital energy. The mean kinetic energy becomes

$$\overline{\mathrm{T}} = -\frac{\overline{\mathrm{U}}}{2}.$$

This theorem that the mean kinetic energy is equal to half the mean potential energy is valid generally for a system of electric charges which act on one another with forces obeying Coulomb's law.

Further, the co-ordinates of the electrical centre of gravity for a charge revolving in a Kepler ellipse are the time averages of the actual co-ordinates ξ and η, thus

(23′) $$\bar{\xi} = -\tfrac{3}{2}\epsilon a$$

and, by symmetry,

$$\bar{\eta} = 0.$$

The electrical centre of gravity is therefore situated on the major axis half-way between the middle point of the ellipse and that focus not occupied by the centre of force.

In the case of the Kepler motions the Fourier series for the rectangular co-ordinates ξ, η and for the distance r are comparatively easy to find. Noting that r/a and ξ/a are even functions, and η/a an uneven function of u, and therefore also of w_1, we can put

$$\frac{r}{a}=\frac{1}{2}B_0+\sum_\tau B_\tau \cos(2\pi w_1\tau)$$

(24)
$$\frac{\xi}{a}=\frac{1}{2}C_0+\sum_\tau C_\tau \cos(2\pi w_1\tau)$$

$$\frac{\eta}{a}=\sqrt{1-\epsilon^2}\left[\frac{1}{2}D_0+\sum D_\tau \sin(2\pi w_1\tau)\right].$$

For the coefficients we obtain the integrals :

$$B_\tau=4\int_0^{\frac{1}{2}}\frac{r}{a}\cos(2\pi w_1\tau)dw_1$$

(25)
$$C_\tau=4\int_0^{\frac{1}{2}}\frac{\xi}{a}\cos(2\pi w_1\tau)dw_1$$

$$D_\tau=4\int_0^{\frac{1}{2}}\frac{\eta}{a\sqrt{1-\epsilon^2}}\sin(2\pi w_1\tau)dw_1.$$

By partial integration we get from these

$$B_\tau=-\frac{2}{\pi\tau}\int_0^{\frac{1}{2}}\sin(2\pi w_1\tau)d\left(\frac{r}{a}\right)$$

$$C_\tau=-\frac{2}{\pi\tau}\int_0^{\frac{1}{2}}\sin(2\pi w_1\tau)d\left(\frac{\xi}{a}\right)$$

$$D_\tau=+\frac{2}{\pi\tau}\int_0^{\frac{1}{2}}\cos(2\pi w_1\tau)d\left(\frac{\eta}{a\sqrt{1-\epsilon^2}}\right).$$

Now by (16) and (17) we have

$$d\left(\frac{r}{a}\right)=\epsilon\sin u\,du$$

$$d\left(\frac{\xi}{a}\right)=-\sin u\,du$$

$$d\left(\frac{\eta}{a\sqrt{1-\epsilon^2}}\right)=\cos u\,du.$$

If now we introduce u as an integration variable from (15), we obtain

$$B_\tau=-\frac{2\epsilon}{\pi\tau}\int_0^\pi \sin[\tau(u-\epsilon\sin u)]\sin u\,du$$

$$C_\tau=\frac{2}{\pi\tau}\int_0^\pi \sin[\tau(u-\epsilon\sin u)]\sin u\,du$$

$$D_\tau=\frac{2}{\pi\tau}\int_0^\pi \cos[\tau(u-\epsilon\sin u)]\cos u\,du.$$

A simple trigonometrical transformation leads to :

$$B_\tau=\frac{\epsilon}{\pi\tau}\left\{\int_0^\pi \cos\left[(\tau+1)u-\tau\epsilon\sin u\right]du-\int_0^\pi \cos\left[(\tau-1)u-\tau\epsilon\sin u\right]du\right\}$$

$$C_\tau=\frac{1}{\pi\tau}\left\{-\int_0^\pi \cos\left[(\tau+1)u-\tau\epsilon\sin u\right]du+\int_0^\pi \cos\left[(\tau-1)u-\tau\epsilon\sin u\right]du\right\}$$

$$D_\tau=\frac{1}{\pi\tau}\left\{\int_0^\pi \cos\left[(\tau+1)u-\tau\epsilon\sin u\right]du+\int_0^\pi \cos\left[(\tau-1)u-\tau\epsilon\sin u\right]du\right\}.$$

The integrals appearing here are Bessel functions [1] defined by

$$\mathfrak{J}_\tau(x)=\frac{1}{\pi}\int_0^\pi \cos(\tau u-x\sin u)du.$$

We have therefore

$$B_\tau=\frac{\epsilon}{\tau}\left[\mathfrak{J}_{\tau+1}(\tau\epsilon)-\mathfrak{J}_{\tau-1}(\tau\epsilon)\right]$$

$$C_\tau=\frac{1}{\tau}\left[\mathfrak{J}_{\tau-1}(\tau\epsilon)-\mathfrak{J}_{\tau+1}(\tau\epsilon)\right]$$

$$D_\tau=\frac{1}{\tau}\left[\mathfrak{J}_{\tau+1}(\tau\epsilon)+\mathfrak{J}_{\tau-1}(\tau\epsilon)\right].$$

Since these formulæ fail for $\tau=0$ we must calculate B_0, C_0, D_0 from (25). We find:

$$B_0=4\int_0^{\frac{1}{2}}\frac{r}{a}dw_1=\frac{2}{\pi}\int_0^\pi(1-\epsilon\cos u)^2du=2+\epsilon^2$$

$$C_0=4\int_0^{\frac{1}{2}}\frac{\xi}{a}dw_1=\frac{2}{\pi}\int_0^\pi(\cos u-\epsilon)(1-\epsilon\cos u)du=-3\epsilon$$

$$D_0=0.$$

If, finally, we substitute the calculated values of the coefficients in (24) we derive:

$$\frac{r}{a}=1+\frac{\epsilon^2}{2}+\epsilon\sum_{\tau=1}^{\infty}\frac{1}{\tau}\left[\mathfrak{J}_{\tau+1}(\tau\epsilon)-\mathfrak{J}_{\tau-1}(\tau\epsilon)\right]\cos(2\pi w_1\tau)$$

(26)
$$\frac{\xi}{a}=-\frac{3}{2}\epsilon+\sum_{\tau=1}^{\infty}\frac{1}{\tau}\left[\mathfrak{J}_{\tau-1}(\tau\epsilon)-\mathfrak{J}_{\tau+1}(\tau\epsilon)\right]\cos(2\pi w_1\tau)$$

$$\frac{\eta}{a}=\sqrt{1-\epsilon^2}\,.\sum_{\tau=1}^{\infty}\frac{1}{\tau}\left[\mathfrak{J}_{\tau+1}(\tau\epsilon)+\mathfrak{J}_{\tau-1}(\tau\epsilon)\right]\sin(2\pi w_1\tau).$$

§ 23.—Spectra of the Hydrogen Type

The calculations given in § 22 provide us now with a basis for the explanation of certain line spectra. According to the conception of

[1] The Bessel functions are here indicated by Gothic J's, to avoid confusion with the action variables.

atomic structure described in the Introduction, the hydrogen atom in the uncharged (neutral) state consists of a nucleus of charge $+e$ and considerable mass M and an electron of charge $-e$ and small mass m. Of similar structure are the singly ionised helium atom (He^+) and the doubly ionised lithium atom (Li^{++}), only the nuclear charge is $2e$ and $3e$ respectively in the two cases. In all of these atoms, therefore, we have a Z-fold charged nucleus and one electron; their mechanics is consequently included in the theory given in § 22.

The energy in the stationary states is, by (4), § 22,

$$W=-\frac{cRhZ^2}{n^2}, \tag{1}$$

where

$$R=\frac{2\pi^2\mu e^4}{ch^3}. \tag{2}$$

R is known as the Rydberg Constant, because Rydberg was the first to notice that it occurred in the representations of numerous spectra. Since

$$\mu=\frac{mM}{m+M}=m\frac{1}{1+\frac{m}{M}}, \tag{3}$$

R depends on the ratio of the electron mass m to the nuclear mass M. The limiting value for infinitely heavy nuclei is

$$R_\infty=\frac{2\pi^2 me^4}{ch^3}. \tag{4}$$

For other atoms

$$R=R_\infty\frac{1}{1+\frac{m}{M}}. \tag{5}$$

The correction factor is here very nearly 1, since even for hydrogen $m/M=1/1830$; in the majority of cases, therefore, R may, to a sufficient approximation, be replaced by R_∞.

Spectroscopists prefer to specify spectral lines not in frequencies but in wave numbers, *i.e.* number of waves per cm. We will follow the usual notation and write ν for the wave number of a line or term in §§ 23–29. This should not be confused with the earlier use of ν for the mechanical frequency in an orbit.

The wave numbers of the spectral lines corresponding to the terms (1) are

$$\nu=\frac{1}{hc}(W^{(1)}-W^{(2)})=RZ^2\left(\frac{1}{n_2{}^2}-\frac{1}{n_1{}^2}\right). \tag{6}$$

According to the correspondence principle all transitions between the stationary states occur, since in the Fourier series for the motion (26), § 22, the coefficients of all the harmonics differ from zero.

For Z=1 the spectrum of the hydrogen atom is obtained from equation (6), and, for $n_2=2$, in particular, the long-familiar Balmer series:

$$\nu=R_H\left(\frac{1}{2^2}-\frac{1}{n_1{}^2}\right) \qquad (n_1=3, 4 \ldots).$$

The strongest support of the Bohr theory consists in the agreement of the quantity R_H, determined from the spectroscopic measurements of this series, with that expressed by (4) and (5), in terms of atomic constants (the difference between R_H and R_∞ is smaller than the relative errors of measurement of the atomic constants).

According to deviation experiments on cathode rays

$$\frac{e}{m}=1{\cdot}77 \, . \, 10^7 \, \frac{\text{E.S.U.}}{\text{gm.}},$$

by Millikan's measurement of the smallest charge on a drop

$$e=4{\cdot}77 \, . \, 10^{-10} \text{ E.S.U.},$$

according to heat radiation measurements and determinations of the limit of the continuous X-ray spectrum (see later)

$$h=6{\cdot}54 \, . \, 10^{-27} \text{ erg sec};$$

with these numerical values one finds from (4)

$$cR=3{\cdot}28 \, . \, 10^{15} \text{ sec}^{-1},$$
$$R=1{\cdot}09 \, . \, 10^5 \text{ cm}^{-1};$$

the value deduced directly from the observed spectrum is

$$R_H=109678 \text{ cm}^{-1}.$$

The agreement of the two numbers lies within the limits of accuracy in the value calculated from (4) using the observed values of e, e/m, and h.

This gives for the work done in separating the electron when in the one-quantum orbit

$$W_1=-cRh=2{\cdot}15 \, . \, 10^{-11} \text{ erg}.$$

This value can also be expressed in kilocalories per gram molecule by multiplying by Avogadro's number $N=6{\cdot}06 \, . \, 10^{23}$ and dividing by the mechanical equivalent of heat $4{\cdot}18\times10^{10}$ ergs per kcal. The result is 312 kcal. Finally, as a measure of the energy, use is often made of the potential V in volts through which an electron must pass in order to gain the energy under consideration ; we have

$$W=\frac{eV}{300}.$$

The value 13·53 volts is found for the energy of the hydrogen electron. The general transformation formula is

$$(7) \qquad 1 \text{ volt}=23{\cdot}0 \frac{\text{kcal.}}{\text{gm. mol.}}=1{\cdot}59 \,.\, 10^{-12} \text{ erg}=8{\cdot}11 \,.\, 10^{3} \text{ cm}^{-1}.$$

It is the potential V which is directly measured in the method of electron impact (see Introduction, § 3).

The formula (6) contains, in addition to the Balmer series, the following hydrogen series :

1. The ultra-violet Lyman series,

$$\nu=R_H\left(1-\frac{1}{n_1^2}\right) \qquad (n_1=2, 3 \ldots).$$

Since the constant term in this series formula corresponds to the normal state of the atom, the series occurs in "non-excited" atomic hydrogen as an absorption series.

2. The infra-red Paschen series,

$$\nu=R_H\left(\frac{1}{3^2}-\frac{1}{n_1^2}\right) \qquad (n_1=4, 5 \ldots).$$

For Z=2 we obtain the spectrum of ionised helium (the "spark spectrum" of helium). In this spectrum the lines which correspond to even quantum numbers (n=2N),

$$\nu=4R_{He}\left[\frac{1}{(2N_1)^2}-\frac{1}{(2N_2)^2}\right]=R_{He}\left(\frac{1}{N_1^2}-\frac{1}{N_2^2}\right),$$

are situated in close proximity to the hydrogen lines,

$$\nu=R_H\left(\frac{1}{N_1^2}-\frac{1}{N_2^2}\right).$$

This similarity between the spark spectrum of helium and the spectrum of hydrogen was responsible for the fact that the former used to be written in the form

$$\nu=R\left(\frac{1}{\left(\frac{n_1}{2}\right)^2}-\frac{1}{\left(\frac{n_2}{2}\right)^2}\right),$$

and the lines, observed in certain stars and nebulæ, which fitted this formula were ascribed to hydrogen. Bohr made the situation clear and showed that the difference between the two Rydberg constants R_H and R_{He} was due to the differences in the nuclear masses M in (3).

The hitherto unobserved spectrum of doubly ionised lithium (Li^{++}) is given by putting $Z=3$.

In addition to the quantitative agreement of the spectra the orders of magnitude are also in favour of Bohr's model of the atom. For the radius of the normal orbit of the hydrogen atom, considered as a circle, we have by (10), § 22, for $\mu=m$

$$a_H=\frac{h^2}{4\pi^2me^2}=0{\cdot}532\,.\,10^{-8}\text{ cm}\,; \tag{8}$$

this falls within the order of magnitude of estimates deduced from the kinetic theory of gases and other atomic theories. For the semi-major axis of the excited hydrogen ellipses we have by (10), § 22,

$$a=a_H\,.\,n^2\,; \tag{9}$$

the radii of the corresponding orbits of He^+ and Li^{++} are smaller in the ratio 1 : 2 and 1 : 3 respectively.

§ 24.—The Series Arrangement of Lines in Spectra not of the Hydrogen Type

We proceed now to those spectra not of the hydrogen type. As we have already mentioned in § 21 we endeavour, following Bohr, to ascribe the production of these spectra to transitions between stationary states of the atom, each of these stationary states being characterised essentially by the motion of a single " radiating " or " series " electron in an orbit under the influence of the core, which is represented approximately by a central field of force. This conception explains some of the most important regularities of the series of spectra, namely, the existence of several series, each of which is more or less similar to the hydrogen type, and the possibility of combinations between these.

In a (non-Coulomb) central field of force the motion depends, according to § 21, on the subsidiary quantum number k in addition to the principal quantum number n. k has a simple mechanical significance, being in fact the total angular momentum of the electron measured in units of $h/2\pi$.

The Bohr relation between frequencies of radiation and energy differences of the radiating system,

$$\tilde{\nu}=\frac{1}{h}(W^{(1)}-W^{(2)}),$$

corresponds to the general observation that the regularities which occur in observed spectra can be expressed by writing the wave number of a line as the difference of two terms, the number of terms being less than the number of lines ordered by means of them. In our simple atomic model the terms depend on two integers n and k and can therefore be denoted by the symbol n_k. We found, by applying the correspondence principle, that only such terms may combine with one another as have values of k differing by ± 1 (see (11′), § 21).

With this theoretically predicted spectrum we compare that actually observed. The empirical set of terms of any one spectrum is arranged by spectroscopists in a number of term series ;[1] an individual term is denoted by its number in the term series and by the name of this series. The usual designation of these term series is derived from the historical designation of the corresponding line series : *s* (sharp or second subordinate series), *p* (principal series), *d* (diffuse or first subordinate series), *f* (fundamental series, often called also *b*, Bergmann series), *g* (called sometimes *f′* or *f**), etc. There is therefore a series of *s*-terms, one of *p*-, *d*-, *f*- . . . terms ; further, each of these may be multiple, but this possibility we shall disregard for the time being.[2]

With the usual spectroscopic numbering of the terms in the series we derive the following scheme :

1*s*	2*s*	3*s*	4*s*	5*s*	6*s*	. . .
	2*p*	3*p*	4*p*	5*p*	6*p*	. . .
		3*d*	4*d*	5*d*	6*d*	. . .
			4*f*	5*f*	6*f*	. . .
				5*g*	6*g*	. . .

In each of these series the terms with increasing order number decrease towards zero.

In order to see how our numbers n and k are related to these letters, we refer to the following observations respecting the combination of the terms. Under normal conditions (*i.e.* when the atoms are in direct interaction with the radiation without being disturbed by external influences) the following rules hold :[3]

---

[1] The word "sequence" is sometimes used for a term series, and the word "series" is then restricted to mean a series of lines in the spectrum.

[2] The multiplicity of the terms cannot be explained on the assumption of a point electron and a central field of force. It was first ascribed to a space quantisation of the orbit of the radiating electron with respect to an axis in the core, and later to a spin of the electron itself (*cf.* p. 155).

[3] They are obeyed strictly in the more simply constructed types of spectra, *e.g.* those of the alkalies and of Cu and Ag. In the other spectra also they are for the

1. Two terms of the same term series never combine.
2. The only combinations are *s*- with *p*-terms, *p*- with *s*- and *d*-terms, *d*- with *p*- and *f*-terms, etc.

From this it is clear that the separate term series differ in the quantum number k and that taking the term series in the order *s*, *p*, *d*, *f* . . . the number k increases or decreases by 1 from one to the next. Since *s* represents the end of the series of combinations, presumably in the term series *s*-, *p*-, *d*-, *f*- . . ., k is to be put equal to 1, 2, 3, 4 respectively.[1]

We shall now see what can be said regarding the magnitudes of the terms.

The field of force of the core of an atom is, at a sufficiently great distance, a Coulomb field of force. In the case of the neutral atom it corresponds to the " effective " nuclear charge $Z=1$, in the case of the 1-, 2- . . . fold ionised atom $Z=2, 3$ . . . respectively. The orbits of the radiating electron at a large distance are therefore similar to those in the case of hydrogen. They differ from the Kepler ellipses only by the fact that the perihelion executes a slow rotation in the plane of the orbit. The semi-axes and parameter of the ellipses are, by (9), (10), and (11) of § 22,

$$a=n^2a_{\mathrm{H}}$$

$$b=\frac{nka_{\mathrm{H}}}{Z}$$

$$l=\frac{k^2a_{\mathrm{H}}}{Z}.$$

The perihelion radius vector is :

$$a(1-\epsilon)=a\left(1-\sqrt{1-\frac{k^2}{n^2}}\right)=\frac{a_{\mathrm{H}}}{Z}n^2\left(1-\sqrt{1-\frac{k^2}{n^2}}\right);$$

for a fixed value of k this distance lies between $l/2$ and l, the exact value depending on the value of n. The larger the value of k the more of the orbit is situated in the Coulomb part of the field of force; for large values of k the terms are consequently similar to those of hydrogen. This confirms the adopted numbering of the series by the values of k, for observation shows that the terms

most part valid ; the exceptions point to a deficiency of our model (they may depend on quantum transitions of the core electrons, or to interactions of the series electron with the core which cannot be represented by a central field).

[1] A. Sommerfeld, *Sitz.-Ber. d. Bay. Akad. d. Wiss., Math. Phys. Cl.*; p. 131, 1916, and A. Sommerfeld and W. Kossel, *Verh. d. Dtsch. Phys. Ges.*, vol. xxi, p. 240, 1919. This co-ordination is possible only in those spectra where one electron can be singled out as the radiating electron. In the case of more complicated spectra the designations *s*-, *p*-, *d*-terms must be associated with the resultant angular momentum of all the external electrons.

approximate more and more nearly to those of hydrogen the further we proceed in the order s, p, d, f. . . .

From the term series the line series are obtained by keeping one term fixed and allowing the other to traverse a term series. The most commonly observed series by far, and those which have given their names to the terms, are the following:

Principal series (H.-S.)	$\nu=1s-mp$
Diffuse (1st subordinate) series (I. N.-S.) .	$\nu=2p-md$
Sharp (2nd subordinate) series (II. N.-S.) .	$\nu=2p-ms$
Fundamental (Bergmann) series (F.-S.) . .	$\nu=3d-mf$.

In addition to these the following combinations occur:

Second principal series	$\nu=2s-mp$
Second diffuse series	$\nu=3p-md$
	$\nu=3d-mp$
	$\nu=4f-md$.

Not only these term differences, but also the terms themselves, have a physical significance. Thanks to our hypothesis regarding the potential energy, which we have supposed to vanish at infinity, the magnitude $|W|$ of the energy constant denotes the work which is necessary to remove an electron from its stationary orbit to infinity and to bring it to rest there (relatively to the nucleus). If the stationary orbit of the electron is that of the normal state, then this work is the work of ionisation.

Also the energies W converge to zero, with increasing n,[1] as in the case of hydrogen, and further the empirical terms of a single term series likewise converge to zero, so the energy values ascribed theoretically are in agreement with the empirical terms; the wave number of a term multiplied by hc is therefore a measure of the work required to remove the electron from the orbit to a state of rest at infinity.

The largest existing term corresponds to the orbit of the electron in the normal state and gives a measure of the ionisation potential. If this term is an s-term, as is the case for several of the simpler spectra, the ionisation potential is the frequency of the limit ($n=\infty$) of the principal series multiplied by h; if the largest term is a p-term, the ionisation potential is the frequency of the common limit of the two subordinate series multiplied by h. Simple spectra are also known for which a d-term corresponds to the normal state (*e.g.* Sc^{++}).

All that we can expect of our simple atomic model, by means of

[1] This result arises from the behaviour of the integral (6), § 21, for negative values of W tending to zero, when $U(r) \propto 1/r$ for r large.

which we replace the non-mechanical motion of the radiating electron by a mechanical one based on the assumption of a spherically symmetrical field of force for the core, is that it shall give a rough indication of the general characteristics of the line spectra. As a matter of fact it makes comprehensible the series arrangement of the lines and terms as well as the increasing similarity of the higher series to those of hydrogen. Of the most important remaining unexplained facts we mention once more the multiplicity of the terms. In all of the alkali spectra the *p*-, *d*- . . . terms are double, in the alkaline earths there are also triple *p*-, *d*- . . . terms. Other elements, *e.g.* Sc, Ti, Va, Cr, Mn, Fe exhibit still higher multiplicities. We mention further the fact that many elements have term systems of the structure described here, *e.g.* the alkaline earths have a complete system of single terms as well as a system with single *s*-terms and triple *p*-, *d*- . . . terms. Finally, exceptions occur to the above-mentioned rule for the change of k in quantum transitions.

The multiplicity may be accounted for in principle by assuming deviations from the central symmetry of the core. If these deviations are small, they produce a secular precession of the angular momentum vector of the radiating electron and core about the axis of the resultant angular momentum of the system. Space quantisation occurs, a somewhat different energy value becoming associated with each orientation. But this argument leads to multiplicities which do not correspond exactly to those observed.[1] Pauli[2] has shown that these could be explained by ascribing four quantum numbers to each electron instead of three; and to account for the fourth quantum number Uhlenbeck and Goudsmit[3] suggested that the electron had a quantised spin about an axis. This hypothesis has been very fruitful for the understanding of spectra with multiple terms, but it will not be considered in this volume.

§ 25.—Estimation of the Energy Values of Outer Orbits in Spectra not of the Hydrogen Type

We found that the orbit of the radiating electron was hydrogen-like for large values of k, since it is situated in an approximately Coulomb field of force. For smaller values of k the orbit approaches

[1] For multiplicities and Zeeman effects *cf.* E. Back and A. Landé, *Zeemaneffekt und Multiplettstruktur der Spektrallinien*, Berlin, Julius Springer, 1925, vol. i of the German series, *Struktur der Materie*; and F. Hund, *Linienspektra*, vol. iv of the same series.

[2] W. Pauli, *Zeitschr. f. Physik*, vol. xxxi, p. 765, 1925.

[3] G. E. Uhlenbeck and S. Goudsmit, *Naturwissenschaften*, vol. xiii, p. 953, 1925; *Nature*, vol. cxvii, p. 264, 1926.

the region of the core electrons. As long as it does not penetrate this region it will be permissible, to a first approximation, to expand the potential energy of the central field of force in powers of $1/r$ when calculating the value of a term.[1] We write

$$\text{(1)} \qquad U(r) = -\frac{e^2Z}{r}\left(1 + c_1\left(\frac{a}{r}\right) + c_2\left(\frac{a}{r}\right)^2 + \dots\right),$$

where a denotes a length which may conveniently be put equal to a_H (see (8), § 23). The radial action integral is then, by (4), § 21 :

$$J_r = \oint\left[-A + 2\frac{B}{r} - \frac{C}{r^2} + \frac{D}{r^3} + \dots\right]^{\frac{1}{2}} dr,$$

where

$$A = -2mW,$$
$$B = me^2Z,$$
$$C = \frac{k^2h^2}{4\pi^2} - 2me^2Za_Hc_1,$$
$$D = \qquad + 2me^2Za_H{}^2c_2.$$

We assume now that in the expansion for $U(r)$ the term quadratic in a/r is small in comparison with the linear term, and calculate as a first approximation the influence of the subsidiary term c_1a/r in the potential energy on the value of the term. This calculation may be carried out rigorously for all values of c_1. The phase integral has the same form as in § 22, and we obtain by complex integration (*cf.* (5), Appendix II) :

$$J_r = (n-k)h = 2\pi\left(-\sqrt{C} + \frac{B}{\sqrt{A}}\right),$$

and from this

$$A = -2mW = \frac{4\pi^2B^2}{[(n-k)h + 2\pi\sqrt{C}]^2}.$$

If we substitute for B and C their values and introduce the Rydberg constant R from (2), § 23, we get

$$\text{(2)} \qquad W = -\frac{cRhZ^2}{(n+\delta)^2},$$

where

$$\delta = -k + \sqrt{k^2 - \frac{8\pi^2me^2Z}{h^2}a_Hc_1} = -k + \sqrt{k^2 - 2Zc_1}$$

(using (8), § 23). If the deviation from the Coulomb field is small only, we can write

[1] See A. Sommerfeld, *Atomic Structure and Spectral Lines* (Methuen), p. 596.

(3) $$\delta = -\frac{Zc_1}{k}.$$

The influence of the additional term in the potential energy on the value of the term may be expressed as follows: If the energy be written in the form $-\frac{cRhZ^2}{n^{*2}}$, the "effective quantum number" n^* differs from the integral value n, which it has for hydrogen, by a small amount δ. The difference depends on k, but not on n, and its amount will be smaller the larger the value of k. The deviation from the Coulomb field, caused by the core electrons, will consist mainly of a more rapid variation of the potential with r, since as r decreases the attractive action of the highly charged nucleus will be less and less weakened by the core electrons. Assuming that the first term of the expansion is the determining factor, this means that in our expansion (1) c_1 is positive. δ is then negative, so that we should expect the magnitude n^*, the effective quantum number, to be smaller than n.

The form of the orbit is, as in every multiply-periodic central motion, a rosette. Its equation is easily found. In order to derive it we again introduce the co-ordinates r, ψ in the orbital plane. By (12), § 21, we obtain then for the differential equation of the orbit:

$$\frac{d\psi}{dr} = \frac{\frac{J^2}{2\pi}}{r^2\sqrt{2\mu W + \frac{2\mu e^2 Z}{r} - \left(\frac{J_2^2}{4\pi^2} - 2\mu e^2 Z c_1 a_H\right)\frac{1}{r^2}}}$$

or

(4) $$\frac{d\psi}{dr} = \frac{1}{\gamma} \cdot \frac{\sqrt{C}}{r^2\sqrt{-A + \frac{2B}{r} - \frac{C}{r^2}}}.$$

The equation has almost the same form as in the case of the Kepler motion; A and B have the same meaning as there:

$$A = 2\mu(-W), \qquad B = \mu e^2 Z;$$

C is somewhat different:

$$C = \frac{J_2^2}{4\pi^2} - 2\mu e^2 Z a_H c_1 = \frac{J_2^2}{4\pi^2} - \frac{h^2 Z}{2\pi^2} c_1,$$

and γ has the value

(5) $$\gamma = \sqrt{1 - \frac{2h^2 Z}{J_2^2} c_1}.$$

The integration of the equation (4) is carried out in precisely the same way as in the case of the Kepler motion, and leads to (*cf.* § 22)

$$r=\frac{C}{B+\sqrt{B^2-AC}\cos\gamma(\psi-\psi_0)}.$$

If we introduce here the abbreviations (*cf.* (6), § 22)

$$\frac{C}{B}=l,$$

$$1-\frac{AC}{B^2}=\epsilon^2,$$

we get

$$r=\frac{l}{1+\epsilon\cos\gamma(\psi-\psi_0)}. \tag{6}$$

The equation of the path differs from that of an ellipse with the parameter l and eccentricity ϵ by the factor γ. While r goes through one libration, the true anomaly ψ increases by $2\pi/\gamma$. The path approaches more nearly to an ellipse the smaller the coefficient c_1 of the additional term in the potential energy, and for $c_1=0$ it becomes an ellipse. For small values of c_1 we can regard the path as an ellipse, whose perihelion slowly rotates with the angular velocity

$$\omega_1\left(\frac{1}{\gamma}-1\right)=\omega_1\frac{h^2Z}{J_2^{\ 2}}c_1+\ldots=\omega_1\frac{c_1Z}{k^2}+\ldots.$$

ω_1 is here the mean motion of the point on the ellipse.

We now take into account the term $c_2(a/r)^2$ in (1), but only in the case where its influence is small. We find then by complex integration (*cf.* (10), Appendix II):

$$J_r=(n-k)h=2\pi\left(-\sqrt{C}+\frac{B}{\sqrt{A}}+\frac{BD}{2C\sqrt{C}}\right),$$

and from this

$$A=-2mW=\frac{4\pi^2B^2}{\left[(n-k)h+2\pi\sqrt{C}-\pi\frac{BD}{C\sqrt{C}}\right]^2}$$

and

$$W=-\frac{cRhZ^2}{n^{*2}}=-\frac{cRhZ^2}{(n+\delta)^2}, \tag{2}$$

where this time

$$\delta=-k+\sqrt{k^2-2Zc_1}-\frac{Z^2c_2}{\sqrt{k^2-2Zc_1}^{\,3}} \tag{7}$$

$$=-\frac{Zc_1}{k}-\frac{Z^2c_1^{\ 2}}{2k^3}-\frac{Z^2c_2}{k^3}+\cdots.$$

The following term $c_3(a/r)^3$ may be taken into account in a similar way and would lead to a dependence of the quantity δ on n in the form

$$\delta=\delta_1+\frac{\delta_2}{n^2}.$$

However, we shall not carry out the calculation in this way; instead, we will again calculate the influence of the additional terms in the potential energy, this time with the help of the method of secular perturbations, § 18. The result will be of less generality only inasmuch as we must suppose the quantity c_1 to be small as well as $c_2, c_3 \cdots$. We write

$$H=H_0+H_1,$$

where H_0 is the Hamiltonian function of the Kepler motion, consequently

$$H_0=W_0=-\frac{cRhZ^2}{n^2},$$

and we regard

$$H_1=-\frac{e^2Z}{r}\left[c_1\left(\frac{a_H}{r}\right)+c_2\left(\frac{a_H}{r}\right)^2+\cdots\right]$$

as the perturbation function. The unperturbed motion is doubly degenerate; the perturbation makes it singly degenerate. We obtain the secular motion of the angle variables now no longer degenerate, and the influence of the perturbation on the energy, by averaging H_1 over the unperturbed motion. In this way we find

$$W_1=-e^2Z[c_1a_H\overline{r^{-2}}+c_2a_H{}^2\overline{r^{-3}}+c_3a_H{}^3\overline{r^{-4}}+c_4a_H{}^4\overline{r^{-5}}+\cdots].$$

The mean values are by (19), § 22:

$$\overline{r^{-2}}=\frac{1}{ab}=\frac{Z^2}{a_H{}^2n^3k},$$

$$\overline{r^{-3}}=\frac{1}{b^3}=\frac{Z^3}{a_H{}^3n^3k^3},$$

$$\overline{r^{-4}}=\frac{a\left(1+\frac{\epsilon^2}{2}\right)}{b^5}=\frac{\left(3-\frac{k^2}{n^2}\right)Z^4}{2a_H{}^4n^3k^5},$$

$$\overline{r^{-5}}=\frac{a^2\left(1+\frac{3}{2}\epsilon^2\right)}{b^7}=\frac{\left(5-3\frac{k^2}{n^2}\right)Z^5}{2a_H{}^5n^3k^7}.$$

On introducing the Rydberg constant

$$R=\frac{e^2}{2a_{\mathrm{H}}hc}$$

we get

$$(8)\qquad W=-\frac{cRhZ^2}{n^2}\left[1+\frac{2Zc_1}{nk}+\frac{2Z^2c_2}{nk^3}+\frac{Z^3\left(3-\frac{k^2}{n^2}\right)c_3}{nk^5}+\frac{Z^4\left(5-3\frac{k^2}{n^2}\right)c_4}{nk^7}+\cdots\right].$$

Writing W in the form

$$(9)\qquad W=-\frac{cRhZ^2}{n^{*2}},$$

we find, on neglecting products of the c_i's,

$$(10)\qquad n^*=n+\delta=n-\frac{Zc_1}{k}-\frac{Z^2c_2}{k^3}+Z^3c_3\left(-\frac{3}{2k^5}+\frac{1}{2k^3n^2}\right)+Z^4c_4\left(-\frac{5}{2k^7}+\frac{3}{2k^5n^2}\right)+\cdots$$

or

$$(11)\qquad n^*=n+\delta_1+\frac{\delta_2}{n^2}+\cdots,$$

where

$$\delta_1=-\frac{Zc_1}{k}-\frac{Z^2c_2}{k^3}-\frac{3Z^3c_3}{2k^5}-\frac{5Z^4c_4}{2k^7}-\cdots,$$

$$\delta_2=\frac{Z^3c_3}{2k^3}+\frac{3Z^4c_4}{2k^5}+\cdots.$$

We now compare these theoretical formulæ with observation. The terms derived from observations of spectra of the non-hydrogen type may in fact be written in the form

$$\frac{RZ^2}{(n+\delta)^2},$$

where, in general, δ depends very little on n. Rydberg [1] was the first to suggest this form and verified it by measurements of numerous spectra. We shall therefore denote the quantity δ as the Rydberg correction. The remaining deviations have been represented by

[1] J. R. Rydberg, *K. Svenska Akad. Handl.*, vol. xxiii, 1889: an expansion in $1/n^2$ equivalent to the Rydberg formula has been given independently by H. Kayser and C. Runge (*Berlin. Akad.*, 1889 to 1892).

Ritz,[1] who gave a series expansion for the difference between n^* and the whole number

$$\delta=\delta_1+\delta_2\frac{1}{n^2}+\ldots \tag{12}$$

Ritz used also the implicit formula

$$\nu=\frac{RZ^2}{(n+\delta_1+\bar{\delta}_2\nu)^2}. \tag{13}$$

§ 26.—The Rydberg-Ritz Formula

The Rydberg-Ritz formula can be established empirically not only for the terms of the outer orbits, but also for orbits which penetrate the core and which we shall call " penetrating orbits." It may in fact be derived theoretically for very general cases.

We show next that for an arbitrary central field the formula

$$\nu=\frac{RZ^2}{(n+\delta_1+\bar{\delta}_2\nu)^2} \tag{1}$$

corresponds to a reasonable series expansion.[2]

The connection between the quantum numbers and the wave number ν of the term is given by the equation (*cf.* (4), § 21)

$$(n-k)h=\oint\sqrt{-2m[h\nu+U(r)]-\frac{h^2k^2}{4\pi^2r^2}}dr.$$

($U(r)$ is negative, see § 21.) We compare this with the expression

$$(n^*-k)h=\oint\sqrt{-2m\left[h\nu-\frac{e^2Z}{r}\right]-\frac{h^2k^2}{4\pi^2r^2}}dr,$$

which, for the same ν, corresponds to a Coulomb field of force. For this n^* is of course not an integer, but has the value given by

$$\nu=\frac{RZ^2}{n^{*2}}.$$

The difference of the two integrals is a function of ν and k alone. If we imagine it expanded in terms of ν and put equal to

$$-h[\delta_1(k)+\bar{\delta}_2(k)\nu+\ldots],$$

we obtain

$$n^*-n=\delta_1+\bar{\delta}_2\nu+\ldots$$

---

[1] W. Ritz, *Ann. d. Physik*, vol. xii, p. 264, 1903; *Physikal. Zeitschr.*, vol. ix, p. 521, 1908; see also *Ges. Werke*, Paris, 1911.

[2] G. Wentzel, *Zeitschr. f. Physik*, vol. xix, p. 53, 1923.

and

$$\nu = \frac{RZ^2}{(n+\delta_1+\bar{\delta}_2\nu+\ldots)^2}.$$

Since for larger values of n the term ν rapidly approaches zero, we can conclude from this consideration that the correction $\delta_1+\bar{\delta}_2\nu$ rapidly converges to a fixed limiting value for increasing n.

The following argument due to Bohr,[1] goes much further towards providing a theoretical basis for the Rydberg-Ritz formula (1), and gives this formula greater physical significance.

The real object of the introduction of the central field was to describe, by means of a simple model, the (certainly non-mechanical) interaction between core and radiating electron, for which no exchange of energy between core and electron occurs. Now this assumption regarding the constancy of the energy of the radiating electron is alone enough to enable us to deduce the series formula, without special assumptions regarding the field of force; this derivation is, in consequence, not only valid for any atom whose spectrum can be ascribed to a single series electron, but even for molecules. Certainly molecules do not emit line but band spectra; these, however, are also produced chiefly by transitions of a radiating electron, on which are superimposed the quantum transitions of the molecule as a whole from one state of rotational or oscillatory motion to another.

Further, this derivation is altogether independent of whether an exchange of angular momentum between core and electron takes place or not, *i.e.* whether or not an azimuthal quantum number k can be defined in a manner analogous to that in the case of central motion.

The only assumption which we make is that the core (which includes one nucleus in the case of one atom and several in the case of a molecule) is small in comparison with the dimensions of the path of the radiating electron. The field will then closely resemble a Coulomb field over most of the path outside the core; the distance of the aphelion from the centre point of the core will be determined only by the potential energy in the aphelion, it is therefore equal for all loops of the path independently of whether these loops are similar to one another (as for a central field) or not. Accordingly an effective quantum number n^* may be so defined that the relation

---

[1] We are indebted to Professor Bohr for kindly communicating the ideas on which the following paragraphs are based.

holds which is valid in the Coulomb field, between n^* and aphelion distance and energy respectively :

$$W=-\frac{cRhZ^2}{n^{*2}}. \tag{2}$$

We assume, on account of the periodicity of the electron motion, that it has a principal quantum number n ; W is then a function of $J=nh$, and for the radial period τ of the motion (*i.e.* the time from aphelion to aphelion) we have

$$\frac{1}{\tau}=\frac{\partial W}{\partial J}=\frac{1}{h}\frac{\partial W}{\partial n}. \tag{3}$$

The radial period τ^* of the motion in the Kepler ellipse with the same energy (2) is

$$\frac{1}{\tau^*}=\frac{1}{h}\frac{\partial W}{\partial n^*}. \tag{4}$$

In a single term series we consider the variation of energy with the principal action integral J or principal quantum number n, for constant values of the other quantum numbers ; for such a variation we may invert the derivatives (3) and (4), and find for a term series

$$\frac{d(n-n^*)}{dW}=\frac{1}{h}(\tau-\tau^*).$$

Now the Rydberg correction δ is equal to n^*-n (compare (2) with (2), § 25), and W is hc times the wave number ν of the corresponding term in the spectrum, so that for a term series

$$\frac{d\delta}{d\nu}=c(\tau^*-\tau). \tag{5}$$

The radial motion in the two orbits is only different over that part of the actual orbit where the field of the core is appreciable ; the proportion of a radial period spent in this part of the orbit is small, if the core is small compared to the dimensions of the orbit of the series electron as assumed, so $\tau^*-\tau$ is small compared to τ. If it can be taken to have a constant value

$$\tau^*-\tau=\bar{\delta}_2/c$$

over the range of ν covered by the term series, (5) integrates directly to

$$\delta=\delta_1+\bar{\delta}_2\nu,$$

whence the Ritz formula (1) follows at once.

If $\tau^*-\tau$ cannot be taken as constant, it seems probable that it will be expansible in a power series in W or ν (this can certainly be done if the field is central); integration of (5) then gives δ as a power series in ν—the "extended Ritz formula."

In order to provide a survey of the validity of this formula we give the values of the effective quantum number n^* for the terms of two typical spectra, those of Na and Al:

Na.										
s	1·63		2·64			3·65			4·65	
p		2·12			3·13			4·14		
d				2·99			3·99			4·99
f							4·00			5·00

Al																
s		2·19		3·22				4·23			5·23			6·23		
p	1·51		2·67			3·70			4·71			5·72				
d			2·63		3·42			4·26			5·16			6·11	7·08	8·07
f							3·97			4·96			5·96			

The Na-spectrum and the *s*-, *p*-, and *f*-series of the Al-spectrum show the behaviour which we find for almost all term series, namely, very little dependence of the Rydberg correction n^*-n on the term number n. The *d*-series of aluminium and a few other known series form the exception, inasmuch as the limiting value of the correction is reached only for comparatively high term number.

Since, for the time being, we do not know the quantum number n only the fractional part of δ can yet be found, the integer is undetermined. If we choose the integers here so that the magnitudes of δ decrease with increasing k and at the same time are as small as possible, we obtain as limiting values for large n:

	s	*p*	*d*	*f*
Na	−1·35	−0·86	−0·01	0·00
Al	−1·77	−1·28	−0·93	−0·04

Now if the analysis of § 25 were applicable, $|\delta|$ would increase as $1/k$ or $1/k^3$ or $1/k^5$ (*cf.* (10), § 25), as k decreased and the orbit at perihelion came closer to the nucleus; it will be seen from these examples, and from all other series spectra, that there comes a stage at which the increase of $|\delta|$ with decreasing k is very much more rapid than that given by any of these inverse powers. The large values of δ show us, moreover, that we can no longer regard it as a small correction of n.

The large deviations of the term values from the hydrogen terms may be explained if we consider that the orbit of the series electron is not always situated entirely outside the core, even in the excited states, but penetrates into it. Such a penetrating orbit (Tauchbahn) is in its innermost parts much more strongly subject to the influence of the nucleus; it traverses, therefore, a field of force similar to a Coulomb field of force with a higher nuclear charge. Under such conditions use of (1), § 25, for the potential energy will not be justified.

In the case of Na a noticeable irregularity is present in the course of the δ-values between the d- and p-terms; this suggests that the d-orbits are situated entirely outside the core and that the s- and p-orbits penetrate into the core.

§ 27.—The Rydberg Corrections of the Outer Orbits and the Polarisation of the Atomic Core

We now consider in greater detail the physical influences which cause a departure of the field of force outside the core from a Coulomb field of force.[1] First we can determine approximately which power of a/r is especially important in the potential. We write the orbital energy in the form

$$W=-\frac{cRhZ^2}{\left(n+\delta_1+\frac{\delta_2}{n^2}\right)^2}.$$

An additional term $-\frac{e^2Z}{r}\cdot c_1\frac{a_H}{r}$ in the potential energy gives by (10), § 25, a " Rydberg correction "

$$\delta_1=-\frac{Zc_1}{k}$$

and a " Ritz correction "

$$\delta_2=0.$$

An additional term $-\frac{e^2Z}{r}\cdot c_2\frac{a_H{}^2}{r^2}$ gives

$$\delta_1=-\frac{Z^2c_2}{k^3},\qquad \delta_2=0;$$

an additional term $-\frac{e^2Z}{r}\cdot c_3\frac{a_H{}^3}{r^3}$ gives

[1] M. Born and W. Heisenberg, *Zeitschr. f. Physik*, vol. xxiii, p. 388, 1924; the numerical values of the following tables are taken from this work. For further work on this subject, see D. R. Hartree, *Proc. Roy. Soc.*, vol. cvi, p. 552, 1924; E. Schrödinger, *Ann. d. Physik*, vol. lxxvii, p. 43, 1925; A. Unsold, *Zeitschr. f. Physik*, vol. xxxvi, p. 92, 1926; B. Swirles, *Proc. Camb. Phil. Soc.*, vol. xxiii, p. 403, 1926.

$$\delta_1 = -\frac{3}{2}\frac{Z^3c_3}{k^5}, \qquad \delta_2 = \frac{Z^3c_3}{2k^3}, \qquad \frac{\delta_2}{\delta_1} = -\frac{k^2}{3},$$

and an additional term $-\frac{e^2Z}{r} \cdot c_4 \frac{a_H{}^4}{r^4}$ gives

$$\delta_1 = -\frac{5}{2}\frac{Z^4c_4}{k^7}, \qquad \delta_2 = \frac{3Z^4c_4}{2k^5}, \qquad \frac{\delta_2}{\delta_1} = -\frac{3}{5}k^2.$$

The following table gives the values of the Rydberg and Ritz corrections and their ratio, determined from the spectra of the alkali metals, whose structure is especially simple.

		Li	Na	K	Rb	Cs
p	$-\delta_1$	0·049				
	δ_2	0·031	T	T	T	T
	$-\delta_2/\delta_1$	0·63				
d	$-\delta_1$	..	0·015	0·25	0·35	
	δ_2	..	0·036	0·80	0·99	T
	$-\delta_2/\delta_1$	..	2·4	3·2	2·8	
f	$-\delta_1$	..	0·0020	0·009	0·36	0·032
	δ_2	..	0·0064	0·035	0·35	0·16
	$-\delta_2/\delta_1$	..	3·2	3·9	9·8	5·0

The letter T in the table denotes that the Rydberg correction is too large so that an expansion of the potential in powers of $1/r$ does not appear justifiable.

The large value of $-\delta_2/\delta_1$ shows that the higher powers of $1/r$ are present in the potential to an appreciable extent. For the terms with c_3/r^4 and c_4/r^5 we obtain theoretically the values

	k	$-\delta_2/\delta_1$. for $\frac{c_3}{r^4}$	for $\frac{c_4}{r^5}$
p	2	1·33	2·4
d	3	3·0	5·4
f	4	5·33	9·6

From this it appears that the term containing c_3/r^4 is the essential additional term.

Now such an additional term in the potential energy has in fact a theoretical significance. For if the core of the atom, instead of being regarded as absolutely rigid, is considered to be capable of deformation, it will acquire an electric moment in the field of the series electron. If the electron is at a sufficient distance from the core, the field $|\mathbf{E}| = e/r^2$ produced by it in the vicinity of the core may be considered as homogeneous. The induced moment of the core is proportional to this field: $p=\alpha e/r^2$. The moment of such a doublet produces an electric field in its neighbourhood; if it be considered to arise from the approach of two charges p/l at a distance l apart it will be seen that the force exerted on the radiating electron, in the direction of its axis, will be

$$\lim_{l\to 0}\frac{pe}{l}\left[\frac{1}{r^2}-\frac{1}{(r+l)^2}\right]=pe\frac{d}{dr}\left(-\frac{1}{r^2}\right)=\frac{2pe}{r^3}=\frac{2\alpha e^2}{r^5}.$$

Its potential is $-\alpha e^2/2r^4$. If the other deviations from the Coulomb field be neglected, we have

$$U(r)=-\frac{e^2Z}{r}\left(1+\frac{\alpha}{2Za_{\mathrm{H}}{}^3}\frac{a_{\mathrm{H}}{}^3}{r^3}\right)$$

and

$$\delta_1=-\frac{3}{4}\frac{Z^2\alpha}{a_{\mathrm{H}}{}^3k^5},\qquad \delta_2=\frac{Z^2\alpha}{4a_{\mathrm{H}}{}^3k^3}.$$

Our assumption, that the departure of the field of force from a Coulomb field is due essentially to the induced doublet in the core, may be tested by calculating the "polarisability" α, from the empirical values of δ_1 and δ_2. It must be assumed that the cores of the alkalies Li, Na, K, Rb, Cs are similar in structure to the neutral atoms of the inert gases (containing the same number of electrons) He, Ne, A, Kr, X (see further, § 30). The values of α for these atoms may be determined from the dielectric constants; between them and the α-values of the alkali cores a simple relation should exist.

From the empirical δ_1-values of the alkalies we get

	Li^+	Na^+	K^+	Rb^+	Cs^+
$\alpha\cdot 10^{24}=$	0·314	0·405	1·68	..	6·48

For this the f-terms are used with the exception of Li, the p-term of which serves for the calculations; Rb is omitted on account of its somewhat anomalous Rydberg and Ritz correction. The polarisabilities of the inert gases are related to the dielectric constants ϵ or with the refractive indices n for infinitely long waves by the Lorentz-Lorenz formula

$$\alpha=\frac{3}{4\pi N}\frac{\epsilon-1}{\epsilon+2}=\frac{3}{4\pi N}\frac{n^2-1}{n^2+2},$$

where N is the number of atoms per unit volume. If the optically measured refractive indices be extrapolated for infinitely long waves, one finds

	He	Ne	A	Kr	X
$\alpha\cdot 10^{24}=$	0·20	0·39	1·63	2·46	4·00

The α-values of the alkali ions must be somewhat smaller since the volumes of the ions must be less than those of the preceding inert gas atoms on account of the higher nuclear charge.

We find consequently that the α-values calculated from the spectrum have the right order of magnitude, but that they are all rather too large. One might be inclined to account for the difference by assuming that, in addition to the induced moment, still another deviation from the Coulomb law of force is present, likewise corresponding to an auxiliary term of the approximate form c_3/r^4. We cannot at this point prove whether such an assumption is admissible. It should, however, be mentioned that our knowledge of the structure of the ions of the inert gas type hardly admits of such a possibility.

If the explanation given here of the Rydberg correction as being due to polarisation of the core be retained, then a contradiction remains which, from the standpoint of our quantum rules, cannot be removed. We have, however, already referred to the fact that the explanation of the finer details of the spectra (the multiplets and the closely allied anomalous Zeeman effect) does not appear possible within the range of a quantum theory of multiply-periodic systems. One is led by the theory of these phenomena to the formal remedy of giving to the quantum number k half integral values, *i.e.* to give it the values $\frac{1}{2}$, $\frac{3}{2}$, $\frac{5}{2}$, etc. It is to be expected that in the further development of the theory the real quantum numbers will remain integral as before and that the quantity k, occurring in our approximate theory, is not itself such a quantum magnitude, but is built up indirectly out of them. We shall not go into these questions in the present book ; we shall content ourselves with seeing what values are obtained for α when we choose half values for k in our formulæ. We find, then, from the spectroscopic values of δ, the following α-values :

	Li^+	Na^+	K^+	Rb^+	Cs^+
$\alpha \cdot 10^{24} =$	0·075	0·21	0·87	..	3·36

These numbers are related in the right sense to the α-values of the inert gases. This connection can be traced still further by considering the α-values of other (multiple-valued) ions of inert gas type, which may be determined partly from the Rydberg corrections of spectra of the ionised element (spark spectra), partly from the refractive indices of solid salts (ionic lattice). In this way further support is obtained for the view that the Rydberg correction of the terms of the outer orbits in the spectra under consideration is due to the polarisation of the atomic core and that the quantum number k is to be given half values.[1]

The investigations dealt with in this volume are otherwise independent of a decision for whole or half values for k.

§ 28.—The Penetrating Orbits

In § 26 we have ascribed the large values of the Rydberg corrections to the fact that the electron penetrates deeply into the atomic core, and is thus subjected to an increased nuclear influence.

An estimate of the orders of magnitude to be expected for the δ-values for such "penetrating orbits" may be obtained by a procedure due to E. Schrödinger.[2] He considers the core of the atom replaced by a spherical shell uniformly charged with negative electricity, external to which there is then a Coulomb field of force, corresponding to the nuclear charge $Z^{(a)}$ (1 for a neutral, 2 for a singly ionised atom), and in the interior of which there is likewise a Coulomb field, but corresponding to a higher nuclear charge $Z^{(i)}$. As soon as the perihelion distance of a quantum orbit, calculated as an ellipse in the field of force with the nuclear charge $Z^{(a)}$, becomes smaller than the radius of this spherical shell, the orbit penetrates into the interior; it consists then of two elliptic arcs which join smoothly at the intersection with the spherical shell (fig. 14).

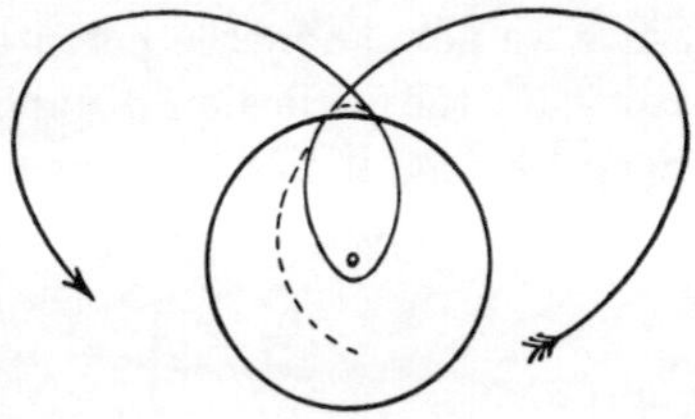

FIG. 14.

For given quantum numbers n and k, given shell radius, and given charges of the shell and nucleus, the effective quantum number n^* or the correction δ may be calculated.

We shall not repeat Schrödinger's calculations here; we shall show only that by means of such an atomic model, which may even consist of several concentric shells with surface charges, the relation between quantum numbers and energy may be expressed in terms of

---

[1] This evidence is by no means conclusive, since values of the polarisability α deduced from terms of spectra corresponding to external orbits depend to a considerable extent on the term series from which they are deduced, so conclusions drawn from comparison of values of α deduced from a single series with values deduced from other phenomena must be regarded with caution. We may also mention here that the polarising field on the core due to an electron in an orbit radius $9a_H$ (the radius of the 3-quantum circular orbit of hydrogen) is about 10^6 times the field in strong sunlight, and the displacement of the electrons in the core polarised by this field may be an appreciable fraction of the core radius.

[2] E. Schrödinger, *Zeitschr. f. Physik*, vol. iv, p. 347, 1921.

elementary functions.[1] Let the shell radii be $\rho_1, \rho_2 \ldots$, arranged in decreasing order of magnitude, and their charges $-z_1e, -z_2e \ldots$. The potential energy in the space between the shells ρ_s and ρ_{s+1} is

$$U_s(r) = -Z_s\frac{e^2}{r} + c_s,$$

where

$$Z_0 = Z^{(a)}$$

$$Z_s = Z^{(a)} + \sum_{\sigma=1}^{s} z_\sigma,$$

and c_s is determined by the condition that at the shells the potential varies continuously. It follows from this that

$$c_s = \sum_{\sigma=1}^{s} \frac{e^2}{\rho_\sigma} z_\sigma.$$

Since we now know the potential energy as a function of r, we can calculate the perihelion distance $r_{\min}$ and state within which shells $\rho_1, \rho_2 \ldots \rho_p$ it lies. The radial action integral has, according to (4), § 21, the form

$$J_r = 2\int_{\rho_1}^{r_{\max}} \sqrt{-A_0 + 2\frac{B_0}{r} - \frac{C}{r^2}}\,dr$$

$$+2\int_{\rho_2}^{\rho_1} \sqrt{-A_1 + 2\frac{B_1}{r} - \frac{C}{r^2}}\,dr + 2\int_{\rho_3}^{\rho_2} \sqrt{-A_2 + 2\frac{B_2}{r} - \frac{C}{r^2}}\,dr$$

$$+ \ldots + \int_{r_{\min}}^{\rho_p} \sqrt{-A_p + 2\frac{B_p}{r} - \frac{C}{r^2}}\,dr,$$

where

$$A_s = -2m(W - c_s)$$

$$B_s = me^2 Z_s$$

$$C = \frac{k^2h^2}{4\pi^2}.$$

All the integrals may be expressed in terms of elementary functions; in this way we obtain J_r and hence $(n-k)$ as a function of W and k, and finally W as a function of n and k.

Following van Urk [2] we shall make use of Schrödinger's conception of the charged shells to estimate the δ-values for the penetrating orbits. It will be seen that the larger the radius of the spherical shell the larger will be the radial action integral, for a given external ellipse; for the larger this radius, the longer will the electron move

[1] *Cf.* also G. Wentzel, *Zeitschr. f. Physik*, vol. xix, p. 53, 1923, especially p. 55.
[2] A. Th. van Urk, *Zeitschr. f. Physik*, vol. xiii, p. 268, 1923.

under the influence of the full nuclear charge. One obtains, therefore, from the Schrödinger model, on the assumption that an orbit is of the penetrating kind, a lower limit for the magnitude of δ by choosing the radius of the shell so that it touches the external ellipse. If we wish to find the value to which δ tends for large values of n (the dependence on n is extremely small in the case of the Schrödinger model), we can take as the perihelion distance of the external ellipse that of the parabola; in the case of the s-orbit, therefore, $\frac{1}{2Z^{(a)}}a_H$, we shall write generally $\frac{\zeta}{Z^{(a)}}a_H$. Since we choose the radius of the sphere equally large, the total orbit of the radiating electron will be given to a close approximation by the two complete ellipses.

We get for the radial action integral

$$J_r = J_r^{(a)} + J_r^{(i)},$$

affix (a) indicating the contribution from the part of the orbit outside the core, and affix (i) the contribution from the part inside. Now the spectrum term is proportional to the work of separation of the outer electron, and consequently equal to the energy of the outer ellipse

$$W = -\frac{cRh^3Z^{(a)2}}{(J_r^{(a)} + J_\psi)^2},$$

where J_ψ is 2π times the common angular momentum for the two ellipses. If we compare this with the form

$$W = -\frac{cRhZ^{(a)2}}{n^{*2}}$$

for the energy, we find for the effective quantum number

$$n^* = \frac{1}{h}(J_r^{(a)} + J_\psi) = \frac{1}{h}(J_r - J_r^{(i)} + J_\psi).$$

But

$$J_r + J_i = nh,$$

so that

$$\delta = n^* - n = -\frac{J_r^{(i)}}{h} = -\left(\frac{J^{(i)}}{h} - k\right), \tag{1}$$

where $J^{(i)}$ is the sum of the action integrals for the inner ellipse. $J^{(i)}$ is determined by the semi-major axis a of the inner ellipse:

$$a = \frac{a_H}{Z^{(i)}}\left(\frac{J^{(i)}}{h}\right)^2;$$

a is further related to the radius of the shell

$$a(1+\epsilon)=\frac{\zeta}{Z^{(a)}}a_{\mathrm{H}},$$

where

$$\epsilon=\sqrt{1-\frac{h^2k^2}{J^{(i)2}}}.$$

If a and ϵ be eliminated from these three equations we find

$$\left(\frac{J^{(i)}}{h}\right)^2\left(1+\sqrt{1-\frac{k^2}{(J^{(i)}/h)^2}}\right)=\zeta\frac{Z^{(i)}}{Z^{(a)}},$$

and from this, by solving for $\frac{J^{(i)}}{h}$ and substituting in (1):

$$\delta=-\frac{\zeta\frac{Z^{(i)}}{Z^{(a)}}}{\sqrt{2\zeta\frac{Z^{(i)}}{Z^{(a)}}-k^2}}+k. \tag{2}$$

The equation (1) is also approximately valid if the outer ellipse cuts the shell at a small angle instead of touching it, so long as the shell radius is small in comparison with the major axis of the outer ellipse (which is certainly the case for large values of the principal quantum number) and if $Z^{(i)}$ is considerably greater than $Z^{(a)}$. The error which is then made in replacing the action integral over the outer portion of the orbit by that over the complete outer ellipse is then small; likewise the error made in replacing the inner portion by the complete inner ellipse; the aphelion of the inner ellipse is situated only slightly outside the shell (on account of the rapid decrease of the potential energy in the field with the nuclear charge $Z^{(i)}$). The sum $J^{(i)}$ of the action integrals of the inner ellipse is determined uniquely by the major axis of this ellipse, and is consequently almost independent of n.

In the approximation given by formula (1) δ is not dependent on n. This approximation is better the larger the major axis of the outer ellipse; since that is rapidly attained by increasing n, we see how δ very soon assumes a constant value with increasing n.

If there are quantum paths which are contained completely in the interior of the shell, and if $n^{(i)}$ is the principal quantum number of the largest of them, then

$$n^{(i)}<\frac{J^{(i)}}{h}<n^{(i)}+1$$

and

(3) $$\delta = -(n^{(i)} + \epsilon - k) \qquad 0 < \epsilon < 1.$$

This formula is essentially independent of the Schrödinger model of the charged spherical shells, and depends only on the fact that the aphelion distance of the outer orbit is large in comparison with the core radius, and that the electron penetrating the core soon comes into the region of higher effective nuclear charges. Bohr [1] derived it, before v. Urk, in the following way :

The radial action integral $J_r = h(n-k)$ of the orbit is composed of the outer portion of the orbit and of the inner loop :

$$J_r = J_r^{(a)} + J_r^{(i)} = h(n-k).$$

$J_r^{(a)}$ is only slightly smaller than the radial action integral $h(n^*-k)$ of the complete external ellipse :

$$J_r^{(a)} = h(n^* - k - \epsilon_1),$$

and $J_r^{(i)}$ differs but little from the radial action integral $h(n^{(i)}-k)$ of the largest orbit completely contained in the core :

$$J_r^{(i)} = h(n^{(i)} - k + \epsilon_2).$$

It is not necessary here that $n^{(i)}$ should be integral, but it is the sum of the action integrals of the largest possible mechanical (not quantum) orbit divided by h. One obtains consequently

(4) $$\delta = n^* - n = -(n^{(i)} - k - \epsilon_1 + \epsilon_2)$$

and the result may be formulated as follows :

The Rydberg correction for penetrating orbits is not very different [2] from the radial action integral of the largest orbit, completely contained in the core, divided by h.

The question as to the accuracy with which all optical (and X-ray) terms may be consistently represented by a suitable central field has been examined by E. Fues ; [3] he arrived at eminently satisfactory results in the case of the arc spectrum of Na and the analogous spark spectra of Mg^+ and Al^{++}.

§ 29.—The X-ray Spectra

The optical series spectra of the elements provide one of the principal means of obtaining information regarding the structure of

---

[1] Bohr, N., Lectures at Göttingen, June 1922 (unpublished).

[2] In practice, $\varepsilon_1 - \varepsilon_2$ is not always small compared to 1 ; comparison with observed spectra shows it may be greater than $\frac{1}{2}$.

[3] E. Fues, *Zeitschr. f. Physik*, vol. xi, p. 364 ; vol. xii, pp. 1, 314 ; vol. xiii, p. 211, 1923 ; vol. xxi, p. 265, 1924. See also W. Thomas, *Zeitschr. f. Physik*, vol. xxiv, p. 169, 1924. For further work on penetrating orbits, especially the relations between corresponding terms of different atoms of the same electronic structure, see E. Fues, *Ann. d. Physik*, vol. lxxvi, p. 299, 1924 ; D. R. Hartree, *loc. cit.*, and *Proc. Camb. Phil. Soc.*, vol. xxiii, p. 304, 1926.

atoms. In as far as they can be comprehended on the basis of our theoretical conceptions we can draw conclusions regarding the processes taking place in the exterior portions of atoms only; they afford us little or no information about those occurring in the inner regions. The most important means of investigating the internal structure of the atom is the study of the X-ray spectra. Our theory of the motion of an electron in a central field of force is applicable also to these, since it may be inferred from the observations that we are here concerned with quantum transitions of the atom in which one electron (corresponding to the series electron in the optical spectra) changes its position in the interior of the atom while the rest of the atom remains approximately a structure possessing central symmetry.

Before we follow out these ideas in detail, we shall give a brief summary of some of the results of observations on X-ray spectra. Since the discovery of v. Laue, the natural gratings of crystals have been available for the analysis of these spectra. Each X-ray spectrum consists of a continuous band and a series of lines.

The continuous spectrum has a short-wave limit, whose frequency $\nu_{\max}$ is related to the kinetic energy of the generating cathode rays by the equation

$$h\tilde{\nu}_{\max}=\frac{m}{2}v^2.$$

This result can be looked upon as a kind of converse to the photoelectric effect, on the assumption that the incident cathode rays are retarded in the anti-cathode and that their energy is transformed into radiation according to the Einstein law (§ 2); the highest frequency emitted corresponds then to the total loss of kinetic energy of the incident electrons.

The line spectrum is characteristic of the radiating matter, and is called, therefore, " characteristic radiation." The most important fact relating to it is that every element exhibits the same arrangement of lines, and that with increasing atomic number the lines shift towards the shorter wave-lengths. This line spectrum contains various groups of lines: a short-wave group (called K-radiation) has already been found in the case of the light elements (from elements in the neighbourhood Na and onwards). These become continually shorter for the heavier elements, and are followed by a group of longer waves (L-radiation); behind this group follows, in the case of still heavier elements, a group of still longer wave-lengths (M-radiation).

If these spectral lines are to be related to the motions of the electrons in the atom in accordance with the principles of the quantum theory, the X-ray frequencies must be given in terms of the energies of two stationary electron configurations by the equation

$$h\tilde{\nu}=W^{(1)}-W^{(2)}.$$

The large values of $\tilde{\nu}$ (about 1000 times as great as in the visible spectrum) indicate that we have to do with variations in the orbits of the inner electrons where, on account of the high nuclear charge, a large amount of work must be expended in the displacement of an electron.

The fact that the X-ray lines are arranged in simple series, and may be characterised by small integers, forms the ground for the assumption that, as in the case of the simpler optical spectra, we are here concerned principally with the motion of a single "radiating electron." Although we are compelled to assume that this electron moves in the interior of the atom we shall replace the action of the nucleus and remaining electrons, for reasons analogous to those holding in the case of the visible spectra, by a central symmetrical field of force. By so doing we express once again the fact that no exchange of energy takes place between the radiating electron and the remainder of the atom; the existence of quantum numbers for the radiating electron points to its motion being periodic, and assuming, therefore, the same energy after each revolution.

There is, however, a fundamental difference between the optical spectra and the X-ray spectra. Whereas the lines of the optical spectra can occur also in absorption, the X-ray lines are never observed as absorption lines. The absorption coefficient for Röntgen rays exhibits, in fact, no maxima of the kind which produces absorption lines; it shows rather a continuous variation, broken only at certain places by the so-called "absorption edges," at which a sudden increase in absorption coefficient occurs if the frequency is increased through them (fig. 15).

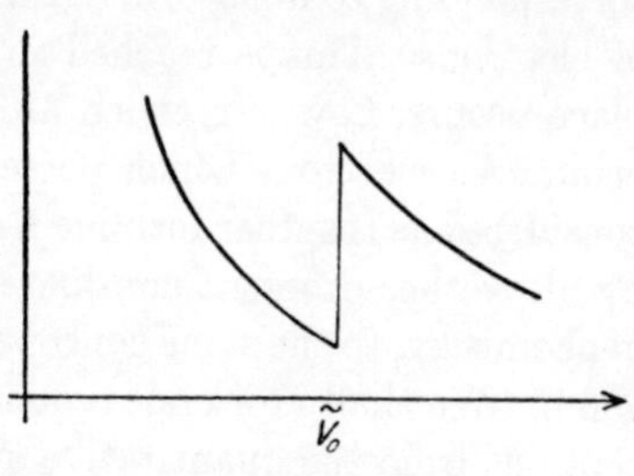

FIG. 15.

An explanation of this phenomenon has been given by Kossel.[1] According to him, the absorption spectra are concerned with the

[1] W. Kossel, *Verhandl. d. Dtsch. physikal. Ges.*, vol. xvi, pp. 899 and 953, 1914, and vol. xviii, p. 339, 1916.

ionisation of the atom in such a way that an inner electron is removed. The frequency condition gives for this process

$$h\tilde{\nu}=-\mathrm{W}+\frac{m}{2}v^2,$$

where v is the velocity of the electron after separation and $-\mathrm{W}$ is the work of separation. It follows then that all frequencies will be absorbed which are greater than the limiting frequency

$$\tilde{\nu}_0=\frac{-\mathrm{W}}{h},$$

which will thus be the frequency of the absorption edge. The hypothesis that in the atom there are electrons with various different binding energies W leads then to a variation of the absorption with frequency in qualitative agreement with observation.

According to Kossel the emission lines are caused by an electron falling in from a higher quantum orbit to replace the ejected electron, whereby the energy of the atom decreases. Further, an electron from a still higher quantum orbit can fall into the vacated place until finally the last gap will be filled by a free electron.

The emission spectra of the X-rays arise then from the re-establishment of a stable state of the atom after its disturbance through the ejection of an inner electron.

We can express this hypothesis of Kossel's, which has been completely verified, as follows: For every system of quantum numbers, corresponding to inner orbits, there corresponds a maximum number of electrons. This is reached in the stable state. An exchange of place occurs, however, when an electron is removed from its inner orbit. All electrons which possess the same quantum numbers are considered as together forming a shell; we shall be led subsequently, by altogether different considerations, principally from the domain of chemistry, to the same conception of a shell-like structure of atoms (§ 30). We shall now endeavour to establish the truth of these conceptions from the quantitative standpoint.

Our model, in which the electron under consideration moves in a central field, gives rosettes for the electron paths, and these are determined by two quantum numbers n and k. Orbits with different values of n must in fact occur in the interior of the atom. The behaviour of the Rydberg corrections shows that, for almost all elements, the p-orbits penetrate; in order that this may be possible the core must at least contain orbits with $n=2$. Of the orbits in the core those with $n=1$ ($k=1$) are nearest to the nucleus, then follow those with $n=2$ ($k=1, 2$), and then perhaps come orbits with $n=3$ ($k=1, 2, 3$).

In the elements of high atomic number the innermost orbits are subject mainly to the attractive force of the nucleus, while the influence of the remaining electrons is comparatively small. The energy of the innermost electron orbit is then given approximately by

$$W=-\frac{cRhZ^2}{n^2}$$

with $n=1$ and Z equal to the atomic number; as we proceed outwards the energy decreases rapidly, partly on account of the decrease of n and also on account of the shielding of the nuclear charge by the remaining electrons. The wave number of the first line to be expected is

$$\nu=RZ^2\left(\frac{1}{1^2}-\frac{1}{2^2}\right)=\frac{3}{4}RZ^2 \tag{1}$$

approximately. The formula requires that $\sqrt{\nu}$ shall increase linearly with the nuclear charge. Moseley,[1] who was the first to study the X-ray spectra systematically, found that for the K-series $\sqrt{\nu}$ is actually very nearly a linear function of the atomic number; by atomic number is understood the number expressing the position of an atom in the series order of the periodic system (1 H, 2 He, 3 Li . . .), thus practically in the order of the atomic weights; the gaps required by chemistry (*e.g.* that of the element 43 homologous to manganese) are to be taken into account as well as the reversals required by chemical behaviour [*e.g.* 18 A (at. wt. 39·88), and 19 K (39·10)].

This provides an excellent verification of the already long-inferred principle first put forward by van den Broek (*cf.* § 3, p. 13), that the atomic number is equal to the number of the nuclear charges.[2] This enables us also to determine uniquely the atomic numbers of elements with very high atomic weights, among which occur long series of elements differing very little chemically from one another (*e.g.* the rare earths), and also to determine accurately the existing gaps.

In order to show the accuracy with which the law (1) holds, we give the values of $\sqrt{\frac{4}{3}\frac{\nu}{R}}$ for some elements.

[1] H. G. J. Moseley, *Phil. Mag.*, vol. xxvi, p. 1024, 1913; vol. xxvii, p. 703, 1914.

[2] Strictly speaking, Moseley's law only confirms that the difference between the atomic number and nuclear charge is the same for all elements whose X-ray spectrum has been observed; it does not show that this constant difference is necessarily zero.

For Na(Z=11) the value is 10·1, for Rb(Z=37) it is 36·3, and for W(Z=74) it is 76·5. We associate therefore the first K-line with the transition of an electron from a two-quantum to a one-quantum orbit. This suggests associating the remaining K-lines with transitions from higher quantum orbits to a one-quantum orbit. The K-lines have actually the theoretically required limit

$$\frac{RZ^2}{1^2}.$$

Situated at the same place is one of the above-mentioned absorption edges.

The principle of linear increase of $\sqrt{\nu}$ is valid also for the L-lines. We attempt to identify these lines as transitions to a two-quantum orbit ($n=2$), and obtain for one of the L-lines the approximate wave number

$$\nu = RZ^2\left(\frac{1}{2^2}-\frac{1}{3^2}\right)=\frac{5}{36}RZ^2. \tag{2}$$

This formula does not hold so well as it does for the K-series; this we can understand since here we are at a greater distance from the nucleus. We can take account of this quantitatively,[1] by writing

$$\nu = R(Z-s)^2\left(\frac{1}{2^2}-\frac{1}{3^2}\right); \tag{3}$$

the empirical values are then in agreement with a value for s which, for medium values of Z, lies approximately between 6 or 7. Here again the series limit coincides with an absorption edge. The M-lines correspond finally to transitions to a three-quantum orbit. We obtain a clearer survey of the stationary orbits of the electrons in the atom if from the system of the X-ray lines we proceed to that of the X-ray terms. The end term of the K-lines we call the K-term, it corresponds to the K absorption edge, and corresponding to it (in our model) are the quantum numbers $n=1$, $k=1$. In order to account for the multiplicity of the L-lines we must assume three end terms (L-terms) for which $n=2$ and $k=1$ or 2. The fact that three terms exist instead of two implies that the quantum numbers n and k are not sufficient to define them; we are confronted here by a phenomenon very closely allied to that of the multiplicity of the optical terms. On the basis of our model we cannot give an explanation of this phenomenon.[2] Again, investigations of the

[1] A. Sommerfeld, *Ann. d. Physik*, vol. li, p. 125, 1916.

[2] A satisfactory interpretation in terms of the "spinning electron" can be given, as for the multiplets of optical spectra (*cf.* p. 155 and footnote 2, p. 152).

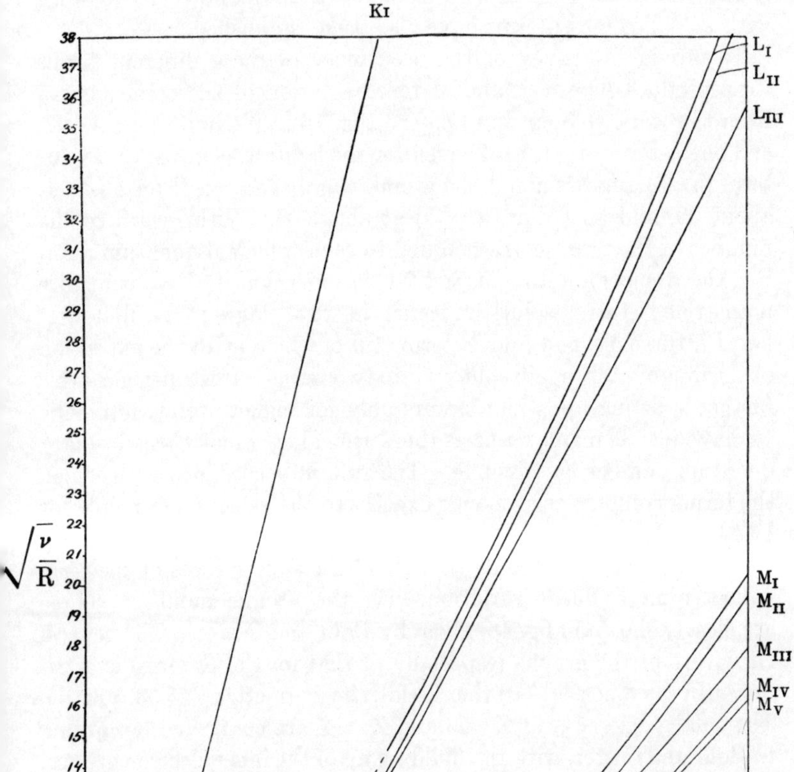

KI
LI
LII
LIII
MI
MII
MIII
MIV
MV
NI
NII
NIII
NIV
NV
NVI
NVII
OI
OII
OIII
OIV
OV
$\sqrt{\frac{\nu}{R}}$
Z
1, 2, 2₂
3, 3₂
4, 3₃
4₂
5, 4₃
5₂
6, 5₃ 4₄
6₂
7, 6₃

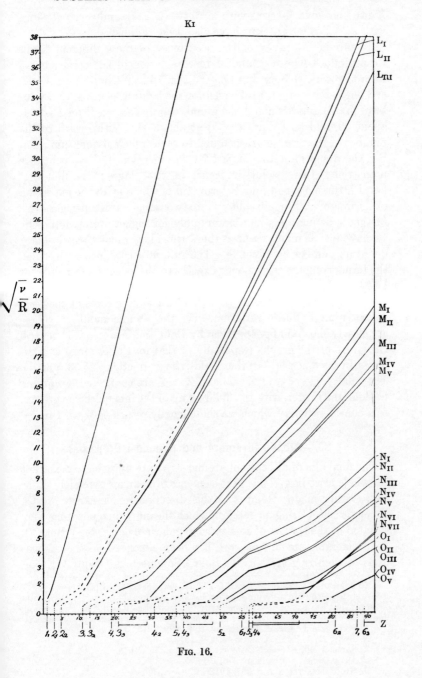

FIG. 16.

X-ray lines give M-terms with $n=3$ ($k=1, 2, 3$), and seven N-terms with $n=4$; some O-terms have also been established.

To provide a survey of the occurrence of these different terms we reproduce here a graphical representation of the terms, taken from the work of Bohr and Coster [1] (fig. 16). We find there the K- and one L-term ($n=1$, $n=2$) even for the lightest elements ; [2] an M-term ($n=3$) appears about the atomic number 21, an N-term ($n=4$) about 39, and an O-term ($n=5$) at about 51. With regard to the number of the terms corresponding to each principal quantum number, the resolution into 3, 5, and 7 terms mentioned above is readily noticeable ; this resolution occurs in two stages ; we find first two L-, three M-, and four N-terms, all of which, with the exception of the first of each, again split up into two terms. If we disregard this further splitting up, which occurs only for higher atomic numbers, we have just as many terms as there are values which the subsidiary quantum number can assume. The rule in accordance with which the terms combine corresponds exactly to the selection principle for k ($\triangle k=\pm 1$).

We refer finally to the departures of the square roots of the term values from a linear variation with the atomic number. These are clearly shown in fig. 16, given by Bohr and Coster. The general curvature of the graphs (especially of that for the K-term) is attributed by Sommerfeld [3] to the "relativity correction" (§ 33, p. 201). The small kinks, *e.g.* at Z=56 and Z=74, are connected, according to Bohr and Coster, with the building up of the inner electron groups, to a consideration of which we shall shortly return (§ 32, p. 191).

§ 30.—Atomic Structure and Chemical Properties

The final aim of a theory of atomic structure must be to construct the whole periodic system of the elements from an atom model. Bohr had already made attempts in this direction in his earlier works. He made use of "ring models," in which the individual electrons were situated at the corners of concentric regular polygons (the "rings"). A considerable amount of work has been expended on the calculations of such ring systems by Bohr,[4] Sommerfeld,[5] Debye,[6] Kroo,[7]

[1] N. Bohr and D. Coster, *Zeitschr. f. Physik*, vol. xii, p. 342, 1923.

[2] A state of the atom giving another L-term presumably exists for the lighter elements, but has not been experimentally determined as it is not involved in any line in the K spectrum, which is the only one of their X-ray spectra yet observed.

[3] A. Sommerfeld, *Ann. d. Physik*, vol. li, p. 125, 1916.

[4] N. Bohr, *Phil. Mag.*, vol. xxvi, p. 476, 1913.

[5] A. Sommerfeld, *Physikal. Zeitschr.*, vol. xix, p. 297, 1918.

[6] P. Debye, *ibid.*, vol. xviii, p. 276, 1917.

[7] J. Kroo, *ibid.*, vol. xix, p. 307, 1918.

Smekal,[1] and others, particularly with reference to the explanation of the X-ray spectra ; the results were, however, altogether unsatisfactory. The most important mechanical result arising out of this was Sommerfeld's observation that such an electron polygon can not only rotate about the nucleus, but that it can execute a motion in which the electrons traverse congruent Kepler ellipses (family of ellipses). Sommerfeld dealt also with the mutual perturbations of such rings for the case in which they are coplanar as well as for that in which they lie in different planes. Models of this kind have indeed a spatial structure just like the real atoms, but they do not show the symmetry of the latter as exhibited chemically (*e.g.* carbon tetrahedra) as well as crystallographically. Landé [2] therefore endeavoured to construct models with spatial symmetry such that, in common with Sommerfeld's family of ellipses, the electrons traverse congruent paths in exact phase relations (*e.g.* simultaneous passage through the perihelion). But these models also failed when it came to quantitative investigations.

Bohr realised that, by purely theoretical considerations and the construction of models, the desired object of explaining the regularities in the structures of atoms (periodic system of the elements) would be very difficult to attain ; he therefore adopted a procedure by means of which, half theoretically and half empirically, making use of all the evidence provided by physics and chemistry, and, especially, by a thorough application of the data derived from the series spectra, there was evolved a picture of the building up of atoms.

The chemical results which are to be taken into account in such an investigation have been expressed in a suitable form by Kossel.[3] He takes as a starting-point the fact that the periods of the system of elements begin with an inert gas, the atoms of which are characterised by the fact that they enter into no combinations and can be ionised only with extreme difficulty. The atoms of the inert gases are, therefore, particularly stable configurations which, perhaps as a result of the high degree of symmetry, are surrounded only by small fields of force and, on account of this great stability, neither take up electrons easily nor part with them. The atoms preceding the inert gases are the halogens (F, Cl, Br, I) which occur readily

---

[1] A. Smekal, *Zeitschr. f. Physik*, vol. v, p. 91, 1921.

[2] A. Landé, *Verhandl. d. Dtsch. physikal. Ges.*, vol. xxi, pp. 2, 644, 653, 1919; *Zeitschr. f. Physik*, vol. ii, pp. 83, 380, 1920.

[3] W. Kossel, *Ann. d. Physik*, vol. xlix, p. 229, 1916 ; see also G. N. Lewis, *Journ. Amer. Chem. Soc.*, vol. xxxviii, p. 762, 1919, and J. Langmuir, *ibid.*, vol. xli, p. 868, 1919.

as singly charged negative ions; this, according to Kossel, is due to the fact that their electron systems lack one electron to make up the stable inert gas configurations and that they endeavour, with loss of energy, to take up the missing electron. Conversely the atoms following the inert gases, the alkalies (Li, Na, K, Rb, Cs), occur always as singly charged positive ions, and so must easily give up an electron; in their case consequently it may be assumed that an easily removable electron revolves outside a stable core of the inert gas type. The positive or negative electrovalency of the remaining atoms may be accounted for in a similar manner; the former is due to the presence of easily separable electrons, after the removal of which the inert gas-like core remains; the latter is due to the endeavour on the part of "incomplete" electron structures to form complete inert gas configurations by taking up electrons.

The application of this principle to the periodic system leads to the conception of the shell structure of atoms (see also § 29, p. 176). The first period, consisting of the elements H and He, represents the structure of the innermost shells. The system of two electrons of the inert gas He must therefore be a very stable arrangement.

The second period commences with Li. This element will have a core of the character of the He atom, external to which a third electron is loosely bound. In the next element, Be, a further outer electron is added, and so on, until at the tenth element, Ne, the second shell has become a stable inert gas configuration with 8 electrons. This completes the second shell.

The first element of the third period, Na, has again the loosely bound outer electron, which represents the commencement of the third shell; this closes with the inert gas A, and, since this has the atomic number 18, the complete third shell is again made up of 8 electrons.

The process is continued in a similar way, the periods, however, becoming longer (they contain first 18, afterwards 32 elements). Among them occur the elements Cu, Ag, Au, which have a certain resemblance to the alkalies; they will thus be characterised by an easily separable electron and a relatively stable core.

By means of these qualitative considerations, Kossel was able to make a considerable part of inorganic chemistry comprehensible from the physical standpoint; this theory proved particularly fruitful in the domain of the so-called complex combinations, *i.e.* combinations in which molecules arise by the superposition of atomic complexes, which, from the standpoint of the simple valency theory, are completely saturated.

Langmuir and Lewis[1] have (independently of Kossel) added to the theory by imagining that the stable configuration of 8 electrons, which we met with in the case of Ne, A, and the ions of the neighbouring elements, is a cube (octet theory), at the corners of which these 8 electrons remain in equilibrium. According, then, to these American investigators, we have to do with static models, a hypothesis which does not agree with our ideas of atomic mechanics, and which will therefore not be considered any further here.

The manner in which Bohr arrives at the building up of the atoms step by step in the order of their atomic number is as follows.

He considers the capture of the most loosely bound electron by the remainder of the atom. This process takes place by transitions of this electron between the stationary orbits, regarding which information is obtained from the arc spectrum of the element. During this process the atom can be thought of as resolved into a core and a radiating electron. The core has the same number of electrons as that of the foregoing atom and a nuclear charge one unit greater. The first question arising is whether the electrons in the core have the same arrangement as in the foregoing neutral atom ? Information is obtained on this point in many cases from the spark spectrum. The second question is, in what orbit does the newly captured electron finally move ? It either takes a place as one of a group of outer electrons already existing in the core, or it traverses an orbit not yet occurring in the core. In the former case it adds further to an already existing shell, in the latter case it commences a new shell. In order to answer these questions we must know the quantum numbers of the orbits in the atom. The answer to the first question is sometimes Yes and sometimes No ; in the latter case the same two questions have to be asked about the last electron but one captured, and so on.

The idea underlying this procedure is called by Bohr the " Aufbauprinzip " (atom building).

§ 31.—The Actual Quantum Numbers of the Optical Terms

Our next problem will be the more exact determination of the number of electrons occupying the individual electron orbits and the values of n and k associated with them. Two methods are available for the solution : the examination of the optical spectra and of the X-ray spectra.

If one goes through the series of the elements, and considers in

---

[1] *Loc. cit.*, see p. 181.

each case the scheme of the spectral terms, the great similarity between the spectra of homologous elements will be recognised. Each alkali spectrum exhibits the same characteristics, likewise each spectrum of the alkaline earths. We attribute this to the equal numbers of outer electrons (*cf.* Kossel, § 30).

We turn to the term values themselves. We imagine them written in the form

$$W = -\frac{cRh}{n^{*2}}.$$

The spectrum of an element can then be expressed by the system of n^*-values. In order to give a survey of the dependence of the spectrum on the atomic number, we give here the effective quantum numbers n^* of the lowest term of each series, for the arc spectra so far analysed, together with the decimal places of the absolute magnitude of the Rydberg correction taken as the limiting value for large values of n.[1]

The table shows that for neutral atoms of almost all elements the *f*-terms are still of hydrogen type. The Rydberg corrections are smallest here for Cu and Ag, apart from the light elements; they are largest for the alkaline earths, and in this case increase in the order of the atomic numbers. The *d*-terms are of hydrogen type in the case of the lightest elements (*i.e.* not heavier than Na); it seems probable also that for Cu, Ag, and perhaps for Cr, Mn, the correction is nearly zero (not approximately equal to another whole number). The Rydberg correction is still relatively small for the alkalies, but increases definitely with the atomic number; in the case of the alkaline earths it is considerably larger. Finally the *p*- and *s*-terms depart considerably from the values in the case of hydrogen. It appears, consequently, that *f*-orbits are in general situated outside the core, that the *d*-orbits in many neutral atoms approach the core too closely to remain hydrogen-like, and in several cases many actually penetrate into the core, and that the *p*- and

[1] The numbers are mostly calculated from the data in Paschen-Götze (*Seriengesetze der Linienspektren*, 1922). In the case of doublets or triplets the mean value of n^* is given; for the alkaline earths the values in the first and second row correspond to the singlet and triplet terms respectively, for O, S they correspond to the triplet and quintet terms, and for He to the singlet and "doublet" (which are possibly really triplet) terms; the figures for Cr, Mo refer to septet terms and those for Mn to octet terms. Except for those of the alkali metals and He, most of these spectra, especially those of Cr, Mn, Mo, include terms which cannot be explained on the assumption of a single radiating electron; only those terms are included in the table which can be so explained. From O onwards only the decimal places of $-\delta$ are given in the columns for the Rydberg corrections. In those places where the known terms permit of no extrapolation for $n = \infty$, the Rydberg correction of the last known is given in brackets.

	n^* of the first				Rydberg Correction for large n of the			
	s-	*p*-	*d*-	*f*-	*s*-	*p*-	*d*-	*f*-
	Terms				Terms			
1 H	1·00	2·00	3·00	4·00	0·00	0·00	0·00	0·00
2 He	0·74	2·01	3·00	4·00	−0·14	+0·01	0·00	0·00
	1·69	1·94	2·99	4·00	−0·30	−0·07	0·00	0·00
3 Li	1·59	1·96	3·00	4·00	−0·40	−0·05	0·00	0·00
					. . .	. . .	. . .	. . .
8 O	1·82	1·00	2·98		14	70	02	
	1·74	2·17	2·97		23	78	04	
10 Ne[1]	1·67	2·15	2·99		30	83	02	
11 Na	1·63	2·12	2·99	4·00	34	85	01	00
12 Mg	1·33	2·03	2·68		52	04	56	
	2·31	1·66	2·83	3·96	63	12	17	06
13 Al	2·19	1·51	2·63	3·97	76	28	93	05
16 S	1·97	1·15	2·65		(20)			
	1·88	2·34			(06)		47	
19 K	1·77	2·23	2·85	3·99	17	70	25	01
20 Ca	1·49	2·07	2·00	3·97	33	93	95	09
	2·49	1·79	1·95	3·92	44	95	92	10
24 Cr	1·42	1·88	2·99		45	(12)	(01)	
25 Mn	2·31	1·63	2·89		60	(37)	08	
29 Cu	1·33	1·86	2·98	4·00	58	(09)	02	00
30 Zn	1·20	1·94	2·87		62	09	20	
	2·34	1·60	2·90	3·98	72	20	08	04
31 Ga	2·16	1·52	2·84		78	27	24	
37 Rb	1·80	2·27	2·77	3·99	13	66	35	03
38 Sr	1·54	2·13	2·06	4·14	(26)	(59)	75	10
	2·55	1·87	1·99	3·91	37	85	80	12
42 Mo	1·36	1·81	2·74		(65)	(01)		
47 Ag	1·34	1·90	2·98	3·99	52	(05)	01	01
48 Cd	1·23	1·95	2·87		57	05	21	
	2·28	1·62	2·89	3·97	67	14	07	03
49 In	2·21	1·55	2·82		73	19	29	
55 Cs	1·87	2·35	2·55	3·98	05	57	45	04
56 Ba	1·62	2·14	1·89	2·85	43	(73)	45	(92)
	2·63	1·94	1·82	3·84	28	67	77	12
79 Au	1·21	1·77	2·97		60		00	
80 Hg	1·14	1·91	2·92		63	00	08	
	2·24	1·59	2·93	3·97	71	10	05	03
81 Tl	2·19	1·56	2·90	3·97	74	19	10	03

[1] The neon spectrum is known to have two systems of terms which converge to different limits. In calculating n^* the term under consideration has to be counted from the limit of the system to which it belongs. The p-term given is the lowest which can be assigned to a definite series. A deep-lying term ($n^*=0{\cdot}79$) is known from measurements on electron impact (G. Hertz, *Zeitschr. f. Physik*, vol. xviii, p. 307, 1923), and from the spectrum in the extreme ultra-violet (G. Hertz, *Zeitschr. f. Physik*, vol. xxxii, p. 933, 1925; T. Lyman and F. A. Saunders, *Proc. Nat. Acad. Sci.*, vol. xii, p. 192, 1926); it corresponds to the normal state, but cannot be explained on the assumption of a single radiating electron.

s-orbits are always penetrating orbits, except in the case of the very lightest elements. (These conclusions, as far as they are based on this table, refer to neutral atoms only; it is not necessarily true that the orbits of the series electron of an ionised atom will be of the same character as those with the same k in a neutral atom of the same atomic structure.)

In order to substantiate this view we consider the radii of the atomic cores. The sizes of the cores in the case of the arc spectra of the alkaline earths, or, what comes to the same thing, the sizes of the singly charged ions of the alkaline earths, can be derived from the spark spectra. These ions possess only one external electron; the aphelion of its orbit is situated in a region where the field of force of the atom has approximately the character of a Coulomb field, and the aphelion distance depends in the same way on the energy, and consequently on n^*, as in the case of hydrogen:

$$\frac{a}{a_{\mathrm{H}}}(1+\epsilon)=\frac{1}{Z}n^{*2}\left(1+\sqrt{1-\frac{k^2}{n^{*2}}}\right).$$

Since the first s-orbit is the normal orbit of the series electron of the ions of the alkaline earths, we take from the spark spectra of the alkaline earths the n^* values corresponding to the first s-terms, and regard the aphelion distances calculated from them as the core radii of the alkaline earths. In the same way we may draw conclusions regarding the cores of the elements Zn and Cd, which are similar to the alkaline earths, since we must assume also of their ions that they have only one external electron. We obtain an upper limit for the radii of the alkali ions and the ions of Cu and Ag from their distances of separation in the crystal gratings of their salts; the separation of the Na^+ and Cl^- ions in the rock-salt grating must, for example, be larger than the sum of the ionic radii. By means of such considerations all radii of all monovalent ions are determined, apart from an additive constant which is additive for positive and subtractive for negative ions. This constant can be determined approximately by putting the two ions K^+ and Cl^-, both of which are similar to the A-atom, equal to one another; this gives upper limits for the radii of the positive ions, since K^+ must be smaller than Cl^- on account of the difference of nuclear charge.[1] A second upper limit for the ionic radii of the alkali metals is given by the known radii of the atoms of the preceding inert gases, deduced from the kinetic theory of gases; the alkali ions we must regard as being similar in structure to the inert gases—their dimensions,

[1] *Cf.* W. L. Bragg, *Phil. Mag.*, ser. 7, vol. ii, p. 258, 1926.

however, must be somewhat smaller on account of the higher nuclear charge.

The ionic radii calculated in this way are collected in the following table. They are expressed in terms of the hydrogen radius a_H as unit.[1]

The table shows the growth in the core radii of homologous elements with atomic number as well as the fact that the radii of the alkaline earth cores are relatively large, while those of Cu and Ag are smaller.

An *f*-orbit has, in a strict Coulomb field, a perihelion distance which is larger than $8a_H$ (*cf.* § 24). Owing to the departures from a Coulomb field of force in the neighbourhood of the atomic cores it will be decreased. We shall not carry out this calculation, however,[2] since for our purpose (the determination of the real quantum

	Upper Limit of the Radius		Radius calculated from n^*
	From the Kinetic Theory of Gases	From Grating Separation	
3 Li^+	1·8	1·7	
11 Na^+	2·2	2·4	
12 Mg^+			3·3
19 K^+	2·6	2·9	
20 Ca^+			4·3
29 Cu^+		1·2–1·4	
30 Zn^+			2·5
37 Rb^+	3·0	3·2	
38 Sr^+			4·7
47 Ag^+		0·9–2·2 [3]	
48 Cd^+			2·6
55 Cs^+	3·3	3·7	
56 Ba^+			5·2

numbers) a qualitative consideration suffices. We see that an *f*-orbit can most easily approach the core in the case of the heavy alkaline earths; we understand the large Rydberg correction in the case of Ba and the relatively large ones in the case of Sr and Ca; we find generally a complete correspondence between the core radii

[1] There are still other methods of determining the radii of the alkali cores, which we shall not enter into here. The results are in agreement with the upper limits given here. *Cf.* the summary by K. F. Herzfeld, *Jahrb. d. Radioakt. u. Elektronik*, vol. xix, p. 259, 1922.

[2] The calculations have been carried out by F. Hund, *Zeitschr. f. Physik*, vol. xxii, p. 405, 1924.

[3] The values obtained from different Ag salts are widely different.

and the Rydberg corrections. This connection enables us to draw conclusions regarding the ionic radius also in the case of the few other elements the Rydberg corrections of which are known; we conclude in this way that it is rather smaller for Al than for Mg, and that in the case of Hg and Tl it is of the same order of magnitude as for Zn and Cd.

The d-orbits in the hydrogen atom have a perihelion distance of more than $4{\cdot}5a_H$ (the circular orbit $n=3$ has radius $9a_H$); in the field exterior to the cores, which deviates appreciably from a Coulomb field, they are smaller. The very small Rydberg corrections in the case of Cu and Ag we ascribe to the fact that in these cases the d-orbits are situated at a considerable distance from the core. The small values for the alkalies and for Zn, Cd, and Hg show that in these cases also the d-orbits are still external paths; in the case of Rb and Cs, they must approach very close to the boundary of the core. In the case of the heavier alkaline earths, Ca, Sr, Ba, we must assume that penetration occurs. In this connection it is striking, that in spite of the increase in the core radius from Ca to Ba, the n^* values (for large n) increase; this leads to the assumption that the Rydberg corrections in the table are to be altered by whole numbers and are, for Ca, $-0{\cdot}95$, $-0{\cdot}92$ respectively; for Sr, $-1{\cdot}75$, $-1{\cdot}80$ respectively; for Ba, $-2{\cdot}45$, $-2{\cdot}77$ respectively. In the case of Ca the lowest d-term would still correspond to a 3_3-orbit, in the case of Sr to a 4_3-, and in the case of Ba to a 5_3-orbit. The cases are worthy of note in which the Rydberg corrections of the f- and d-orbits do not go hand in hand. Thus in the case of Zn the magnitude of the f-correction is larger, that of the d-correction smaller than for K; Cd and Hg have considerably smaller d-corrections than Rb and Cs, whereas the f-corrections are about the same. The explanation of this is the high degree of symmetry of the alkali ions; this causes the potential in the vicinity of their boundaries to vary in accordance with a high power of r, while, in the case of the less symmetrical cores of Zn, Cd, and Hg, it varies more slowly with r.

In the case of the very light elements, the p-orbits are still external; the smallness of the Rydberg corrections, and small core radii, suggest that this may also be the case for Cu, Ag, and Au, but the magnitude of the doublet separations and the variation of the value of the correction for different atoms of the same atomic structure (Cu, Zn^+, Ga^{++}, Ge^{+++}, etc.[1]) seem to show conclusively that the p-orbits penetrate. The apparently small Rydberg corrections for

---

[1] See J. A. Carroll, *Phil. Trans. Roy. Soc.*, vol. ccxxv, p. 357 (1926).

Mg (—0·04 and —0·12), Zn (—0·09 and —0·20), Cd (—0·05 and —0·14), as well as Hg (—0·00 and —0·10), have certainly to be increased by a whole number; their magnitudes would otherwise be no larger than those of the *d*-corrections. If we again note that the n^*-values in the series of the alkalies increase with increasing core radius, we must assume that the real *n*-values are 3 for Na, 4 for K, 5 for Rb, 6 for Cs, and that the Rydberg corrections are —0·85, —1·70, —2·66, and —3·57 respectively. Their magnitudes for the alkaline earths must be somewhat larger; we assume, therefore, —1·04, —1·12 respectively for Mg; —1·93, —1·95 respectively for Ca; —2·59, —2·85 respectively for Sr; —3·73, —3·67 respectively for Ba.

The *s*-orbits penetrate from Li onward. In order that the magnitudes of the Rydberg corrections may increase with increasing atomic radius, we must take $\delta = -1{\cdot}34$ for Na (—0·34 would be smaller in amount than the *p*-correction); —2·17 for K; —3·13 for Rb, and —4·05 for Cs. The somewhat larger values for the alkaline earths may likewise be found uniquely from the table. For Al we assume —1·76; for Cr to Ga values ranging from —2 to —3; for Ag, Cd from —3 to —4; for Hg and Tl values between —4 to —5 are very probable. According to the estimate (4), § 28, of the Rydberg correction, the essential factor is the principal quantum number of the largest *s*-orbit confined to the interior of the core, and this is clearly, in the case of Cu, Zn, Ga, the same as for Rb, and in the case of Ag, Cd, In, the same as for Cs; the values in the sixth period can be inferred by analogy.

We supplement this consideration by another rough estimation of the δ-values for the *s*-terms, namely, that given by van Urk. We replace the electron structure of the atomic cores by charged spherical shells, the radii of which are somewhat larger than $\frac{1}{2}a_H$

	δ_{cal}	δ_{corr}
3 Li	—0·06	—0·40
11 Na	—0·74	—1·35
19 K	—1·24	—2·18
29 Cu		—2·59
37 Rb	—2·08	—3·14
47 Ag		—3·54
55 Cs	—2·74	(—4·06)
87 —	—3·69	

(they must be as large as this for the *s*-orbits to be penetrating orbits), and imagine the full charge of the nuclei (equal to the order in the periodic system) to be operative in the interior of the shells. Since the *s*-orbits under consideration have the same angular momentum as the innermost orbits of the core but smaller amounts of energy, and since the field of the core again resembles a Coulomb one in the vicinity of the nucleus, it follows that the inner loops of these *s*-orbits have the same parameter as the core orbits next to the nucleus; they are therefore subjected to the undiminished nuclear charge. Application of the equation (2), § 28, leads to the δ-values (δ_{cal}) given in the following table. Together with these the only δ-values (δ_{corr}) which can be in agreement with these lower limits and the empirical terms are given.

As a consequence of this we can regard the actual principal

	Negative Rydberg Corrections $(-\delta)$				Quantum Numbers of the First Terms of each Series			
	s	*p*	*d*	*f*				
1 H	0·00	0·00	0·00	0·00	1_1	2_2	3_3	4_4
2 He	0·14	−0·01	0·00	0·00	1_1	2_2	3_3	4_4
	0·30	0·07	0·00	0·00	2_1			
3 Li	0·40	0·05	0·00	0·00	2_1	2_2	3_3	4_4
8 O	1·14	0·70	0·02					
	1·23	0·78	0·04		3_1	2_2	3_3	4_4
10 Ne	1·30	0·83	0·02		3_1	2_2 [1]	3_3	4_4
11 Na	1·34	0·85	0·01	0·00	3_1	3_2	3_3	4_4
12 Mg	1·52	1·04	0·56	0·06	3_1	3_2	3_3	4_4
	1·63	1·12	0·17		4_1			
13 Al	1·76	1·28	0·93	0·05	4_1	3_2	3_3	4_4
19 K	2·17	1·70	0·25	0·01	4_1	4_2	3_3	4_4
20 Ca	2·33	1·93	0·95	0·09	4_1	4_2	3_3	4_4
	2·44	1·95	0·92	0·10	5_1			
29 Cu	2·58	(2·09)	0·02	0·00	4_1	4_2	3_3	4_4
30 Zn	2·62		0·20	0·04	4_1	4_2	3_3	4_4
	2·72		0·08		5_1			
31 Ga	2·78		0·24		5_1	4_2	3_3	
37 Rb	3·13	2·66	0·35	0·03	5_1	5_2	3_3	4_4
38 Sr	(3·26)	(2·59)	1·75	0·10	5_1	5_2	4_3	4_4
	3·37	2·85	1·80	0·12	6_1			
47 Ag	3·52	(2·05)	0·01	0·01	5_1	5_2	3_3	4_4
48 Cd	3·57		0·21	0·03	5_1	5_2	3_3	4_4
	3·67		0·07		6_1			
49 In	3·73		0·29		6_1	5_2	3_3	
55 Cs	4·05	3·57	0·45	0·04	6_1	6_2	3_3	4_4
56 Ba	4·43	(3·73)	2·45	(0·92)	6_1	6_2	5_3	4_4
	4·28	3·67	2·77	0·12	7_1			
79 Au	4·60	(3·2)	3·00		6_1	6_2	3_3	4_4
80 Hg	4·63		0·08	0·03	6_1	6_2	3_3	4_4
	4·71		0·05		7_1			
81 Tl	4·74		0·10	0·03	7_1	6_2	3_3	4_4

[1] Normal orbit of last electron added. See footnote, p. 185.

quantum numbers and the actual Rydberg corrections of the empirically known terms as determined, with a few exceptions. To summarise these results we now give a table (p. 190) of the negative values $-\delta$ of the true Rydberg corrections (for large n) and the quantum numbers of the first terms of each series. The normal state is denoted by heavy type; it is distinguished by the fact that the lines for which it is the initial state occur in absorption at ordinary temperatures. It must be emphasised that this table only refers to neutral atoms, and it must not be assumed that the relative magnitudes of the terms, or the quantum numbers of the first term in each term series, are necessarily the same for all ions containing the same number of electrons.

§ 32.—The Building Up of the Periodic System of the Elements

We are now in a position to deal with the building up of the periodic system step by step, for which purpose we have now at our disposal all of the data hitherto collected, namely, the properties of the X-ray spectra (§ 29), the chemical behaviour (§ 30), and the characteristics of the optical spectra collected in the table on p. 190 and similar data for many ions.

As a reminder of the order of the elements in the periodic system we give the scheme (fig. 17) often used by Bohr and dating back to J. Thomsen.

In the normal state, hydrogen (1 H) has an electron in an orbit with the principal quantum number 1. As long as the orbit is regarded as an exact Kepler ellipse the subsidiary quantum number is undetermined. We shall see, however, on taking into account the relativity theory in § 33, that the total angular momentum is also to be fixed by a quantum condition, without thereby appreciably altering the energy. The normal orbit of the electron is thus a 1_1-orbit.

For helium (2 He) in the excited states the core will correspond, according to Bohr's principle, with that of the hydrogen atom in the normal state, the only difference being the higher nuclear charge. Now the orbit of maximum energy, or normal orbit, of the series electron is likewise a 1_1-orbit, so that helium in the normal state would have two (presumably equivalent) 1_1-electron orbits. This system will be considered in greater detail later (§ 48). According to Kossel, a special stability must be ascribed to such a system of two 1_1-orbits, such as is the case with all inert gases; in X-ray terminology this structure comprises the K-shell.

The question why there are two systems of terms—a singlet system (parhelium), to which belongs the normal state, and a doublet system (orthohelium)—and why these cannot combine with one another, cannot be dealt with from the standpoint of our book.

The configuration of two 1_1-orbits occurs again in the core of the excited lithium atom (3 Li). According to the spectroscopic evidence, the normal state in this case is not a 1_1- but a 2_1-orbit. We must conclude from this that, according to the principles which limit the

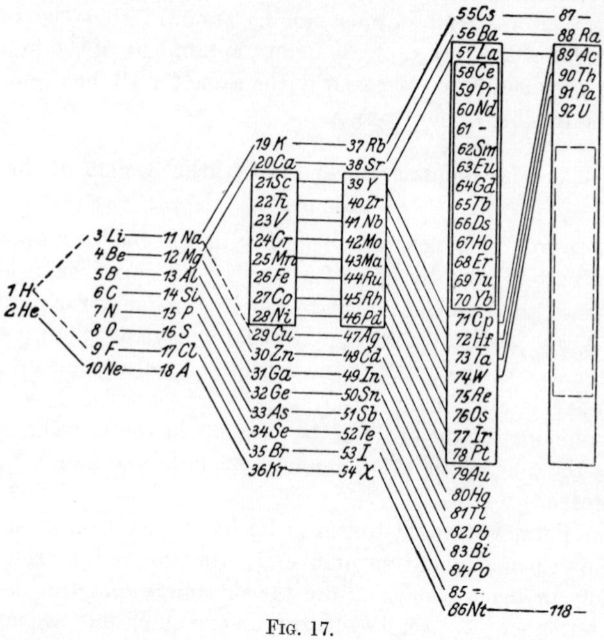

Fig. 17.

number of electrons in orbits with the same n_k,[1] a system of three 1_1-orbits under the influence of a nuclear charge 3 is not possible. The ions Be^+, B^{++}, C^{+++} . . . have a structure similar to that of the lithium atom. Millikan and Bowen [2] were able to confirm experimentally the fact that the spectra of the "stripped atoms" Be^+ to O^{+5} are similar to that of the Li-atom.

The spectra of the two following elements, beryllium (4 Be) and boron (5 B), are not sufficiently well known for us to be able to draw conclusions regarding the electronic orbits. We can conclude only,

[1] These principles have been formulated by W. Pauli (*Zeitschr. f. Physik*, vol. xxxi, p. 765, 1925) but will not be explained in this book.

[2] R. A. Millikan and I. S. Bowen, *Proc. Nat. Acad. Sci.*, vol. x, p. 199, 1924 (B^{++}); *Nature*, vol. cxiv, p. 380, 1925 (Be^+ and C^{+++}); *Phys. Rev.*, vol. xxviii, p. 256, 1926 (Be^+); *Phys. Rev.*, vol. xxvii, p. 144, 1926 (O^{+5}).

from the bivalent character of beryllium and trivalent character of boron, that the newly added electron occupies orbits with the principal quantum number 2, and that the number of 1_1-orbits remains equal to two; the K-shell is therefore closed with the He configuration. The spectra of B^+ and C^{++} are known,[1] at least in part; they are presumably similar to the spectrum of neutral Be, and their lowest terms indicate that the normal orbit of the series electron is a 2_1-orbit. Also the spark spectrum of carbon is known;[2] the lowest term occurring in it is the 2_2-term. Since the boron atom is most probably similar in structure to the single-charged carbon ion, we may assume that, in addition to the K-shell, one 2_2- and two 2_1-orbits exist in boron. We arrive here at the same result as for lithium, that not more than two equivalent electrons with $k=1$ exist.

A further electron is added in carbon (6 C) and occupies, in all probability, a 2_2-orbit. Such a system of two 2_1- and two 2_2-orbits does not necessarily possess the tetrahedral symmetry with which one is familiar from the chemical and physical properties (*e.g.* diamond lattice) of the carbon atom. Since, however, nothing is known regarding the complicated motions in the atom, this does not necessarily imply a contradiction.

Too little is known spectroscopically regarding the next elements (7 N, 8 O, 9 F). The chemical evidence affirms that N, O, F have an affinity for three, two, and one electrons, and the spectrum of O shows that the normal orbit of the last electron is a 2_2-orbit. The eight-shell required by Kossel's theory must be reached in the case of the inert gas neon (10 Ne); we can assume, therefore, that the eight electrons added since Li are bound in orbits with the principal quantum number 2. The question as to how they are distributed among the 2_1- and 2_2-orbits we leave unanswered.[3]

The conception of the fully occupied eight-shell is confirmed by the well-known spectrum of sodium (11 Na). The normal orbit of the series electron is a 3_1-orbit, the p-orbit of maximum energy being a 3_2-orbit. Outside the core, then, no more orbits occur with $n=2$. We conclude from this, that the series of electrons for which $n=2$ is completed by the number 8 reached in the case of neon. Using the terminology of the X-ray spectra we call this structure

---

[1] R. A. Millikan and I. S. Bowen, *Phys. Rev.*, vol. xxvi, p. 310, 1925.

[2] A. Fowler, *Proc. Roy. Soc.* (A), vol. cv, p. 299, 1924.

[3] Later investigations by E. C. Stoner (*Phil. Mag.*, vol. xlviii, p. 719, 1924) and W. Pauli, jr. (*loc. cit.*), have shown that two of the electrons traverse 2_1-orbits and six 2_2-orbits. Here and in the following, however, we shall not enter further into these details.

the L-shell. The construction of this L-shell is therefore completed in the second period of the system of elements, while the K-shell is built up in the first period.

Since in the case of magnesium (12 Mg) the normal orbit of the series electron is again a 3_1-orbit, we assume, in accordance with the double valency, that the magnesium atom in the normal state has two equivalent 3_1-electrons in addition to the K- and L-shells.

In aluminium (13 Al), a 3_2-orbit appears as the normal orbit. We see, therefore, that a system of three 3_1-orbits cannot be formed as the outside shell. In the case of Li and C^+ we arrived at a similar conclusion, namely, the impossibility of the existence of three 1_1- or 2_1-orbits.

In the case of silicon (14 Si) we meet with an instance in which the spectrum can no longer be accounted for with the help of one "radiating electron."[1] We conclude from the tetravalent character that the L-ring is surrounded by four orbits with $n=3$.

With regard to the following elements (15 P, 16 S, 17 Cl) the only relevant evidence at present available is the affinities for one, two, and three electrons and the spectrum of S which indicates that the normal orbit of the last bound electron is a 3_2-orbit. The final element of the period is the inert gas argon (18 A), in which, again, a closed shell of 8 electrons must exist. The detailed construction of this shell is best considered from the standpoint of the following element potassium (19 K), the core of which must have this structure.

The potassium spectrum indicates a 4_1-orbit as the normal orbit of the radiating electron, and a 4_2-orbit as the p-orbit with maximum energy; the series of 3_1- and 3_2-orbits is therefore completed on the attainment of the eight-shell of argon. The 3_3-orbit of potassium is more loosely bound than the 4_1- and even the 4_2-orbits; it has, in fact, a larger effective quantum number (2·85 in comparison with 2·23 for the 4_2- and 1·77 for the 4_1-orbit). The closed shells in argon do not therefore contain all orbits with the principal quantum number 3, but only the 3_1- and 3_2-orbits.

In the case of the divalent calcium (20 Ca), chemical and spectroscopic results both point to a second electron occupying a 4_1-orbit.

The elements now following exhibit very complicated spectra, for

[1] Experimental determinations by J. C. McLennan and W. W. Shaver, *Trans. Roy. Soc. Canada*, vol. xviii, p. 1, 1924, and A. Fowler, *Phil. Trans. Roy. Soc. London* (A), vol. ccxxv, p. 1, 1925. Theoretical interpretation by F. Hund, *Zeitschr. f. Physik*, vol. xxxiii, p. 345, 1925; vol. xxxiv, p. 296, 1925.

whose resolution into series very few data are at present available.[1] Their terms have a very high multiplicity, *e.g.* the terms of Mn and others are octets; further, the elements have each several systems of terms, so that, for example, an element can have several *p*- or *d*-terms of the same multiplicity, which do not belong to a series; the normal state is not always, as hitherto, an *s*- or *p*-state; *d*- and *f*-terms also occur as normal terms, but the spectroscopic character

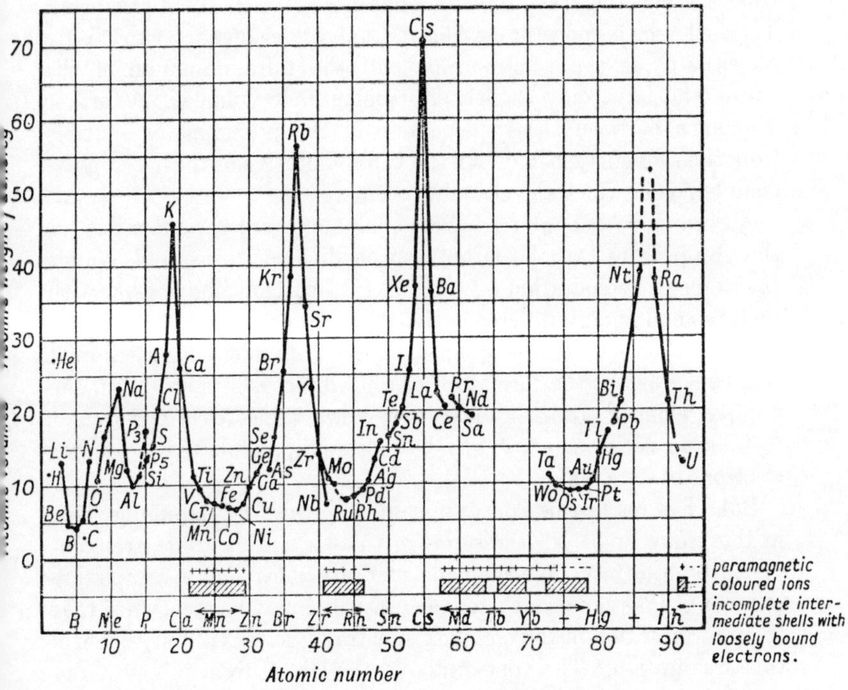

FIG. 18.

of these terms is not determined by one electron only. Here too for the first time we meet ions having electron arrangements different from those of the neutral atoms with the same number of electrons; for some of these ions the normal orbit of the series electron is a *d*-orbit (see p. 200).

The elements from scandium to nickel also form, chemically, a special group. With regard to their chemical valency, they do not form a continuation of the series K, Ca; rather they exhibit multiple valencies which vary irregularly though their maximum

[1] For the connection between these spectra and the periodic system, see F. Hund, *Zeitschr. f. Physik*, *loc. cit.*

values correspond in general to their position in the general scheme of the periodic system (Ti 4-, V 5-, Cr 6-, M 7-valent); the minimum valency may be as low as 2. At this juncture the well-known curve (fig. 18) of atomic volumes, after Lothar Meyer, can be used as an example of the relations between different elements (atomic weights and densities in the solid state). The alkali elements form sharply defined maxima on this curve, which, according to our ideas, arises from the fact that they have one outer electron in an elliptic orbit. The fact which concerns us here is that the elements Ti to Ni are all situated in the neighbourhood of the third minimum of the curve, and have only slightly different atomic volumes. A further difference between these elements and the preceding ones arises from their magnetic behaviour and the colouration of the heteropolar compounds in which the elements occur as ions.

According to Ladenburg,[1] these compounds are paramagnetic for the group Ti to Cu (the latter only in divalent form) and exhibit characteristic colouration (*cf.* fig. 18), *i.e.* electron jumps exist with such a small energy difference that they absorb visible light. Previous to Bohr's system of quantum numbers Ladenburg attributed this behaviour to the formation of an " intermediate shell " in the group of elements from Sc to Ni. The newly added electrons are not to take up positions externally but internally, while the two outer electrons of Ca remain.

Bohr has made this conception more precise by assuming that, in the group Sc to Ni, the series of the 3_1- and 3_2-orbits are completed by 3_3-orbits. We shall consider later how such a completion of inner groups can occur; for the present it may be mentioned that the interpretation of the complex spectra of Sc to Ni[2] fully confirm this assumption. The appearance of the last M-term in the X-ray spectra of Cu (*cf.* fig. 16, p. 179) shows that 3_3-orbits are actually present in the interior of the atoms of the following elements. The 3_3-orbits in the core do not prevent the existence of excited 3_3-orbits in the exterior, as the table on p. 190 shows for Cu, Zn, Ga, Rb.

The elements copper (29 Cu) and zinc (30 Zn) resemble the alkalies and alkaline earths respectively in some series of their spectra. In Cu we have to assume an outer electron confined to a 4_1-orbit, and in Zn two such 4_1-electrons. Corresponding to Al, the radiating electron in gallium (31 Ga) is situated on a 4_2-orbit. In the eighth place after Ni we have the inert gas krypton (36 Kr), so that the group

[1] R. Ladenburg, *Zeitschr. f. Elektrochem.*, vol. xxvi, p. 262, 1920. Fig. 18 is taken from this paper.

[2] F. Hund, *loc. cit.*

Cu to Kr resembles very closely the second and third periods. We assume, therefore, that in this group the eight four-quantum electron orbits (4_1- and 4_2-orbits) are added to the complete three-quantum shell completed in the case of Ni.

The fact that in Kr the N-ring ($n=4$) is closed is shown by the spectra of rubidium (37 Rb) and strontium (38 Sr); they prove, in conjunction with the chemical behaviour of these elements, that, in the normal state, we have one and two outer electrons respectively in 5_1-orbits. The following elements, yttrium (39 Y) to palladium (46 Pd) (like the group Sc to Ni), do not form a simple continuation of the series, but exhibit multiple and rapidly changing valency. This suggests that in these elements the 4_3-orbits, hitherto absent, appear for the first time; in the case of silver (47 Ag) we actually observe a corresponding X-ray term. The occurrence of 4_3-orbits in the core, again, does not prohibit electrons in an excited state from moving in a 3_3-orbit outside the core, as is the case in Ag, Cd, and In.

The elements silver (47 Ag), cadmium (48 Cd), and indium (49 In) correspond in their spectra and chemical behaviour to the elements Cu, Zn, Ga. In their case one 5_2- and two 5_1-orbits are superposed on the four-quantum shell (4_1-, 4_2-, 4_3-orbits). In xenon (54 X) we must, for the time being, regard the 5_1- and 5_2-groups as closed.

The sixth period begins with cæsium (55 Cs) and barium (56 Ba) in analogy with the fifth; the normal orbits of the radiating electrons are 6_1-orbits. Lanthanum (57 La) and the elements immediately preceding platinum (78 Pt) resemble the group Y to Pd. We may assume there the building up of the 5_3-group; a 5_3-X-ray term occurs, in fact, soon after platinum. In this group is included a further group of elements which all have very much the same chemical behaviour, the rare earths; we may ascribe them to the formation of the 4_4-orbits, which have not occurred hitherto; a 4_4-X-ray term occurs in the case of tantalum (73 Ta). The elements gold (79 Au) to niton (86 Nt) correspond to the elements Ag to X, and involve the initial formation of the 6_1- and 6_2-orbits. The last period involves the superposition of 7_1-orbits.

We would expect that in the seventh period the addition of 5_4-orbits would give a group of elements of very similar chemical properties, analogous to the rare earths. The heaviest known elements do not appear to belong to such a group, so the addition of 5_4-orbits must begin later in the seventh period than the addition of 4_4-orbits in the sixth period; this difference is probably to be ascribed to the greater eccentricity and consequent looser binding of the 5_4-orbits of an element of the seventh period, as compared with the 4_4-orbits of the corresponding element of the sixth period.[1]

If we again cast a glance over the periodic system and omit for the moment those groups (framed in fig. 17) having special chemical and spectroscopic behaviour, we see that, in the first period, two 1_1-electrons are added and in each following period altogether eight n_1- and n_2-electrons. The iron group (Sc to Ni) introduces ten further electrons in three-quantum orbits, so that altogether we obtain 18 three-quantum orbits. The palladium group (Y to Pd) introduces 10, and the group of the rare earths 14 further four-quantum orbits, the number of which is thereby raised to 32.

A corroboration of this conception of the building up of inner electron groups is found (according to Bohr and Coster) in the diagram of the X-ray terms (fig. 16, p. 179), where marked kinks occur in the curves for the values of Z concerned in this process.

For convenience we give a table of the numbers of electrons occupying the various shells.[2]

In order to be able to derive deductively the construction of the periodic table, one must be able to deduce theoretically the maximum number of electrons which can occupy orbits of the same n_k. This can now be done; consideration of physical[3] and chemical[4] experimental evidence first suggested the rule that the maximum number of electrons which can occupy equivalent n_k-orbits in a single atom is $2(2k-1)$; a theoretical explanation of this rule can now be given,[5] but it lies outside the scope of this book.

If these maximum numbers of occupation be regarded simply as given, then the order of addition of the quantum orbits becomes, to a certain degree, comprehensible. We must suppose that the addition of a fresh electron to an already existing configuration takes place in such a way that the electron finally enters that quantum orbit in which it has the least energy (in which it is most firmly bound), and that it remains in this orbit during the capture of subsequent electrons. And here it must be borne in mind that an atom

---

[1] Calculations by Y. Sugiura and H. C. Urey (*Det. Kongel. Danske Vidensk. Selskab.*, vol. vii, No. 13, 1926) suggest that in the seventh period the group analogous to the rare earths should begin with the element atomic number 95.

[2] The table gives the numbers of occupying electrons only in as far as they are determined to a fair degree of certainty from our considerations. Later investigations permit of these numbers being given with a fair degree of probability also in the case of the remaining elements. See F. Hund, *Zeitschr. f. Physik*, *loc. cit.*

[3] E. C. Stoner, *Phil. Mag.*, vol. xlviii, p. 719, 1924.

[4] J. D. Main Smith, *Journ. Soc. Chem. Ind.*, vol. xliii, p. 323, 1924; vol. xliv, p. 944, 1925; H. G. Grimm and A. Sommerfeld, *Zeitschr. f. Phys.*, vol. xxxvi, p. 36, 1926.

[5] This explanation depends on the work of Pauli (*loc. cit.*) and the concept of the spinning electron.

DISTRIBUTION OF ELECTRONS AMONG THE n_k-ORBITS

	1_1	2_1 2_2	3_1 3_2 3_3	4_1 4_2 4_3 4_4	5_1 5_2 5_3 5_4 5_5	6_1 6_2 6_3 6_4 6_5 6_6	7_1 7_2
1 H	1						
2 He	2						
3 Li	2	1					
4 Be	2	2					
5 B	2	2 1					
6 C	2	2 (2)					
— —	—	— —					
10 Ne	2	8					
11 Na	2	8	1				
12 Mg	2	8	2				
13 Al	2	8	2 1				
14 Si	2	8	2 (2)				
— —	—	— —	— —				
18 A	2	8	8				
19 K	2	8	8	1			
20 Ca	2	8	8	2			
21 Sc	2	8	8 1	(2)			
22 Ti	2	8	8 2	(2)			
— —	—	— —	— — —	—			
29 Cu	2	8	18	1			
30 Zn	2	8	18	2			
31 Ga	2	8	18	2 1			
— —	—	— —	— — —	— —			
36 Kr	2	8	18	8			
37 Rb	2	8	18	8	1		
38 Sr	2	8	18	8	2		
39 Y	2	8	18	8 1	(2)		
40 Zr	2	8	18	8 2	(2)		
— —	—	— —	— — —	— — —	—		
47 Ag	2	8	18	18	1		
48 Cd	2	8	18	18	2		
49 In	2	8	18	18	2 1		
— —	—	— —	— — —	— — —	— —		
54 X	8	8	18	18	8		
55 Cs	2	8	18	18	8	1	
56 Ba	2	8	18	18	8	2	
57 La	2	8	18	18	8 1	(2)	
58 Ce	2	8	18	18 1	8 1	(2)	
59 Pr	2	8	18	18 2	8 1	(2)	
— —	—	— —	— — —	— — — —	— — —	—	
71 Cp	2	8	18	32	8 1	(2)	
72 Hf	2	8	18	32	8 2	(2)	
— —	—	— —	— — —	— — — —	— — —	—	
79 Au	2	8	18	32	18	1	
80 Hg	2	8	18	32	18	2	
81 Tl	2	8	18	32	18	2 1	
— —	—	— —	— — —	— — — —	— — —	— —	
86 Nt	2	8	18	32	18	8	
87 —	2	8	18	32	18	8	1
88 Ra	2	8	18	32	18	8	2
89 Ac	2	8	18	32	18	8 1	(2)
90 Th	2	8	18	32	18	8 2	(2)
— —	—	— —	— — —	— — — —	— — —	— — —	—
— —	—	— —	— — —	— — — —	— — — — —	— — —	— —
118 —	2	8	18	32	32	18	8

is not produced from the preceding one by the addition of an electron, but from its own positive ion; this certainly has the same number of electrons as the preceding atom, but a somewhat higher nuclear charge. That this nuclear charge may on occasion be an important factor in deciding which orbit of the added electron is most firmly bound is shown by the following arguments.

We assume that an ion contains a number of fully occupied quantum orbits, and we inquire now which of those not occupied is the most strongly bound. We can give an answer to this in two limiting cases. If the nuclear charge is much greater than the number of electrons, the field of force in the ion and its surroundings is nearly a Coulomb field and the energies of the orbits are in the same order as in the case of hydrogen, only the *p*-, *d*-, etc., orbits with a given n are slightly less firmly bound than the *s*-orbits with the same n; the order is, therefore: $1_1, 2_1, 2_2, 3_1, 3_2, 3_3, 4_1 \ldots$

If now we imagine, say, the uranium atom to be produced by a nucleus of charge 92 collecting 92 electrons in turn, it will first capture two 1_1-electrons, then altogether eight 2_1- and 2_2-electrons, eighteen 3_1-, 3_2-, 3_3-electrons, etc. Since now the number of electrons gradually becomes comparable with the nuclear charge, the order of capture is no longer quite certain. The Bohr-Coster diagram of the X-ray terms (fig. 16, p. 179) shows us, however, that the energies of the orbits, at any rate in completed atoms, are in the order $4_1, 4_2, 4_3, 4_4, 5_1 \ldots$

If the number of electrons is only one less than the nuclear charge, that is, if we have to do with the addition of the last electron and the consequent formation of the neutral atom, we can fall back on the rough estimation of the effective quantum number given by (4), § 28, as soon as we have to do with orbits of the penetrating type. For *s*-orbits we have

$$n^* = n - (n^{(i)} - 1 - \epsilon_1 + \epsilon_2).$$

Since the aphelia of the *s*-orbits of the core determine its magnitude, it follows that $n^{(i)}$ is the real quantum number of the largest *s*-orbit in the core, and therefore $n^{(i)} = n - 1$. We shall then have approximately

$$n^* = 2.$$

In the case of the *p*-orbits $n^{(i)}$ will be somewhat larger than the quantum number of the *p*-orbit completely contained in the core, so that we get

$$2 < n^* < 3.$$

These values agree in a certain measure with the empirical values (first table of § 31).[1] In general, the dimensions of the *d*-orbits of

[1] For half integral values of k one finds $n^* = 1{\cdot}5$ for *s*-terms, $n^* = 1{\cdot}5$ to $2{\cdot}5$ for *p*-terms.

neutral atoms are such that they do not penetrate into the core, or penetrate to such a small extent that the equation (4), § 28, does not seem to be applicable ; the 3_3-orbit is then the most firmly bound *d*-orbit and its n^* will be somewhat less than 3. Only in the case of Sr and Ba do the *d*-orbits appear to penetrate more deeply. The estimate would lead to

$$3<n^*<4,$$

the empirical value is approximately 2, but is still higher than for the *s*-orbits. In either case, then, the first *s*-term of a neutral atom (whatever the value of *n*) is likely to be more firmly bound than the first *d*-orbit.

This estimation affords an explanation of the fact that after the completion of an n_1- and n_2-group, an outer electron of a neutral atom will become bound in an $(n+1)_1$-orbit, and that, in consequence, after the closing of the 3_1- and 3_2-groups in A or K^+, the next electron in K traverses a 4_1- (not a 3_3-) orbit, or after completion of the 4_1- and 4_2-groups in Kr or Rb^+, Rb begins a 5_1- (not a 4_3- or 4_4-) group. Whilst in the successive capture of electrons by a slightly ionised atom the 3_2-orbit is followed by a 4_1-orbit, for atoms of high atomic number with the same number of electrons, which are highly ionised, the 3_2-orbit is succeeded by a 3_3-orbit. Consequently, if we traverse the series of potassium-like ions K, Ca^+, Sc^{++}, Ti^{+++}, $V^{(4)}$ . . . $U^{(73)}$ we must, sooner or later, arrive at a point where the outermost electron is confined to a 3_3-orbit. Actually, in the spectrum of K, the 3_3-orbit ($n^*=2{\cdot}85$) is less strongly bound than the 4_1-orbit ($n^*=1{\cdot}77$), for Ca^+ the difference is much less ($n^*=2{\cdot}31$; $2{\cdot}14$) ; in Sc^{++} the n^* of the *s*-term will be still larger than in the case of Ca^+ (in accordance with the general behaviour of the penetrating orbits), so that the *d*-orbit could be more strongly bound than the *s*-orbit.[1] It has recently been confirmed by experiment[2] that for Sc^{++}, Ti^{+++}, V^{+4} the lowest *d*-term (3_3-orbit) is lower than the lowest *s*-term (4_1-orbit), and similarly[3] in the next row of the periodic table the lowest *d*-term for Yt^{++}, Zr^{+++} is lower than the lowest *s*-term. It may therefore be assumed that, in the building up of the Sc-atom from the argon-like configuration of Sc^{+++}, a 3_3-orbit is added and subsequently two 4_1-orbits, and in the case of Ti from Ti^{++++}, two 3_3- and then two 4_1-orbits.[4]

---

[1] See N. Bohr, *Zeitschr. f. Physik*, vol. ix, p. 1, 1922.
[2] R. E. Gibbs and H. E. White, *Proc. Nat. Acad. Sci.*, vol. xii, p. 598, 1926.
[3] R. A. Millikan and I. S. Bowen, *Phys. Rev.*, vol. xxviii, p. 923, 1926.
[4] This hypothesis is supported by the investigations of these spectra and their theoretical significance (F. Hund, *loc. cit.*), even though the conception of a single "radiating electron" is no longer adequate.

In order to represent the numbers of electrons occupying the quantum orbits with different n, a two-dimensional diagram must be employed, for in order to include all the elements together with all their ions down to the bare nucleus the values of n must be shown as a function of both the atomic number Z and of the numbers of electrons z. An illustration of the ideas in question is provided by fig. 19, in

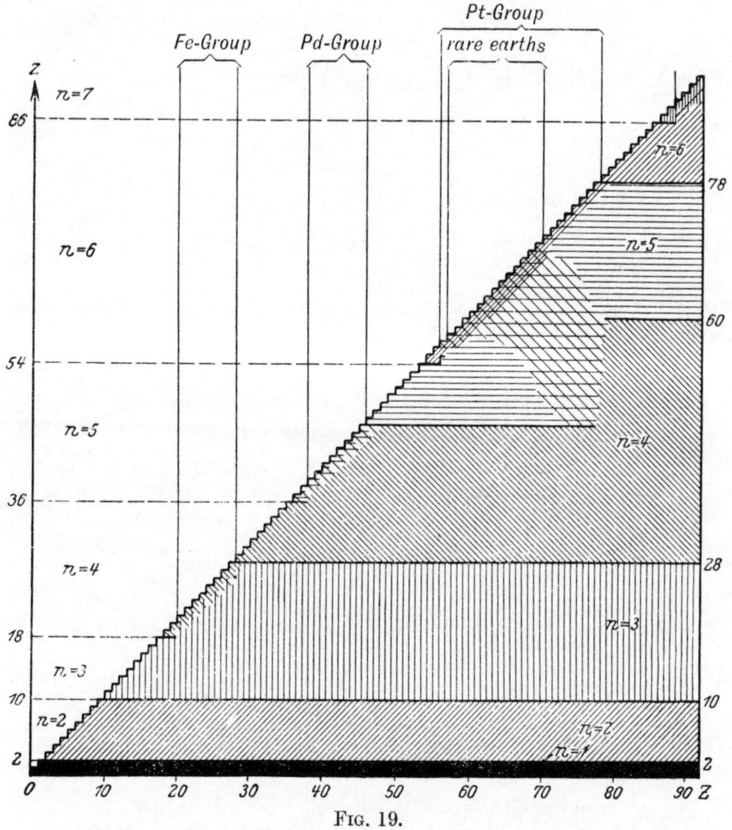

FIG. 19.

which only the group is represented (by shading) which is in process of completion, *i.e.* the quantum orbit of the last electron added. The regions where this quantum orbit is not uniquely determined are doubly shaded.

§ 33.—The Relativistic Kepler Motion

In our investigations of the periodic system we found the non-relativistic mechanics adequate. The more rigorous treatment of the orbits in the case of hydrogen requires, however, that the relativity theory should be taken into account.

A simple calculation shows in fact that already in the one-quantum circular orbit of the hydrogen atom the velocity of the electron attains a value whose ratio to the velocity of light c is not negligible for all purposes. This velocity is

$$v_{\mathrm{H}} = \frac{p}{ma_{\mathrm{H}}} = \frac{h}{2\pi m a_{\mathrm{H}}};$$

if for a_{H} we substitute the value (8), § 23,

$$a_{\mathrm{H}} = \frac{h^2}{4\pi^2 m e^2},$$

we find for the ratio α

$$\alpha = \frac{v_{\mathrm{H}}}{c} = \frac{2\pi e^2}{hc} = 7{\cdot}29 \,.\, 10^{-3}. \tag{1}$$

For observations which attain this order of accuracy, the ordinary mechanics will therefore no longer suffice. Consequently we must investigate the motion of an electron in a Coulomb field of force arising from a nucleus of charge Z, taking the relativity theory into consideration; in this investigation we follow Sommerfeld.[1]

Here also the Hamiltonian function is identical with the total energy (*cf.* (11), § 5). We have

$$\mathrm{H} = m_0 c^2\left(\frac{1}{\sqrt{1-\beta^2}} - 1\right) - \frac{e^2 \mathrm{Z}}{r} = \mathrm{W}, \tag{2}$$

where $\beta = v/c$. The components of the momentum are by (10), § 5,

$$p_x = \frac{m_0 \dot{x}}{\sqrt{1-\beta^2}}, \qquad p_y = \frac{m_0 \dot{y}}{\sqrt{1-\beta^2}}, \qquad p_z = \frac{m_0 \dot{z}}{\sqrt{1-\beta^2}}, \tag{3}$$

which, on squaring and adding, gives

$$p_x^2 + p_y^2 + p_z^2 = \frac{m_0^2 c^2 \beta^2}{1-\beta^2} = m_0^2 c^2\left(\frac{1}{1-\beta^2} - 1\right)$$

and

$$\frac{1}{\sqrt{1-\beta^2}} = \sqrt{1 + \frac{1}{m_0^2 c^2}(p_x^2 + p_y^2 + p_z^2)}.$$

Therefore, by (2),

$$\mathrm{H} = m_0 c^2\left[\sqrt{1 + \frac{1}{m_0^2 c^2}(p_x^2 + p_y^2 + p_z^2)} - 1\right] - \frac{e^2 \mathrm{Z}}{r} = \mathrm{W}. \tag{4}$$

[1] A. Sommerfeld, *Ann. d. Physik*, vol. li, p. 1, 1916.

If we calculate from this the sum of the squares of the momenta, we find :

$$(5)\qquad \frac{1}{2m_0}(p_x{}^2+p_y{}^2+p_z{}^2)=\mathrm{W}+\frac{e^2\mathrm{Z}}{r}+\frac{1}{2m_0c^2}\left(\mathrm{W}+\frac{e^2\mathrm{Z}}{r}\right)^2.$$

This equation differs from the corresponding one in the non-relativistic Kepler motion by the term

$$\frac{1}{2m_0c^2}\left(\mathrm{W}+\frac{e^2\mathrm{Z}}{r}\right)^2$$

only. Since this term depends on r only, the present problem is likewise separable in polar co-ordinates.

Now, however, we have single degeneration only. Following the notation introduced in § 21 for the central motion, we write

$$\begin{aligned}\mathrm{J}_1&=\mathrm{J}_r+\mathrm{J}_\phi+\mathrm{J}_\theta=nh\\ \mathrm{J}_2&=\qquad\ \mathrm{J}_\phi+\mathrm{J}_\theta=kh.\end{aligned}$$

The action integrals J_ϕ and J_θ are the same as before, in particular

$$\mathrm{J}_\phi+\mathrm{J}_\theta=2\pi p$$

is 2π times the angular momentum. J_r takes the same form (2), § 22, as before

$$\mathrm{J}_r=\oint\sqrt{-\mathrm{A}+\frac{2\mathrm{B}}{r}-\frac{\mathrm{C}}{r^2}}dr,$$

but here A, B, and C have a somewhat different meaning :

$$\begin{aligned}\mathrm{A}&=2m_0(-\mathrm{W})-\frac{\mathrm{W}^2}{c^2}=m_0{}^2c^2\left[1-\left(1+\frac{\mathrm{W}}{m_0c^2}\right)^2\right]\\ \mathrm{B}&=m_0e^2\mathrm{Z}+\frac{\mathrm{W}e^2\mathrm{Z}}{c^2}\quad=m_0e^2\mathrm{Z}\left(1+\frac{\mathrm{W}}{m_0c^2}\right)\\ \mathrm{C}&=p^2-\frac{e^4\mathrm{Z}^2}{c^2}\qquad\ =\frac{k^2h^2}{4\pi^2}\left(1-\frac{\alpha^2\mathrm{Z}^2}{k^2}\right),\end{aligned}$$

α being given by (1). The evaluation of the integral gives as before (*cf.* (5), Appendix II),

$$\mathrm{J}_r=(n-k)h=2\pi\left(-\sqrt{\mathrm{C}}+\frac{\mathrm{B}}{\sqrt{\mathrm{A}}}\right),$$

therefore

$$(n-k)h=-kh\sqrt{1-\frac{\alpha^2\mathrm{Z}^2}{k^2}}+\frac{2\pi e^2\mathrm{Z}\left(1+\dfrac{\mathrm{W}}{m_0c^2}\right)}{c\sqrt{1-\left(1+\dfrac{\mathrm{W}}{m_0c^2}\right)^2}}.$$

If the equation be solved for $1+\frac{W}{m_0c^2}$ we find

$$(6) \qquad 1+\frac{W}{m_0c^2}=\frac{1}{\sqrt{1+\frac{\alpha^2Z^2}{(n-k+\sqrt{k^2-\alpha^2Z^2})^2}}}.$$

We have here the exact expression for the energy. As in the case of every multiply-periodic central motion, we know that the orbit is a rosette.

Only the case in which α is very small is of interest to us. The first few terms of the expansion in α are therefore sufficient. We find

$$1+\frac{W}{m_0c^2}=1-\frac{\alpha^2Z^2}{2n^2}+\frac{\alpha^4Z^4}{2n^4}\left(\frac{3}{4}-\frac{n}{k}\right).$$

If the value (1) be substituted for α and the Rydberg constant R be introduced, in accordance with (2), § 23, we obtain

$$(7) \qquad W=-\frac{cRhZ^2}{n^2}\left[1+\frac{\alpha^2Z^2}{n^2}\left(\frac{n}{k}-\frac{3}{4}\right)\right].$$

Before we enter into a fuller discussion of this equation, we shall give another deduction of it, this time using the theory of secular perturbations.

We take as our starting-point the expression (4) for the Hamiltonian function. In this the second term under the root is of the order of magnitude β^2; if we expand in terms of this we get

$$H=\frac{1}{2m_0}(p_x{}^2+p_y{}^2+p_z{}^2)-\frac{1}{8m_0{}^3c^2}(p_x{}^2+p_y{}^2+p_z{}^2)^2+\ldots-\frac{e^2Z}{r}=W.$$

If we put

$$H_0=\frac{1}{2m_0}(p_x{}^2+p_y{}^2+p_z{}^2)-\frac{e^2Z}{r}=W_0$$

$$H_1=-\frac{1}{8m_0{}^3c^2}(p_x{}^2+p_y{}^2+p_z{}^2)^2=W_1,$$

H_0 is the Hamiltonian function of the non-relativistic Kepler motion, which we regard as the unperturbed motion, and H_1 is a perturbation function. In order to find the influence of this perturbation on the Kepler motion, we have to average H_1 over the unperturbed motion. If we express the sum of the squares of the momenta occurring in H_1 with the help of the equation for W_0, we obtain

$$\overline{H}_1=-\frac{1}{2m_0c^2}[W_0{}^2+2e^2ZW_0\,.\,\overline{1/r}+e^4Z^2\overline{1/r^2}]=W_1.$$

This additional term in the energy corresponds to the additional term in (5), only in this case W is replaced by W_0, in accordance with our degree of approximation. We have already calculated the mean values of $1/r$ and $1/r^2$ for the Kepler motion in (19) and (20), § 22 :

$$\overline{1/r}=\frac{1}{a}, \qquad \overline{1/r^2}=\frac{1}{ab},$$

so that

$$W_1=-\frac{1}{2m_0c^2}\left[W_0^{\,2}+\frac{2e^2Z}{a}W_0+\frac{e^4Z^2}{a^2}\cdot\frac{a}{b}\right].$$

Remembering that

$$-\frac{e^2Z}{2a}=W_0, \qquad \frac{a}{b}=\frac{n}{k},$$

we get for the relativity contribution to the energy

$$W_1=-\frac{1}{2m_0c^2}W_0^{\,2}\left(4\frac{n}{k}-3\right),$$

or, if we again introduce a and R,

(8) $$W_1=-\frac{cRhZ^2}{n^2}\cdot\frac{a^2Z^2}{n^2}\left(\frac{n}{k}-\frac{3}{4}\right),$$

in agreement with (7).

The smaller the principal quantum number the larger is the relativity correction (8), and it is therefore greatest for the 1_1-orbit. For the same value of n it is greater the greater the eccentricity of the orbit. The frequency of rotation of the perihelion will be

$$\nu_2=\frac{\partial W}{\partial J_2}=\frac{1}{h}\frac{\partial W_1}{\partial k}=\frac{cRZ^2}{n^3}\cdot\frac{a^2Z^2}{k^2}=\nu_1\cdot\frac{a^2Z^2}{2k^2},$$

where ν_1 is the frequency of revolution of the electron in its ellipse.

The terms of the spectrum (H, He^+, Li^{++}) represented by (7) do not form a singly ordered set, as do the terms obtained by the non-relativistic calculation, but a doubly ordered one.

Since the influence of k on the magnitude of the term is small in comparison with that of n, we can regard the modification brought about by the relativity correction as a splitting up of the non-relativistic terms. The arrangement of the terms (with considerable magnification of the relativistic " fine structure ") is as follows :

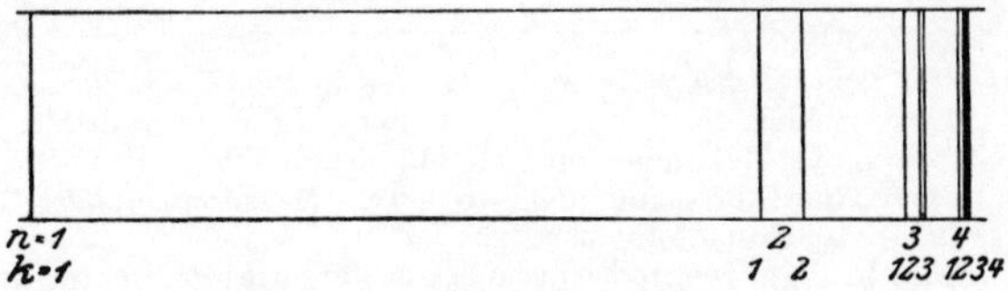

FIG. 20.

In the absence of external disturbances, only those terms combine, according to the correspondence principle (§ 17), for which the subsidiary quantum number k differs by ± 1. The line series whose limiting term is $n=1$ (in H the Lyman series) consists of single lines; the line series having the limiting term $n=2$ (in H the Balmer series) consists of triplets, the lines of the remaining series show a still more complex character.

As a measure of the relativistic fine structure we take, following Sommerfeld, that of the limiting term ($n=2$) of the Balmer series of hydrogen. This has the theoretical value

$$\Delta\nu_{\mathrm{H}}=\frac{\mathrm{R}\alpha^2}{16}=0{\cdot}365\ \mathrm{cm}^{-1}.$$

The value for the corresponding term in the case of a general value of Z is

$$\mathrm{Z}^4\Delta\nu_{\mathrm{H}},$$

e.g. for He^+ it is $16\Delta\nu_{\mathrm{H}}$. The quantity $\Delta\nu_{\mathrm{H}}$ will be the approximate amount by which all terms of the Balmer series are split up, for the separations of the variable terms ($n=3, 4 \ldots$) will be very small.

With regard to the verification of this theory by observation, measurements on hydrogen and helium have actually disclosed the expected components. Regarding the magnitude of the effect, however, the experimental results are not in agreement with one another, measurements on H_α, $\mathrm{H}_\beta \ldots$, for instance, for which theoretically $\Delta\nu_{\mathrm{H}}$ must be $0{\cdot}365\ \mathrm{cm}^{-1}$, vary between 0·29 and 0·39.[1] In the case of He^+ the fine structure may be observed in the series

$$4\mathrm{R}\left(\frac{1}{3^2}-\frac{1}{n^2}\right) \quad \text{and} \quad 4\mathrm{R}\left(\frac{1}{4^2}-\frac{1}{n^2}\right).$$

Paschen has made measurements with direct currents as well as with alternating currents; in the latter case many more lines appear, since, on account of the rapidly changing field strengths, disturbances arise as a result of which the selection rule based on the correspondence principle breaks down. The numbers of components, as well as the relative magnitudes of the separations, are in agreement with the theory.[2]

---

[1] Compare the comprehensive report by E. Lau in *Physikal. Zeitschr.*, vol. xxv, p. 60, 1924; Lau considers the value 0·29 to 0·30 as the most probable. The new measurements by J. C. McLennan and G. M. Shrum (*Proc. Roy. Soc.*, vol. cv, p. 259, 1924) give, however, again 0·33 to 0·37. Measurements by G. Hansen (*Diss.*, Jena, 1924) also support the theory.

[2] In the report by Lau, referred to above, matters are represented as if in the case of He also the measurements by Paschen gave values smaller than those

Sommerfeld[1] has used the relativity correction to explain the multiplicity of the X-ray terms and the departures from Mosley's law, (1), (2), and (3), § 29. The numerical agreement is surprisingly good throughout the whole periodic system; the foundations of the theory are, however, too uncertain to justify its treatment in this volume.

§-34.—The Zeeman Effect

Hitherto we have considered atoms as isolated systems; we now proceed to investigate the action of constant external influences on them, commencing with that of a constant external magnetic field, the Zeeman effect.

We can start out from a very general atomic model with a stationary nucleus and any number of revolving electrons. We assume that the energy of the undisturbed system (without magnetic field) is a function of certain action variables $J_1, J_2 \ldots$

$$W_0(J_1, J_2 \ldots).$$

If now a homogeneous magnetic field exists, the potential energy of the system is invariant with respect to a rotation about the direction of the field. The azimuth ϕ of an arbitrary point of the system is then a cyclic variable, as proved in § 6 and § 17, and the corresponding conjugated momentum p_ϕ is the angular momentum of the system about the direction of the field.

The principal function

$$S = \pm\frac{1}{2\pi}\phi \cdot J_\phi + S^{(1)}(q_1 q_2 \ldots J_1 J_2 \ldots J_\phi)$$

defines angle variables $w_1 w_2 \ldots w_\phi$; w_ϕ is the mean azimuth about the direction of the field.

In the absence of a magnetic field J_ϕ does not appear in the Hamiltonian function, the motion is degenerate and w_ϕ is constant.

If now we wish to find the influence of the magnetic field on the energy, we meet with the case, mentioned in § 4, where the forces which act on the various particles of the system depend on the velocities. Owing to the magnetic field **H** (supposed for the moment

---

required by the theory. This is due to the fact that Lau bases his observations only on the direct current measurements of Paschen, whereas Paschen includes also the alternating current measurements.

[1] A. Sommerfeld, *Ann. d. Physik*, vol. li, p. 125, 1916. A. Landé (*Zeitschr. f. Physik*, vol. xxv, p. 46, 1924) has shown that even certain optical doublets, in the case of terms not of the hydrogen type, follow the appropriate relativity formula. Millikan and Bowen (*Phys. Rev.*, vol. xxiii, p. 1, 1924, and vol. xxv, p. 295, 1925) have brought forward much empirical evidence in support of this. These effects are now ascribed in part to a spin of the electron (*cf.* footnote, p. 152).

to depend arbitrarily on x, y, z), an electron of charge $-e$ is subjected to the so-called Lorentz force [1]

$$\mathbf{K}=-\frac{e}{c}[\mathbf{vH}]. \tag{1}$$

According to § 4 we have to determine a function M such that

$$\frac{d}{dt}\frac{\partial \mathrm{M}}{\partial \dot{x}}-\frac{\partial \mathrm{M}}{\partial x}=\mathbf{K}_x.$$

The function

$$\mathrm{M}=\frac{e}{c}\mathbf{Av}=\frac{e}{c}(\mathbf{A}_x\dot{x}+\mathbf{A}_y\dot{y}+\mathbf{A}_z\dot{z})$$

has this property ; $\mathbf{A}$ is the vector potential of the magnetic field, defined by

$$\mathbf{H}=\operatorname{curl}\mathbf{A}.$$

We have :

$$\begin{aligned}\frac{d}{dt}\frac{\partial \mathrm{M}}{\partial \dot{x}}-\frac{d\mathrm{M}}{\partial x}&=\frac{d}{dt}\left(\frac{e}{c}\mathbf{A}_x\right)-\frac{e}{c}\left(\frac{\partial \mathbf{A}_x}{\partial x}\dot{x}+\frac{\partial \mathbf{A}_y}{\partial x}\dot{y}+\frac{\partial \mathbf{A}_z}{\partial x}\dot{z}\right)\\ &=-\frac{e}{c}\left[\dot{y}\left(\frac{\partial \mathbf{A}_y}{\partial x}-\frac{\partial \mathbf{A}_x}{\partial y}\right)-\dot{z}\left(\frac{\partial \mathbf{A}_x}{\partial z}-\frac{\partial \mathbf{A}_z}{\partial x}\right)\right]\\ &=-\frac{e}{c}[\mathbf{vH}]_x=\mathbf{K}_x.\end{aligned}$$

The Lagrangian function is by (8), § 4 :

$$\mathrm{L}=\mathrm{T}-\mathrm{U}-\frac{e}{c}\sum(\mathbf{A}_x\dot{x}+\mathbf{A}_y\dot{y}+\mathbf{A}_z\dot{z}), \tag{2}$$

where the sum is to be taken over all the electrons. From this we calculate the momenta. For one electron they are :

$$\begin{aligned}p_x&=\frac{\partial \mathrm{L}}{\partial \dot{x}}=m\dot{x}-\frac{e}{c}\mathbf{A}_x\\ p_y&=\frac{\partial \mathrm{L}}{\partial \dot{y}}=m\dot{y}-\frac{e}{c}\mathbf{A}_y\\ p_z&=\frac{\partial \mathrm{L}}{\partial \dot{z}}=m\dot{z}-\frac{e}{c}\mathbf{A}_z.\end{aligned} \tag{3}$$

The Hamiltonian function becomes, by (3), § 5 :

$$\begin{aligned}\mathrm{H}&=\sum(\dot{x}p_x+\dot{y}p_y+\dot{z}p_z)-\mathrm{L}\\ &=\sum\frac{m}{2}(\dot{x}^2+\dot{y}^2+\dot{z}^2)+\mathrm{U}=\mathrm{T}+\mathrm{U}.\end{aligned} \tag{4}$$

[1] See, for example, M. Abraham, *Theorie der Elektrizität*, vol. ii, third edition, Leipzig, 1914, § 4, p. 20, or H. A. Lorentz, *Theory of Electrons*, p. 15.

It is, therefore, equal to the total energy in this case also. No additional term occurs in the energy, corresponding to the magnetic field, since the magnetic forces do no work; the force $-\frac{e}{c}[\mathbf{vH}]$ is always perpendicular to $\mathbf{v}$. If in H we express the velocity components in terms of the momenta we get

$$\mathrm{H}=\sum\left[\frac{1}{2m}(p_x{}^2+p_y{}^2+p_z{}^2)+\frac{e}{cm}(\mathbf{A}_x p_x+\mathbf{A}_y p_y+\mathbf{A}_z p_z)\right.$$
$$\left.+\frac{e^2}{2mc^2}(\mathbf{A}_x{}^2+\mathbf{A}_y{}^2+\mathbf{A}_z{}^2)\right]+\mathrm{U}.$$

We restrict ourselves in the following to the case where the field is so weak that we can neglect the squares of $\mathbf{A}_x$, $\mathbf{A}_y$, $\mathbf{A}_z$. We can then write

$$\mathrm{H}=\sum\left[\frac{1}{2m}(p_x{}^2+p_y{}^2+p_z{}^2)+\frac{e}{c}\mathbf{Av}\right]+\mathrm{U}, \tag{5}$$

so that the Hamiltonian function differs only by the term

$$\sum\frac{e}{c}\mathbf{Av}$$

from its value for no field.

We now examine the effect of a homogeneous magnetic field $\mathbf{H}$ on the motion of the electrons. The vector potential of such a field is

$$\mathbf{A}=\tfrac{1}{2}[\mathbf{Hr}],$$

where $\mathbf{r}$ is the position vector from an arbitrary origin, which we take as the nucleus. In the additional term we have therefore

$$\sum\mathbf{Av}=\sum\tfrac{1}{2}[\mathbf{Hr}]\mathbf{v}=\sum\tfrac{1}{2}\mathbf{H}[\mathbf{rv}]=\frac{1}{2m}\mathbf{Hp}=\frac{1}{2m}|\mathbf{H}|\,p_\phi,$$

where $\mathbf{p}$ is the resultant angular momentum of the system of electrons, and p_ϕ, as above, its component in the direction of the field. Apart from terms proportional to $\mathbf{H}$, p_ϕ is the momentum conjugate to an absolute azimuth. If we pass over to the angle and action variables $w_1, w_2 \ldots w_\phi$, $\mathrm{J}_1, \mathrm{J}_2 \ldots \mathrm{J}_\phi$ of the motion in the absence of a field, (5) takes the form [1]

$$\mathrm{H}=\mathrm{W}_0(\mathrm{J}_1\mathrm{J}_2\ldots)\pm\frac{e|\mathbf{H}|}{2mc}\cdot\frac{\mathrm{J}_\phi}{2\pi}. \tag{6}$$

From this we can deduce at once the influence of the magnetic

[1] The double sign is due to the fact that p_ϕ can be positive or negative, whereas, by definition, J_ϕ is only positive.

field **H** on the motion of the electrons. The angle and action variables of the motion in the absence of a field remain angle and action variables in the presence of a magnetic field, since the total energy depends only on the J_k's. The angle variable w_ϕ is, however, no longer constant, but has the frequency $\nu_\phi = \pm\nu_m$, where

$$\nu_m = \left|\frac{\partial H}{\partial J_\phi}\right| = \frac{1}{2\pi}\frac{e|\mathbf{H}|}{2mc}, \tag{7}$$

corresponding to a wave number

$$\nu_m/c = 4{\cdot}70 \,.\, 10^{-5}\,|\mathbf{H}|\ \mathrm{cm}^{-1},$$

while the frequencies of all the remaining angle variables are expressed in terms of the J_k, in just the same way as with no field acting. The sole effect of the magnetic field **H** is then to superpose on the motion occurring in the absence of a field a uniform precession of the whole system with the frequency ν_m (the Larmor precession).

The motion of an electron may then be resolved into oscillations parallel to the field with frequencies $(\nu\tau) = \nu_1\tau_1 + \nu_2\tau_2 + \ldots$ independent of the field, and into oscillations perpendicular to the field with the frequencies $(\nu\tau) + \nu_m$ and $(\nu\tau) - \nu_m$. This, on the classical theory, would give rise to radiation of frequency $(\tau\nu)$ polarised parallel to the field and to radiation with the frequencies $(\nu\tau) \pm \nu_m$ circularly polarised about the direction of the field.

We shall see that the quantum theory leads to the same resolution of a line into three components.

Since $J_1, J_2 \ldots$ are adiabatic invariants (*cf.* § 16) they remain constant in a magnetic field slowly generated, so on switching on the field the only change in the motion of the electrons is the superposition on the already existing motion of a uniform precession of frequency ν_ϕ.

To the quantum conditions of the unperturbed system

$$J_k = n_k h$$

there is now added a new condition

$$J_\phi = mh\,; \tag{8}$$

it states that the angular momentum of the electron system in the direction of the magnetic field can have only certain values. For a weak magnetic field we have here an example of spatial quantisation, which we have dealt with generally in § 17. If the angular momentum $J/2\pi$, where J is one of the quantities $J_1, J_2 \ldots$, is fixed by the quantum number j,

$$J = jh,$$

the angle α between the directions of the angular momentum and the magnetic field is given by

$$\cos \alpha = \frac{m}{j}. \tag{9}$$

The axis of the angular momentum can therefore be orientated only in $2j+1$ different directions ($m=j, j-1 \ldots -j$) with respect to the axis of the field.

The additional magnetic energy is, by (6), (7), and (8),

$$W_m = \pm h\nu_m \, . \, m \, ; \tag{10}$$

each term will, in consequence, be split up into $2j+1$ equidistant terms separated by a distance ν_m.

According to the correspondence principle, the quantum number m can change by 1, 0, -1 where, for the transition $m \rightarrow m$, the light radiated is polarised parallel to the direction of the field and for the transition $m \pm 1 \rightarrow m$ it is circularly polarised about the direction of the field. A decrease in m corresponds to a Larmor precession in the positive sense in the classical theory, and therefore to positive circularly polarised radiation; an increase of m corresponds to negative circularly polarised radiation.

The frequency radiated in the transition $m \rightarrow m$ is the same as the frequency ν_0 radiated in the absence of a magnetic field for the same variations of the remaining quantum numbers. The frequency radiated in the transition $m \pm 1 \rightarrow m$ is

$$\nu = \nu_0 \pm \nu_m.$$

One finds consequently for longitudinal observation, as in the classical theory, a doublet of circularly polarised spectral lines, situated symmetrically with respect to ν_0. The line with the greater frequency corresponds to the transition $m+1 \rightarrow m$; it is therefore positively circularly polarised with respect to the field, *i.e.* left-handed to an observer looking in the opposite direction to that of the field. For transverse observation a triplet is observed, the centre line of which is situated at ν_0 and is polarised parallel to the lines of force, the outer lines being separated from ν_0 by $\pm \nu_m$ and polarised in a perpendicular direction (fig. 21).

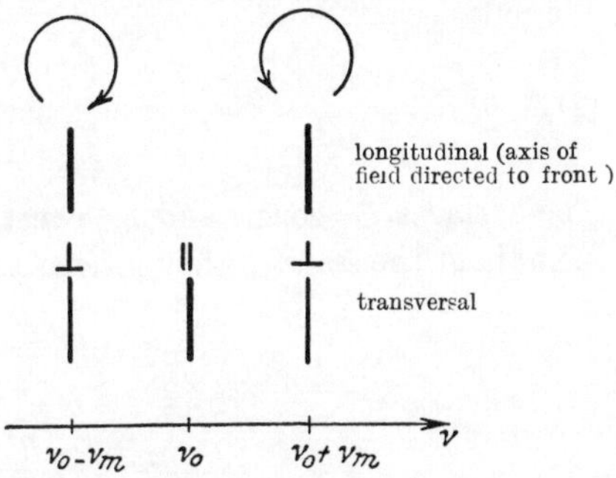

FIG. 21.

This result is the same as in the classical theory of H. A. Lorentz. It is verified experimentally for such lines of the other elements as are simple (singlets). This simple theory (which is analogous to the classical theory of Lorentz), does not suffice for the explanation of the complicated Zeeman effects which occur in the case of multiplets. The theory of these " anomalous Zeeman effects " lies outside the scope of this book.[1]

§ 35.—The Stark Effect for the Hydrogen Atom

The next example of the action of an external field which we shall consider is that of the Stark effect for the hydrogen atom, *i.e.* the influence of a homogeneous electric field **E** on the motion in the hydrogen atom (more generally in an atom with only one electron). We shall treat this problem in considerable detail, in order to illustrate the various methods employed for its solution.

The first method to which we resort is that of the introduction of separation variables;[2] afterwards we shall calculate the secular perturbations by two different methods. The result will, of course, be the same in every case.

If we choose the z-axis of a rectangular co-ordinate system as the direction of the field, the energy function becomes

$$H=\frac{m}{2}(\dot{x}^2+\dot{y}^2+\dot{z}^2)-\frac{e^2Z}{r}+eEz, \qquad E=|\mathbf{E}|. \tag{1}$$

It is easy to see that the Hamilton-Jacobi differential equation is separable neither in rectangular nor in polar co-ordinates. It may, however, be made separable by introducing parabolic co-ordinates. We put

$$\begin{aligned} x&=\xi\eta\cos\phi \\ y&=\xi\eta\sin\phi \\ z&=\tfrac{1}{2}(\xi^2-\eta^2). \end{aligned} \tag{2}$$

The surfaces ξ=const. and η=const. are then paraboloids of rotation about the z-axis; they intersect the (x, z)-plane in the curves

$$x^2=2\xi^2\left(\frac{\xi^2}{2}-z\right)$$

$$x^2=2\eta^2\left(\frac{\eta^2}{2}+z\right),$$

---

[1] *Cf.* E. Back and A. Landé, *Zeemaneffekt und Multiplettstruktur der Spektrallinien*, vol. i of the German series, *Struktur der Materie* (Springer).

[2] First worked out by P. S. Epstein, *Ann. d. Physik*, vol. l, p. 489, 1916; vol. lviii, p. 553, 1919; and K. Schwarzschild, *Sitzungsber. d. Berl. Akad.*, 1916, p. 548.

i.e. in parabolas with their focus at the origin, and having the parameters ξ^2 and η^2; ϕ is the azimuth about the direction of the field. In the new co-ordinates the kinetic energy is

(3) $$T=\frac{m}{2}[(\xi^2+\eta^2)(\dot{\xi}^2+\dot{\eta}^2)+\xi^2\eta^2\dot{\phi}^2];$$

which gives for the momenta conjugated to ξ, η, ϕ:

(4) $$\begin{aligned} p_\xi&=m\dot{\xi}(\xi^2+\eta^2)\\ p_\eta&=m\dot{\eta}(\xi^2+\eta^2)\\ p_\phi&=m\dot{\phi}\xi^2\eta^2. \end{aligned}$$

If we substitute these in T and add the potential energy

$$-\frac{2e^2Z}{\xi^2+\eta^2}+\tfrac{1}{2}eE(\xi^2-\eta^2)$$

we get

(5) $$H=\frac{1}{2m(\xi^2+\eta^2)}\left[p_\xi^{\,2}+p_\eta^{\,2}+\left(\frac{1}{\xi^2}+\frac{1}{\eta^2}\right)p_\phi^{\,2}+meE(\xi^4-\eta^4)-4me^2Z\right].$$

If this be equated to W and the resulting equation multiplied by $2m(\xi^2+\eta^2)$ it becomes separable. We have first:

$$p_\phi=\frac{\partial S}{\partial\phi}=\text{const.}$$

since ϕ is a cyclic co-ordinate, and

$$J_\phi=\oint p_\phi d\phi=2\pi|p_\phi|.$$

Since $p_\phi d\phi$ is never negative, $J_\phi\geqq 0$ always. We find further:

$$p_\xi=\frac{\partial S}{\partial\xi}=\sqrt{f_1(\xi)}$$

$$p_\eta=\frac{\partial S}{\partial\eta}=\sqrt{f_2(\eta)},$$

where

(6) $$\begin{aligned} f_1(\xi)&=2mW\xi^2+2\alpha_1-\frac{1}{\xi^2}\frac{J_\phi^{\,2}}{4\pi^2}-meE\xi^4\\ f_2(\eta)&=2mW\eta^2+2\alpha_2-\frac{1}{\eta^2}\frac{J_\phi^{\,2}}{4\pi^2}+meE\eta^4 \end{aligned}$$

and

(7) $$\alpha_1+\alpha_2=2me^2Z.$$

The action integrals J_ξ and J_η are consequently:

$$(8)\qquad \begin{aligned} J_\xi &= \oint p_\xi d\xi = \oint \sqrt{-A + 2\frac{B_1}{\xi^2} - \frac{C}{\xi^4} + D_1\xi^2} \,.\, \xi d\xi \\ J_\eta &= \oint p_\eta d\eta = \oint \sqrt{-A + 2\frac{B_2}{\eta^2} - \frac{C}{\eta^4} + D_2\eta^2} \,.\, \eta d\eta, \end{aligned}$$

where

$$\begin{aligned} &A = 2m(-W), \\ &B_1 = \alpha_1, \qquad B_2 = \alpha_2, \\ &C = \frac{J_\phi^{\ 2}}{4\pi^2}, \\ &D_1 = -meE, \qquad D_2 = meE. \end{aligned}$$

In order that the integrals (8) shall remain real also for zero external field, α_1 and α_2 must be positive. If the field strength is small, the terms involving D_1 and D_2 are small in comparison with the remaining ones and the integrals may be evaluated approximately by complex integration. We find (*cf.* (11), in Appendix II), if we take the roots in (8) so that the integrals are positive:

$$(9)\qquad \begin{aligned} J_\xi &= \frac{1}{2}\left[-J_\phi + \frac{2\pi\alpha_1}{\sqrt{-2mW}} + \frac{\pi meE}{2\sqrt{(-2mW)^3}}\left(\frac{J_\phi^{\ 2}}{4\pi^2} + \frac{3\alpha_1^{\ 2}}{2mW}\right)\right] \\ J_\eta &= \frac{1}{2}\left[-J_\phi + \frac{2\pi\alpha_2}{\sqrt{-2mW}} - \frac{\pi meE}{2\sqrt{(-2mW)^3}}\left(\frac{J_\phi^{\ 2}}{4\pi^2} + \frac{3\alpha_2^{\ 2}}{2mW}\right)\right]. \end{aligned}$$

α_1 and α_2 are to be eliminated from the three equations (7) and (9) and W evaluated. To a first approximation the term proportional to E in (9) can be omitted and, afterwards, the values of α_1 and α_2, calculated to this first approximation, can be substituted in this correction term. In this way one finds

$$\begin{aligned} \frac{\alpha_1}{\sqrt{-2mW}} &= \frac{2J_\xi + J_\phi}{2\pi} + \frac{meE}{8\pi^2\sqrt{(-2mW)^3}}(6J_\xi^{\ 2} + 6J_\xi J_\phi + J_\phi^{\ 2}), \\ \frac{\alpha_2}{\sqrt{-2mW}} &= \frac{2J_\eta + J_\phi}{2\pi} - \frac{meE}{8\pi^2\sqrt{(-2mW)^3}}(6J_\eta^{\ 2} + 6J_\eta J_\phi + J_\phi^{\ 2}), \end{aligned}$$

and then, using (7),

$$2me^2Z = \frac{1}{\pi}(J_\xi + J_\eta + J_\phi)\sqrt{-2mW} + \frac{3eE}{8\pi^2 W}(J_\xi + J_\eta + J_\phi)(J_\eta - J_\xi).$$

This gives to a first approximation (omitting the term proportional to E) the energy of the motion in the absence of a field

$$(10)\qquad W = -\frac{2\pi^2 me^4 Z^2}{(J_\xi + J_\eta + J_\phi)^2},$$

and, if we substitute this value of W in the correction term, to a second approximation:

$$(11)\qquad W=-\frac{2\pi^2me^4Z^2}{(J_\xi+J_\eta+J_\phi)^2}-\frac{3E}{8\pi^2meZ}(J_\xi+J_\eta+J_\phi)(J_\eta-J_\xi).$$

To our approximation, then, the energy depends only on two linear combinations of the action variables, *i.e.* we have to do with a case of single degeneration. This would no longer be the case if we calculated higher terms in E in the expression for the energy. In accordance with our general considerations (§ 15) we now introduce, in place of J_ξ, J_η, J_ϕ, new action variables, derived from these by an integral transformation with the determinant ±1, and so chosen that the energy (11) depends on only two of the new action variables, and the energy (10) of the unperturbed motion (corresponding to the double degeneration) on only one of the action variables.

We write therefore

$$(12)\qquad \begin{aligned} J_\xi+J_\eta+J_\phi&=J\\ J_\eta-J_\xi&=J_e\\ J_\phi&=J' \end{aligned}$$

and obtain

$$(13)\qquad W=-\frac{2\pi^2me^4Z^2}{J^2}-\frac{3E}{8\pi^2meZ}JJ_e.$$

The motion has two frequencies:

$$(14)\qquad \nu=\nu_0+\nu_e\frac{J_e}{J}$$

and

$$\nu_e=-\frac{3E}{8\pi^2meZ}J.$$

We have two quantum conditions:

$$(15)\qquad \begin{aligned} J&=nh\\ J_e&=n_eh. \end{aligned}$$

If we introduce them into the expression (13) for the energy, we have

$$(16)\qquad W=-\frac{cRhZ^2}{n^2}-\frac{3Eh^2}{8\pi^2meZ}\cdot nn_e,$$

where R is again the Rydberg constant (see (2), § 23). A more accurate calculation gives higher terms which depend also on a third quantum number n'.

J_ϕ has the same meaning as the correspondingly denoted magnitude of the Kepler ellipse in the absence of a field; it can assume values between 0 and J only. The sum of the positive quantities

J_ξ and J_η lies by (12) similarly between 0 and J and their difference J_e between $-J$ and $+J$. The quantum number n_e can therefore have only the values $-n$, $-(n-1)\ldots+n$. As will be seen from a study of the orbits, the values $\pm n$ are also to be excluded.

The parabolic co-ordinates ξ and η execute librations between the zero points of $f_1(\xi)$ and $f_2(\eta)$ in (6). We will consider the character of the motion first for the case in which J_ϕ, and consequently C, does not vanish. Here the region in which $f_1(\xi)$ and $f_2(\eta)$ are positive does not extend to the positions $\xi=0$ and $\eta=0$; the zero points $\xi_{\min}$ and $\eta_{\min}$ are different from 0. The third co-ordinate in this case performs a rotation. The path is confined to the interior of a ring having the direction of the field as axis of symmetry and the

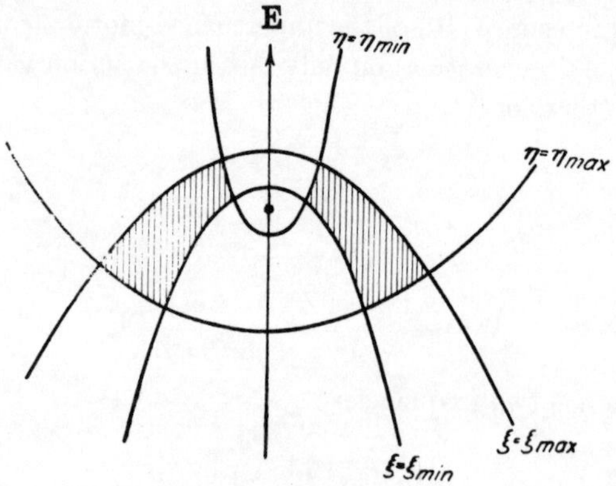

FIG. 22.

cross-section bounded by the parabolas $\xi=\xi_{\max}$, $\xi=\xi_{\max}$, $\eta=\eta_{\min}$, and $\eta=\eta_{\max}$ (*cf.* fig. 22). In particular, if $J_\xi=J_\eta=0$, $\xi_{\min}$ and $\xi_{\max}$ and likewise $\eta_{\min}$ and $\eta_{\max}$ coincide and the path is a circle. Since $\xi_{\min} \neq \eta_{\min}$ its plane does not pass through the nucleus; it is displaced in the opposite direction to that of the external field **E**, as will be seen by a consideration of the equilibrium between the positive nucleus and the orbit of the electron in the field, or by calculating the double roots. If $J_\xi=0$ and $J_\eta>0$, the orbit lies on the paraboloid $\xi=\xi_{\min}$ $=\xi_{\max}$, between the circles of intersection with the paraboloids $\eta=\eta_{\min}$ and $\eta=\eta_{\max}$. Finally, in the general case, for $J_\xi>0$ and $J_\eta>0$, it lies in a three-dimensional ring. If we disregard the motion of ϕ, the (ξ, η) co-ordinates in general fill completely the curvilinear quadrilateral contained between the parabolas for the extreme values of ξ and η, since the frequencies associated with J_ξ and J_η are different and their ratio is rational only for certain values of E.

Proceeding to the case $J_\phi=0$, ϕ remains constant, the motion takes place in a meridional plane parallel to the direction of the field. The region in which $f_1(\xi)$ and $f_2(\eta)$ are positive comprises the values $\xi=0$ and $\eta=0$, since in this case $f_1(\xi)$ and $f_2(\eta)$ remain positive there (*cf.* (6)), *i.e.* the path completely fills the two-dimensional region bounded by $\xi=\xi_{max}$ and $\eta=\eta_{max}$. The orbit approaches therefore indefinitely close to the nucleus.

The case in which the electron approaches infinitely close to the nucleus is to be excluded on principle, just as in the case of central motions (§ 21). This excludes at the same time the case $n_e=\pm n$, since in this case J_ξ or J_η would be equal to $nh=J$ and $J_\phi=0$.

The stationary state represented by the quantum number n in the absence of a field splits up, on application of the field, into $2n-1$ states of different energy with the quantum numbers

$$n_e=-(n-1), \qquad -(n-2)\ .\ .\ .\ +(n-1).$$

We now consider the radiation from such an atom. The radiated frequencies and the possible changes of n and n_e depend on the terms of the Fourier expansion of the electric moment or of the co-ordinates of the electron. To the action variables J_ξ, J_η, J_ϕ correspond angle variables w_ξ, w_η, w_ϕ. With the help of these the Fourier expansion of the co-ordinates may be written in the form

$$\sum_\tau C_\tau e^{2\pi i(\tau_\xi w_\xi+\tau_\eta w_\eta+\tau_\phi w_\phi)}.$$

Since w_ϕ and ϕ are proportional to one another and ϕ performs a uniform rotation about the direction of the field, the values of τ_ϕ for the components of the electric moment perpendicular to the field are ± 1 only, and for the component in the direction of the field the value is 0. The co-efficients τ_ξ and τ_η, on the other hand, do not appear to be restricted (see § 36).

Passing over now to the angle variables which correspond to the action variables J, J_e, J', we have to write (by § 7):

$$w_\xi=w-w_e$$
$$w_\eta=w+w_e$$
$$w_\phi=w+w',$$

and since only J and J_e appear in the energy (see (13)), w' is constant. The Fourier series becomes

$$\sum_\tau D_\tau e^{2\pi i(\tau w+\tau_e w_e)},$$

where

$$\tau=\tau_\xi+\tau_\eta+\tau_\phi, \qquad \tau_e=\tau_\eta-\tau_\xi.$$

w is the angle variable for the motion in the absence of a field and corresponds to the revolution of the electron in the elliptic orbit,

τ may therefore be any integer ; τ_e is also unrestricted, since τ_ξ and τ_η are so. This means that n and n_e can change by any amount consistent with their values, and that frequencies corresponding to all these transitions will be radiated.

The polarisation is derived as follows : If $\tau+\tau_e$, which is equal to $2\tau_\eta+\tau_\phi$, is an even number, τ_ϕ can only be zero. Such a Fourier term represents consequently a motion in the direction of the field ; a light-wave polarised parallel to the field corresponds then to a transition for which $\Delta n+\Delta n_e$ is even. If $\Delta n+\Delta n_e$ is odd, $\tau_\phi=\pm 1$; the wave corresponding to such a transition is polarised perpendicularly to the field.

We illustrate the above remarks by considering the resolution of the Balmer lines H_α, H_β . . . of hydrogen. The terms which combine to give these lines are split up in the following way (the numbers give the energy change as a multiple of $\left.\frac{3Eh^2}{8\pi^2 meZ}\right)$:

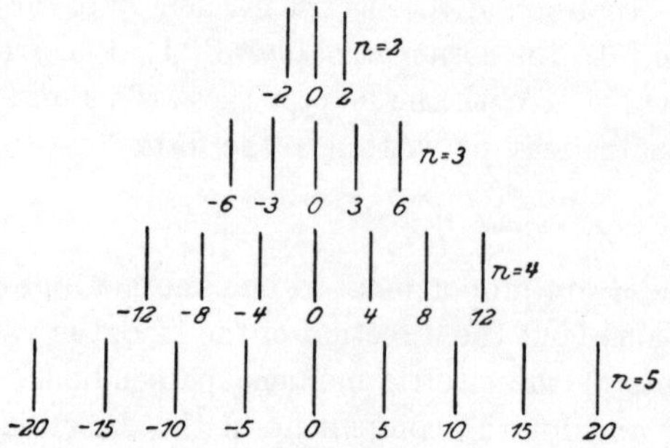

FIG. 23.

We obtain from this for the line $H_\alpha (n=3 \rightarrow n=2)$ the lines :

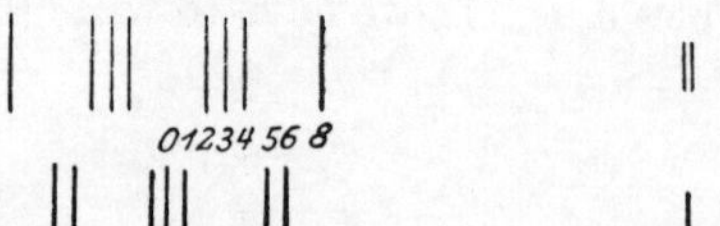

FIG. 24.

For H_β :

FIG. 25.

For H_γ:

FIG. 26.

The calculation of the Stark effect by parabolic co-ordinates allows us to illustrate by an example some previous considerations regarding the restriction of the quantum conditions to non-degenerate action variables.

For $|\mathbf{E}|=0$ the motion of the Stark effect passes over into the simple Kepler motion. This is separable in polar co-ordinates as well as in parabolic co-ordinates. From the separation in polar co-ordinates (§ 22) we obtain the action variables J_r, J_θ, J_ϕ, and the quantum condition

$$J_r+J_\theta+J_\phi=nh.$$

$J_\theta+J_\phi$ is now 2π times the total angular momentum, and J_ϕ is 2π times its component in the direction of the polar axis. The motion remains separable in these co-ordinates if the field is no longer a Coulomb field, but is still spherically symmetrical; in the latter case, however, a second quantum condition,

$$J_\theta+J_\phi=kh,$$

is to be added. To make J_ϕ an integral multiple of h would have no significance, since the direction of the polar axis of the co-ordinate system is altogether arbitrary and the integral value of J_ϕ/h would be destroyed by a rotation of the co-ordinate system. The restriction $J_\theta+J_\phi=kh$, on the other hand, would lead to no impossibility in the case of the simple Kepler motion.

If now we calculate the Kepler motion in parabolic co-ordinates, we have only to put $E=0$ in the above calculations. We obtain the action variables J_ξ, J_η, and J_ϕ (the last has the same significance as in polar co-ordinates) and the quantum condition

$$J_\xi+J_\eta+J_\phi=nh.$$

The second quantum condition

$$J_\xi-J_\eta=n_e h,$$

which we had in the electric field, must now be dropped, since this combination of the J's no longer appears in the energy. It has a meaning only if an electric field is present (though this need only be a weak one).

The stationary motions in a weak electric field are, however, essentially different from those in a spherically symmetrical field differing only slightly from a Coulomb field. In the latter (for which the separation variables are polar co-ordinates) the path is plane ; it is an ellipse with a slow rotation of the perihelion. In the former (separable in parabolic co-ordinates) it is likewise approximately an ellipse, but this ellipse performs a complicated motion in space. If then, in the limiting case of a pure Coulomb field, k or n_e be introduced as second quantum number, altogether different motions would be obtained in the two cases. The degenerate action variable has therefore no significance for the quantisation.

Our considerations lead to yet another result ; the calculation of the Stark effect and the quantising of J_e can have a meaning only if the influence of the relativity theory, or of a departure of the atomic field of force from a Coulomb field, is small in comparison with that of the electric field. Further, our former calculation of the relativistic fine structure is valid only if the influence of the electric fields, which are always present, is small compared with the relativity perturbation.[1]

§ 36.—The Intensity of the Lines in the Stark Effect of Hydrogen [2]

The correspondence principle, which, by its nature, allows of only approximate calculations of intensities, leads to relatively accurate results when we are concerned with ratios of intensities of the lines within a fine structure, *e.g.* in the Stark effect.

Following Kramers,[3] we shall deduce in the following the Fourier expansion for the orbit of an electron which moves round the nucleus under the action of an external field **E** and compare the classical intensity ratios with those observed. In the Fourier coefficients we shall omit all terms proportional to E, E^2, etc., since they lead only to unimportant corrections.

From § 35 we obtain for the principal function S :

$$S=\int\sqrt{f_1(\xi)}d\xi+\int\sqrt{f_2(\eta)}d\eta+\frac{1}{2\pi}\int J_\phi d\phi.$$

[1] Kramers has succeeded in dealing with the simultaneous action of the relativity variation of mass and a homogeneous field for the case in which the corresponding changes in the energy are of the same order of magnitude (H. A. Kramers, *Zeitschr. f. Physik*, vol. iii, p. 199, 1920).

[2] In this section we have given the calculations more shortly than previously in this book.

[3] H. A. Kramers, *Intensities of Spectral Lines*, Copenhagen, 1919.

If the values of α_1 and α_2 be taken from (9), § 35, and the value of W from (10), § 35, both of them for E=0, we find :

$$\begin{aligned}2\pi S=&\int \xi d\xi\sqrt{-\frac{J_\phi{}^2}{\xi^4}+2\frac{2J_\xi+J_\phi}{\kappa J\xi^2}-\frac{1}{\kappa^2J^2}}\\ &+\int \eta d\eta\sqrt{-\frac{J_\phi{}^2}{\eta^4}+2\frac{2J_\eta+J_\phi}{\kappa J\eta^2}-\frac{1}{\kappa^2J^2}}\\ &+J_\phi\,.\,\phi,\end{aligned} \tag{1}$$

where for shortness we write :

$$\kappa=\frac{1}{4\pi^2Ze^2m},\qquad J=J_\xi+J_\eta+J_\phi. \tag{2}$$

For the angle variables w_ξ, w_η, w_ϕ conjugate to J_ξ, J_η, J_ϕ we find from (1) the equations :

$$\begin{aligned}2\pi w_\xi&=2\pi\frac{\partial S}{\partial J_\xi}\\ &=\frac{1}{\kappa J^2}\int\frac{d\xi}{\xi}\,\frac{\kappa J(2J_\eta+J_\phi)\xi^2+\xi^4}{\sqrt{-\kappa^2J_\phi{}^2J^2+2\kappa(2J_\xi+J_\phi)J\xi^2-\xi^4}}\\ &\quad+\frac{1}{\kappa J^2}\int\frac{d\eta}{\eta}\,\frac{-\kappa J(2J_\eta+J_\phi)\eta^2+\eta^4}{\sqrt{-\kappa^2J_\phi{}^2J^2+2\kappa(2J_\eta+J_\phi)J\eta^2-\eta^4}}\\ 2\pi w_\eta&=2\pi\frac{\partial S}{\partial J_\eta}\\ &=\frac{1}{\kappa J^2}\int\frac{d\xi}{\xi}\,\frac{-\kappa J(2J_\xi+J_\phi)\xi^2+\xi^4}{\sqrt{-\kappa^2J_\phi{}^2J^2+2\kappa(2J_\xi+J_\phi)J\xi^2-\xi^4}}\\ &\quad+\frac{1}{\kappa J^2}\int\frac{d\eta}{\eta}\,\frac{\kappa J(2J_\xi+J_\phi)\eta^2+\eta^4}{\sqrt{-\kappa^2J_\phi{}^2J^2+2\kappa(2J_\eta+J_\phi)J\eta^2-\eta^4}}\\ 2\pi w_\phi&=2\pi\frac{\partial S}{\partial J_\phi}\\ &=\frac{1}{\kappa J^2}\int\frac{d\xi}{\xi}\,\frac{-\kappa^2J_\phi J^3-\kappa J(J_\xi-J_\eta)\xi^2+\xi^4}{\sqrt{-\kappa^2J_\phi{}^2J^2+2\kappa(2J_\xi+J_\phi)J\xi^2-\xi^4}}\\ &\quad+\frac{1}{\kappa J^2}\int\frac{d\eta}{\eta}\,\frac{-\kappa^2J_\phi J^3-\kappa J(J_\eta-J_\xi)\eta^2+\eta^4}{\sqrt{-\kappa^2J_\phi{}^2J^2+2\kappa(2J_\eta+J_\phi)J\eta^2-\eta^4}}\\ &\quad+\phi.\end{aligned} \tag{3}$$

Since the calculation of the w's as functions of ξ and η from the above formulæ would obviously be very laborious, it is advisable to write the squares of the variables, ξ^2 and η^2, which oscillate between two fixed limits (*cf*. § 35), in the form

$$\xi^2=a_1+b_1\cos\psi, \qquad \eta^2=a_2+b_2\cos\chi, \tag{4}$$

just as before (§ 22) we found it convenient to introduce the mean and eccentric anomalies. In order that the new variables ψ and χ may increase by 2π during one libration of ξ or η, we must put :

$$\begin{aligned} a_1&=\kappa J(2J_\xi+J_\phi)\,; & b_1&=2\kappa J\sqrt{J_\xi(J_\xi+J_\phi)} \\ a_2&=\kappa J(2J_\eta+J_\phi)\,; & b_2&=2\kappa J\sqrt{J_\eta(J_\eta+J_\phi)}. \end{aligned} \tag{5}$$

This gives :

$$d\psi=\frac{2\xi d\xi}{\sqrt{-\kappa^2J_\phi{}^2J^2+2\kappa(2J_\xi+J_\phi)J\xi^2-\xi^4}}$$

$$d\chi=\frac{2\eta d\eta}{\sqrt{-\kappa^2J_\phi{}^2J^2+2\kappa(2J_\eta+J_\phi)J_\eta{}^2-\eta^4}}$$

and for w_ξ, w_η, w_ϕ we find :

$$\begin{aligned} 2\pi w_\xi&=\frac{1}{2\kappa J^2}(b_1\sin\psi+b_2\sin\chi)+\psi+\pi \\ 2\pi w_\eta&=\frac{1}{2\kappa J^2}(b_1\sin\psi+b_2\sin\chi)+\chi+\pi \\ 2\pi w_\phi&=\frac{1}{2\kappa J^2}(b_1\sin\psi+b_2\sin\chi)+\frac{\psi+\chi}{2} \\ &\quad-\frac{\kappa J_\phi J}{2}\left(\int_0^\psi\frac{d\psi}{a_1+b_1\cos\psi}+\int_0^\chi\frac{d\chi}{a_2+b_2\cos\chi}\right)+\phi+\pi. \end{aligned} \tag{6}$$

In these expressions we have chosen the still arbitrary constants of integration in such a way that the final result takes the simplest possible form.

Introducing the abbreviations

$$\frac{b_1}{2\kappa J^2}=\frac{1}{J}\sqrt{J_\xi(J_\xi+J_\phi)}=\sigma_1\,; \qquad \frac{b_2}{2\kappa J^2}=\frac{1}{J}\sqrt{J_\eta(J_\eta+J_\phi)}=\sigma_2$$

we get

$$\begin{aligned} 2\pi w_\xi&=\sigma_1\sin\psi+\sigma_2\sin\chi+\psi+\pi \\ 2\pi w_\eta&=\sigma_1\sin\psi+\sigma_2\sin\chi+\chi+\pi. \end{aligned} \tag{7}$$

The similarity between these equations and (15), § 22, shows clearly the analogy between ψ, χ, and the eccentric anomaly.

We can now write down without difficulty the Fourier series for the co-ordinates z and $x+iy$. By (2), § 35, $z=\frac{1}{2}(\xi^2-\eta^2)$. Since z does not depend on ϕ, it is also independent of w_ϕ ; we write therefore :

$$z=\tfrac{1}{2}(\xi^2-\eta^2)=\sum A_{\tau_\xi\tau_\eta}e^{2\pi i(\tau_\xi w_\xi+\tau_\eta w_\eta)}, \tag{8}$$

where

$$(9)\qquad A_{\tau_\xi\tau_\eta}=\int_0^1\int_0^1 \frac{\xi^2-\eta^2}{2} e^{-2\pi i(\tau_\xi w_\xi+\tau_\eta w_\eta)}dw_\xi dw_\eta.$$

Now by (7):

$$(10)\qquad dw_\xi dw_\eta=\frac{\partial(w_\xi, w_\eta)}{\partial(\psi, \chi)}d\psi d\chi$$
$$=\frac{1}{4\pi^2}(1+\sigma_1\cos\psi+\sigma_2\cos\chi)d\psi d\chi.$$

Again since, by (4) and (5),

$$z=\frac{a_1-a_2}{2}+\frac{b_1\cos\psi-b_2\cos\chi}{2}$$
$$=\kappa J(J_\xi-J_\eta)+\kappa J^2(\sigma_1\cos\psi-\sigma_2\cos\chi),$$

we have:

$$(11)\quad A_{00}=\frac{1}{4\pi^2}\int_0^{2\pi}\int_0^{2\pi} d\psi d\chi\,.\,[\kappa J(J_\xi-J_\eta)+\kappa J^2(\sigma_1\cos\psi-\sigma_2\cos\chi)]$$
$$.\,(1+\sigma_1\cos\psi+\sigma_2\cos\chi)=\tfrac{3}{2}\kappa J(J_\xi-J_\eta).$$

For the remaining values $A_{\tau_\xi\tau_\eta}$, for which not both the τ's are zero, the constant term $\kappa J(J_\xi-J_\eta)$ in z can be omitted at once, since by (9) it will disappear on averaging. In this way we find $(\tau_\xi+\tau_\eta=\tau)$

$$(12)\quad A_{\tau_\xi\tau_\eta}=\frac{\kappa J^2(-1)^\tau}{4\pi^2}\int_0^{2\pi}\int_0^{2\pi} d\psi d\chi(\sigma_1\cos\psi-\sigma_2\cos\chi)$$
$$.\,(1+\sigma_1\cos\psi+\sigma_2\cos\chi)e^{-i\tau_\xi\psi-i\tau\sigma_1\sin\psi-i\tau_\eta\chi-i\tau\sigma_2\sin\chi}.$$

If in this equation $\cos\psi$ and $\cos\chi$ be replaced by $\frac{1}{2}(e^{i\psi}+e^{-i\psi})$ and $\frac{1}{2}(e^{i\chi}+e^{-i\chi})$ respectively, it will be seen that the integral on the right may be split up into a sum of products, each factor of which is of the form

$$\mathfrak{J}_n(\rho)=\frac{1}{2\pi}\int_0^{2\pi} d\psi\,.\,e^{-in\psi+i\rho\sin\psi};$$

this is the well-known expression for the Bessel function[1] $\mathfrak{J}_n(\rho)$. Using the relations[2]

$$\frac{1}{2}[\mathfrak{J}_{n-1}(\rho)-\mathfrak{J}_{n+1}(\rho)]=\frac{d}{d\rho}\mathfrak{J}_n(\rho)=\mathfrak{J}'_n(\rho)$$

and

$$\mathfrak{J}_{n-1}(\rho)+\mathfrak{J}_{n+1}(\rho)=\frac{2n}{\rho}\mathfrak{J}_n(\rho),$$

[1] E. Jahnke and F. Emde, *Funktionentafeln* (Leipzig, 1909), p. 169; or see, for example, G. N. Watson, *Theory of Bessel Functions* (Cambridge, 1923), p. 20. The Bessel functions are here indicated by Gothic letters to avoid confusion with the action integrals.

[2] Jahnke-Emde, *op. cit.*, p. 165, or Watson, *op. cit.*, p. 17.

we find in this way from (12):

$$(13)\qquad A_{\tau_\xi\tau_\eta}=\frac{\kappa J^2}{\tau}\{\sigma_2\mathfrak{J}_{\tau_\xi}(\tau\sigma_1)\mathfrak{J}'_{\tau_\eta}(\tau\sigma_2)-\sigma_1\mathfrak{J}'_{\tau_\xi}(\tau\sigma_1)\mathfrak{J}_{\tau_\eta}(\tau\sigma_2)\}.$$

Finally we get for z:

$$(14)\quad z=\frac{3}{2}\kappa J(J_\xi-J_\eta)+\kappa J^2\sum_{-\infty}^{+\infty}{}'\frac{1}{\tau}\{\sigma_2\mathfrak{J}_{\tau_\xi}(\tau\sigma_1)\mathfrak{J}'_{\tau_\eta}(\tau\sigma_2)$$
$$-\sigma_1\mathfrak{J}'_{\tau_\xi}(\tau\sigma_1)\mathfrak{J}_{\tau_\eta}(\tau\sigma_2)\}\,.\,e^{2\pi i(\tau_\xi w_\xi+\tau_\eta w_\eta)}.$$

(The dash on the summation sign signifies that $\tau_\xi=\tau_\eta=0$ is to be excluded from the summation.) For $\tau=0$ the expression (13) is indeterminate. It follows, however, directly from (12), that the corresponding $A_{\tau_\xi\tau_\eta}(\tau_\xi+\tau_\eta=0,\ \tau_\xi\neq 0)$ vanish.

In order to calculate the Fourier expansion for $x+iy$ we take from (2), § 35:

$$(15)\qquad x+iy=\xi\eta e^{i\phi}.$$

We can conclude at once from (15) and (3) or (6), that $(x+iy)\,.\,e^{-2\pi i w_\phi}$ depends only on w_ξ and w_η. The most convenient method of procedure is to expand $(x+iy)e^{2\pi i(w_\eta-w_\phi)}$ in a Fourier series:

$$(16)\qquad (x+iy)e^{2\pi i(w_\eta-w_\phi)}=\sum B_{\tau_\xi\tau_\eta}e^{2\pi i[\tau_\xi w_\xi+(\tau_\eta+1)w_\eta]}.$$

In order to write the left side of (16) as a function of ψ and χ we deduce from (6)

$$2\pi(w_\eta-w_\phi)=-\frac{\psi}{2}+\frac{\chi}{2}-\phi+\frac{\kappa J_\phi J}{2}\left(\int_0^\psi\frac{d\psi}{a_1+b_1\cos\psi}+\int_0^\chi\frac{d\chi}{a_2+b_2\cos\chi}\right).$$

On putting

$$c=\sqrt{a_1^2-b_1^2}=\sqrt{a_2^2-b_2^2}=\kappa J_\phi J$$

we have:

$$(17)\qquad \begin{aligned} c\int_0^\psi\frac{d\psi}{a_1+b_1\cos\psi}&=-i\log\frac{\left\{(a_1+b_1)\cos\frac{\psi}{2}+ic\sin\frac{\psi}{2}\right\}^2}{(a_1+b_1)(a_1+b_1\cos\psi)}\\ c\int_0^\chi\frac{d\chi}{a_2+b_2\cos\chi}&=-i\log\frac{\left\{(a_2+b_2)\cos\frac{\chi}{2}+ic\sin\frac{\chi}{2}\right\}^2}{(a_2+b_2)(a_2+b_2\cos\chi)},\end{aligned}$$

and consequently, substituting for $(x+iy)$ from (15) and (4),

$$(18)\quad (x+iy)e^{2\pi i(w_\eta-w_\phi)}$$
$$=e^{i\left(-\frac{\psi}{2}+\frac{\chi}{2}\right)}\frac{\left\{(a_1+b_1)\cos\frac{\psi}{2}+ic\sin\frac{\psi}{2}\right\}\left\{(a_2+b_2)\cos\frac{\chi}{2}+ic\sin\frac{\chi}{2}\right\}}{\sqrt{(a_1+b_1)(a_2+b_2)}}.$$

From this we can deduce at once the $B_{\tau_\xi \tau_\eta}$ (we now write:

$$1+\tau_\xi+\tau_\eta=\tau):$$

$$\text{(19)}\quad B_{\tau_\xi \tau_\eta}=(-1)^\tau \frac{\sqrt{(a_1+b_1)(a_2+b_2)}}{4\pi^2}\int_0^{2\pi}\int_0^{2\pi}(1+\sigma_1\cos\psi+\sigma_2\cos\chi)$$

$$\cdot\left(\cos\frac{\psi}{2}+i\frac{c}{a_1+b_1}\sin\frac{\psi}{2}\right)\left(\cos\frac{\chi}{2}+i\frac{c}{a_2+b_2}\sin\frac{\chi}{2}\right)$$

$$\cdot\, e^{-i(\tau_\xi+\frac{1}{2})\psi-i\tau\sigma_1\sin\psi-i(\tau_\eta+\frac{1}{2})\chi-i\tau\sigma_2\sin\chi}d\psi d\chi.$$

We can express the quantities $\cos\psi$, $\cos\chi$, $\cos\frac{\psi}{2}$, etc., in terms of exponential functions exactly as in equation (12) and so represent $B_{\tau_\xi \tau_\eta}$ as a sum of products of Bessel functions. We obtain finally, in the same way as in the case of the magnitudes $A_{\tau_\xi \tau_\eta}$ $(\tau=1+\tau_\xi+\tau_\eta)$,

$$\text{(20)}\quad B_{\tau_\xi \tau_\eta}=-\frac{\kappa J^2}{\tau}\left\{\frac{1}{J}\sqrt{(J_\xi+J_\phi)(J_\eta+J_\phi)}\mathfrak{J}_{\tau_\xi}(\tau\sigma_1)\mathfrak{J}_{\tau_\eta}(\tau\sigma_2)\right.$$

$$\left.-\frac{1}{J}\sqrt{J_\xi J_\eta}\mathfrak{J}_{\tau_\xi+1}(\tau\sigma_1)\mathfrak{J}_{\tau_\eta+1}(\tau\sigma_2)\right\}.$$

For $\tau=0$ we can calculate $B_{\tau_\xi \tau_\eta}$ directly from (19). It is found that $B_{\tau_\xi \tau_\eta}=0$ for $\tau=0$, with the exception of the values

$$\text{(21)}\quad B_{-1,0}=\tfrac{3}{2}\kappa J\sqrt{J_\xi(J_\eta+J_\phi)};\qquad B_{0,-1}=\tfrac{3}{2}\kappa J\sqrt{J_\eta(J_\xi+J_\phi)}.$$

Finally, as the Fourier series for $x+iy$, we find

$$\text{(22)}\quad x+iy=\frac{3}{2}\kappa J^2\left(\frac{1}{J}\sqrt{J_\xi(J_\eta+J_\phi)}e^{2\pi i(-w_\xi+w_\phi)}\right.$$

$$\left.+\frac{1}{J}\sqrt{J_\eta(J_\xi+J_\phi)}e^{2\pi i(-w_\eta+w_\phi)}\right)$$

$$-\kappa J^2\sum_{-\infty}^{+\infty}{}'\frac{1}{\tau}\left\{\frac{1}{J}\sqrt{(J_\xi+J_\phi)(J_\eta+J_\phi)}\mathfrak{J}_{\tau_\xi}(\tau\sigma_1)\mathfrak{J}_{\tau_\eta}(\tau\sigma_2)\right.$$

$$\left.-\frac{1}{J}\sqrt{J_\xi J_\eta}\mathfrak{J}_{\tau_\xi+1}(\tau\sigma_1)\mathfrak{J}_{\tau_\eta+1}(\tau\sigma_2)\right\}e^{2\pi i(\tau_\xi w_\xi+\tau_\eta w_\eta+w_\phi)}.$$

Now that we have calculated the Fourier coefficients we can proceed to an approximate estimation of the intensities on the basis of the correspondence principle. We assume that the simple degeneration of the variables J_ξ, J_η, J_ϕ, which still existed in (11), § 35, has now been removed, either by including in the energy terms quadratic in E, or by taking account of relativity.

In accordance with the fundamental principles of the quantum theory we must then write

$$J_\xi = n_\xi h; \qquad J_\eta = n_\eta h; \qquad J_\phi = n_\phi h.$$

According to the correspondence principle we find the approximate intensity of a line corresponding to a transition in which n_ξ changes by Δn_ξ, n_η by Δn_η, and n_ϕ by Δn_ϕ, if we examine the intensity of the harmonic $\tau_\xi = \Delta n_\xi$, $\tau_\eta = \Delta n_\eta$, $\tau_\phi = \Delta n_\phi$ in the classical spectrum represented by (14) or (22). This leaves open the question whether the classical spectrum shall be taken to correspond with the initial orbit, the final orbit, or an intermediate one. In the following we shall investigate only the relative intensities within a fine structure. Consequently we shall introduce the magnitudes $\frac{A_{\tau_\xi \tau_\eta}}{\kappa J^2}$, $\frac{B_{\tau_\xi \tau_\eta}}{\kappa J^2}$ as " relative amplitudes " R, and then compare the simple arithmetic mean of the relative intensities R^2 corresponding to the initial and final orbits with the observed relative intensities. One result of introducing the " relative amplitudes " is that in forming the average the initial and final orbits have the same weight attached to them as regards the intensity relations. It may be conjectured that this latter assumption involves a fundamental aspect of the quantum calculation of the intensities; in the case of the Zeeman effect, for example, it implies that the relative intensities in the Zeeman fine structures shall be independent of the principal quantum number, a result that must certainly be expected to hold from analogy with the classical theory and which has always been verified empirically.

From (13) and (20) we find for the z components of the relative amplitudes ($\tau_\phi = 0$, $\tau_\xi + \tau_\eta = \tau$):

$$(23) \quad R_{\tau_\xi \tau_\eta 0} = \frac{1}{\tau}\left\{\frac{1}{n}\sqrt{n_\eta(n_\eta + n_\phi)}\,\mathfrak{J}_{\tau_\xi}(\tau\sigma_1)\mathfrak{J}'_{\tau_\eta}(\tau\sigma_2) - \frac{1}{n}\sqrt{n_\xi(n_\xi + n_\phi)}\,\mathfrak{J}'_{\tau_\xi}(\tau\sigma_1)\mathfrak{J}_{\tau_\eta}(\tau\sigma_2)\right\},$$

for the $(x+iy)$-components ($\tau_\phi = 1$, $\tau_\xi + \tau_\eta + 1 = \tau$):

$$(24) \quad R_{\tau_\xi \tau_\eta 1} = \frac{1}{\tau}\left\{\frac{1}{n}\sqrt{(n_\xi + n_\phi)(n_\eta + n_\phi)}\,\mathfrak{J}_{\tau_\xi}(\tau\sigma_1)\mathfrak{J}_{\tau_\eta}(\tau\sigma_2) - \frac{1}{n}\sqrt{n_\xi n_\eta}\,\mathfrak{J}_{\tau_\xi + 1}(\tau\sigma_1)\mathfrak{J}_{\tau_\eta + 1}(\tau\sigma_2)\right\},$$

where

$$\sigma_1 = \frac{1}{n}\sqrt{n_\xi(n_\xi + n_\phi)}, \qquad \sigma_2 = \frac{1}{n}\sqrt{n_\eta(n_\eta + n_\phi)}, \qquad n = n_\xi + n_\eta + n_\phi.$$

The amplitudes of the z-components correspond to the lines polarised parallel to the field; those of the $(x+iy)$-components to the lines polarised perpendicular to the field.

H_α 6562·8 Å

	Transition	Δ	τ_ξ	τ_η	τ_ϕ	R_a^2	R_e^2	Obser. Intens.	Const. × $(R_a^2+R_e^2)$
∥	111 → 011	2	1	0	0	0·21	0	1·0	0·35
	102 → 002	3	1	0	0	0·26	0	1·1	0·43
	201 → 101	4	1	0	0	0·38	0·33	1·2	1·16
	201 → 011	8	2	−1	0	0	0	..	..
⊥	003 → 002	0	0	0	1	1·00	1·00	2·6	3·4
	111 → 002	0	1	1	−1	0·07	0		
	102 → 101	1	0	0	1	0·56	0·39	1·0	1·56
	102 → 011	5	1	−1	1	0	0	..	..
	201 → 002	6	2	0	−1	0·00	0	..	..

The table gives a comparison between theory and observation for $H_\alpha(n=3\rightarrow n=2)$ 6562·8 Å. The transitions, characterised by the quantum numbers in the initial and final states $(n_\xi^a, n_\eta^a, n_\phi^a \rightarrow n_\xi^e, n_\eta^e, n_\phi^e)$ are given in the first column. The second column gives the displacement Δ of the corresponding lines from their positions for $E=0$ in multiples of the smallest displacement $\frac{3Eh}{8\pi^2 cmeZ}$ (in wave numbers), as calculated by (11), § 35. The third column contains the values of τ_ξ, τ_η, τ_ϕ corresponding to these transitions; in the fourth and fifth columns the quantities R_a^2 and R_e^2, for the initial and final orbits respectively, are given as a measure of the relative intensities. The sixth column contains the intensities observed by Stark. The seventh gives the values of $(R_a^2+R_e^2)$; in order to make a comparison with Stark's values possible a constant factor is introduced, so that the total intensity of the theoretical and observed groups of lines are the same.

We see from the table that the sum of the calculated intensities of the parallel components (1·9), differs considerably from the sum of the intensities of the perpendicular components (5·0), while observation gives for each sum nearly the same value (3·3 and 3·6).

The figs. 27 to 30 [1] represent the comparison between theory and observation in the case of H_α and the other hydrogen lines examined by Stark. An essential point for the agreement between theory and observation is the absence, required by § 35, of the case $J_\phi=n_\phi=0$.

To sum up, we can conclude, from the calculations of the previous

[1] After H. A. Kramers, *loc. cit.*, figs. 1 to 4.

paragraphs, that the correspondence principle, combined with the method of averaging applied here (taking the arithmetic average of

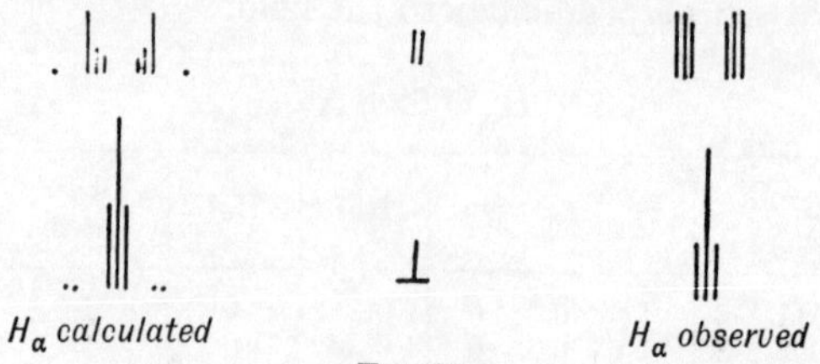

FIG. 27.

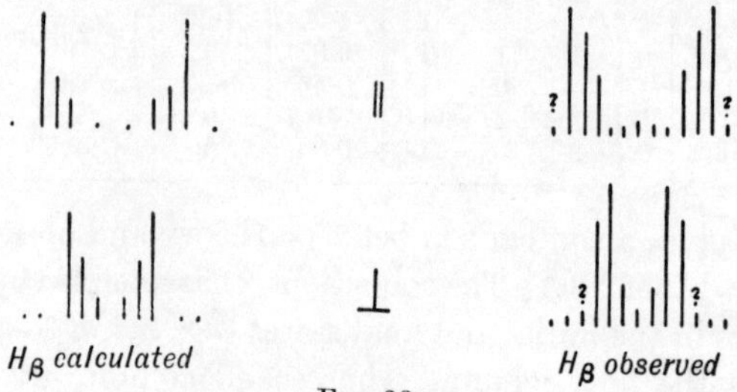

FIG. 28.

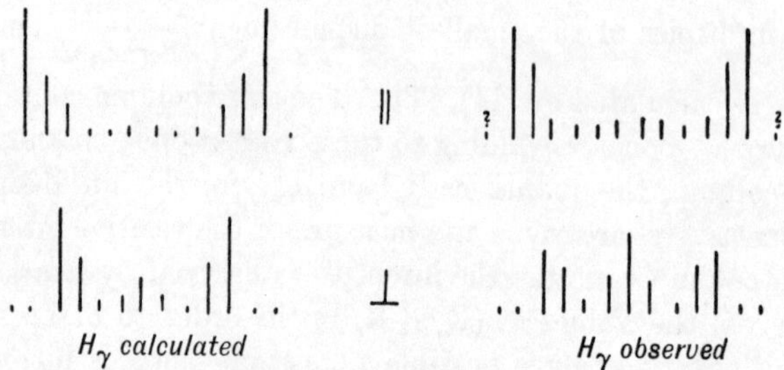

FIG. 29.

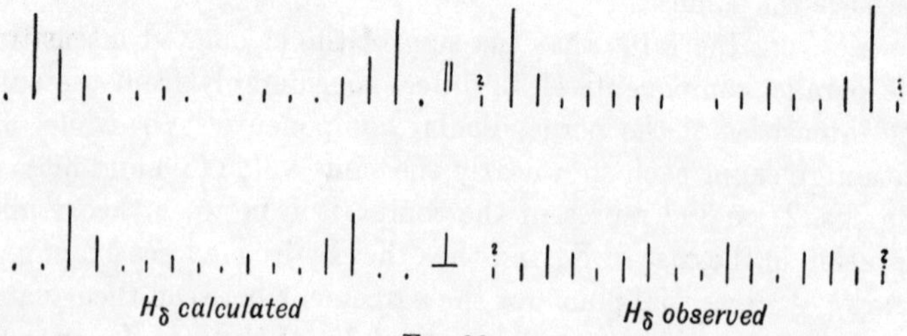

FIG. 30.

the relative intensities of initial and final orbits) approximates closely to the quantum law of intensities. Among other things, the fact that these calculations do not give exactly the true quantum intensities is to be expected, since, according to the above calculations, the resolved lines should exhibit a polarisation as a whole (mentioned above for H_α), the existence of which seems highly improbable both for theoretical reasons and on account of the experimental results.

§ 37.—The Secular Motions of the Hydrogen Atom in an Electric Field

The method so far employed for the treatment of the Stark effect depends on the special circumstance, which might almost be considered accidental, that separation co-ordinates exist having a simple geometrical significance. We shall now show how we may attain our object, without making use of this peculiarity, by a systematic application of the theory of secular perturbations. We shall adopt two different methods of procedure, beginning with one which investigates the secular motions of those angle and action variables which occur as degenerate variables in the investigation of the Kepler motion by polar co-ordinates; the second method, which is more suited to the geometrical aspects of the perturbation, has the advantage of being capable of extension to a more general case (crossed electric and magnetic fields).

We write the Hamiltonian function in the form

(1) $$H=H_0+\lambda H_1.$$

Here

(2) $$H_0=-\frac{cRh^3Z^2}{(J_1^0)^2}$$

is the energy of the Kepler motion in the absence of a field, and

$$\lambda H_1=eEz$$

denotes the perturbation function. (The field strength E may be considered as the small parameter λ.) According to the rules given in § 18, we have to express the mean value over a period of the unperturbed motion,

(3) $$\lambda\overline{H}_1=eE\bar{z}$$

in terms of the degenerate angle variables and the action variables of the unperturbed motion (see § 22), which we now denote by w_2^0, w_3^0, and $J_1^0J_2^0J_3^0$.

If in the unperturbed motion ξ and η are the rectangular co-ordinates of the electron in the plane of the orbit referred to the nucleus as origin and the major axis as the ξ-axis, we have (fig. 31)

$$z=\sin i(\xi \sin 2\pi w_2{}^0+\eta \cos 2\pi w_2{}^0)$$

since apart from a constant of integration which can be taken as zero, $2\pi w_2$ is the angular distance of the perihelion from the nodal line, measured in the plane of the orbit (§ 21, p. 137); and averaging over a period of the unperturbed motion

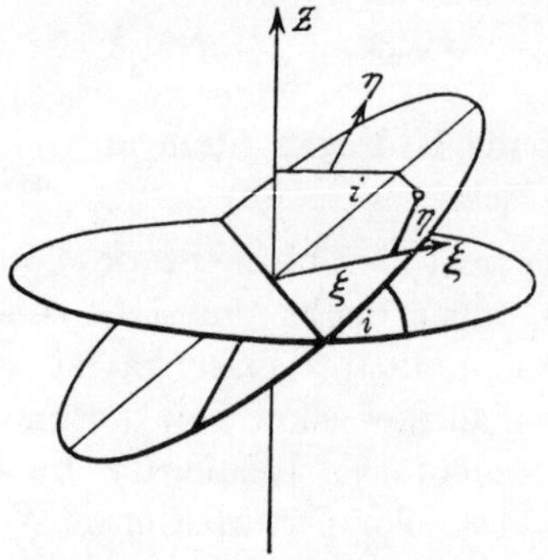

Fig. 31.

$$\bar{z}=\sin i(\bar{\xi} \sin 2\pi w_2{}^0+\bar{\eta} \cos 2\pi w_2{}^0).$$

In § 22 we found for the mean values (see (21), (23′), § 22)

$$\bar{\xi}=-\tfrac{3}{2}\epsilon a, \qquad \bar{\eta}=0\,;$$

they are the co-ordinates of the electrical "centre of gravity" of the moving electron. If we express $\sin i$ and ϵ in terms of $J_1{}^0J_2{}^0J_3{}^0$ we get

$$\bar{z}=-\sin 2\pi w_2{}^0 \cdot \frac{3}{2}a\sqrt{1-\left(\frac{J_3{}^0}{J_2{}^0}\right)^2}\sqrt{1-\left(\frac{J_2{}^0}{J_1{}^0}\right)^2}$$

and

$$(4) \quad W_1=-\lambda\overline{H}_1=-\sin 2\pi w_2{}^0 \cdot \frac{3}{2}a \cdot eE\sqrt{1-\left(\frac{J_3{}^0}{J_2{}^0}\right)^2}\sqrt{1-\left(\frac{J_2{}^0}{J_1{}^0}\right)^2}.$$

The angle variables $w_2{}^0$ and $w_3{}^0$ vary; $w_3{}^0$ varies in a cyclic manner and $J_3{}^0$ remains an action variable of the perturbed motion. $w_2{}^0$ is consequently the only non-cyclic co-ordinate in the averaged perturbation function, and we obtain as the only new action variable

$$(4') \qquad J_2=\oint J_2{}^0 dw_2{}^0.$$

It may be found as a function of W_1, $J_1=J_1{}^0$, and $J_3=J_3{}^0$ from equation (4). On evaluating the integral, W_1 and hence W is found as a function of the action variables.

We write for brevity:

$$(J_1{}^0)^2=A\,; \qquad (J_3{}^0)^2=B\,; \qquad \left(\frac{2W_1}{3aeE}\right)^2=C$$

and

$$(J_2{}^0)^2=x\,;$$

we have then

$$J_2 = \oint \sqrt{x}\frac{dw_2^0}{dx}dx,$$

where

$$\sin^2 2\pi w_2^0 = \frac{C}{\left(1-\frac{x}{A}\right)\left(1-\frac{B}{x}\right)}.$$

If we calculate $\frac{dw_2^0}{dx}$ from the last relation we find

$$d\frac{C}{\sin^2 2\pi w_2^0} = d\left(-\frac{x}{A}-\frac{B}{x}\right)$$

$$\frac{dw_2^0}{dx} = -\frac{\sin^3 2\pi w_2^0}{4\pi C\cos 2\pi w_2^0}\left(\frac{B}{x^2}-\frac{1}{A}\right)$$

$$\frac{dw_2^0}{dx} = \frac{\sqrt{AC}\,.\,(x^2-AB)}{4\pi\sqrt{x}(A-x)(x-B)\sqrt{(A-x)(x-B)-ACx}};$$

thus our integral becomes

$$J_2 = \frac{\sqrt{AC}}{4\pi}\oint\frac{(x^2-AB)dx}{(A-x)(x-B)\sqrt{(A-x)(x-B)-ACx}}.$$

Since the integrand is a rational function of x and the root of an expression quadratic in x, the integral may be evaluated by the method of complex integration. We find (*cf.* (9), Appendix II):

$$J_2 = \frac{1}{2}(\sqrt{A}-\sqrt{B}-\sqrt{AC}),$$

thus

$$J_2 = \frac{1}{2}\left(J_1^0 - J_3^0 - J_1^0\frac{2|W_1|}{3eEa}\right).$$

W_1 may be calculated from this; we find (on putting $J_1^0 = J_1$, $J_3^0 = J_3$):

$$W_1 = \pm\frac{3eEa}{2J_1}\,.\,(J_1 - J_3 - 2J_2)$$

and, if we express a in terms of J_1 by (10), § 22,

$$\text{(5)}\qquad W = -\frac{cRh^3Z^2}{J_1^2} \pm \frac{3Eh^2}{8\pi^2 meZ}J_1(J_1 - J_3 - 2J_2).$$

This equation becomes equation (13), § 35, if we put

$$\text{(6)}\qquad \begin{aligned} J_1 &= J \\ J_1 - J_3 - 2J_2 &= \pm J_e. \end{aligned}$$

We show subsequently that our present considerations lead to the same range of values for J_e as found previously. Once again we have the quantum conditions (15), § 35, and the energy equation (16), § 35.

We now examine the secular motions caused by the electric field. The perihelion of the orbital ellipse alters its position relatively to the line of nodes, and the latter itself moves uniformly about the axis of the field. It follows from (5) that two periods of the perihelion motion occur during one revolution of the line of nodes.

This motion of the perihelion, together with its accompanying phenomena, can best be studied by referring to the curve representing the motion in the $(w_2{}^0, J_2{}^0)$-plane (fig. 32). Its equation is, by (4),

$$\sin 2\pi w_2{}^0 = \frac{K_1}{\sqrt{1-\left(\frac{J_3{}^0}{J_2{}^0}\right)^2}\sqrt{1-\left(\frac{J_2{}^0}{J_1{}^0}\right)^2}}, \tag{7}$$

for shortness, we write here

$$-\frac{2h^2 W_1}{3eEa_{\mathrm{H}}(J_1{}^0)^2} = K_1$$

(using (9), § 23, $a_{\mathrm{H}}(J_1{}^0)^2/h^2$ has been substituted for a in (4)). It is symmetrical with respect to the straight lines $w_2{}^0=\frac{1}{4}$ or $w_2{}^0=\frac{3}{4}$. If $W_1=0$, either $w_2{}^0$ is 0 or $\frac{1}{2}$, or $J_2{}^0$ has one of the values $J_1{}^0$ or $J_3{}^0$. For $W_1<0$, $w_2{}^0$ can no longer have the values 0 or $\frac{1}{2}$, or $J_2{}^0$ the values $J_1{}^0$ or $J_3{}^0$; the curve is confined to the interior of a rectangle bounded by $w_2{}^0=0$, $w_2{}^0=\frac{1}{2}$, $J_2{}^0=J_1{}^0$, $J_2{}^0=J_3{}^0$. When $|W_1|$ is sufficiently small, $w_2{}^0$ can only depart from the immediate vicinity of 0 or $\frac{1}{2}$ when $J_2{}^0$ lies close to $J_1{}^0$ or $J_3{}^0$. The representative curve lies close to the rectangle mentioned and passes over into the circumference of the rectangle for $W_1=0$. The curve becomes less extended for larger values of $|W_1|$, until $w_2{}^0$ can assume only such values as lie in the neighbourhood of $\frac{1}{4}$ ($\sin 2\pi w_2{}^0=1$), and, finally, only this value itself; the curve contracts in this case to a point (*cf.* fig. 32). The same holds for $W_1>0$, only the limiting point is at $w_2{}^0=\frac{3}{4}$. For a given value of W_1, the reversal points for $w_2{}^0$ are situated at those places where $\sin 2\pi w_2{}^0$ is a minimum, or where

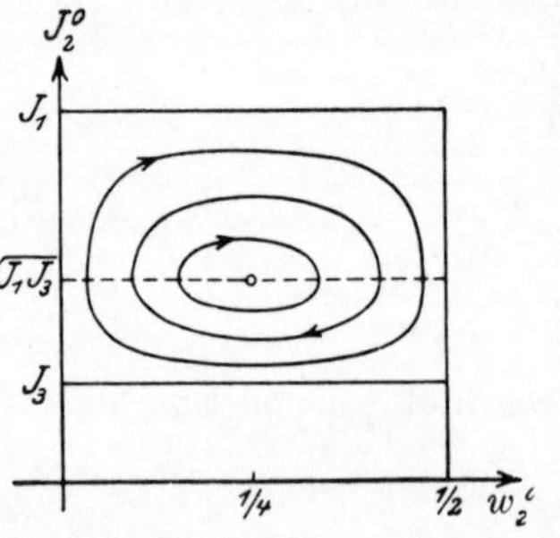

FIG. 32.

$$\left[1-\left(\frac{J_3^0}{J_2^0}\right)^2\right]\left[1-\left(\frac{J_2^0}{J_1^0}\right)^2\right]$$

is a maximum, J_1^0 and J_3^0, and thus

$$\left(\frac{J_3^0}{J_2^0}\right)^2 \cdot \left(\frac{J_2^0}{J_1^0}\right)^2$$

being constant. Now the function

$$(1-x)(1-y),$$

where

$$xy=\text{const.},$$

will be a maximum if $x=y$. Thus w_2^0 reverses when

$$(8) \qquad (J_2^0)^2=J_1^0J_3^0,$$

or when J_2^0 is the geometric mean of J_1^0 and J_3^0.

The secular motions of the orbit under the influence of the electric field are thus as follows: while the line of nodes revolves once, the perihelion of the orbital ellipse performs two oscillations about the meridian plane perpendicular to the line of nodes. For a transit through this meridian plane in one direction, the total momentum $J_2^0/2\pi$ is a maximum and consequently the eccentricity is a minimum; for a transit in the other direction the eccentricity is a maximum. Since the component $J_3^0/2\pi$ of the angular momentum in the direction of the field remains constant, the inclination of the orbital plane oscillates with the same frequency as the eccentricity. It has its maximum or minimum value when the perihelion passes through the equilibrium position, and it assumes both its maximum and minimum value twice during one revolution of the line of nodes. The major axis remains constant during this oscillation of orbital plane and perihelion (since J_1^0 remains constant); the eccentricity varies in such a way that the electrical centre of gravity always remains in the plane

$$z=\frac{W_1}{eE}.$$

In this plane it describes a curve about the direction of the field; since the inclination and rotation of the line of nodes have the frequency ratio 2 : 1, the curve is closed and, in the course of one revolution, the electrical centre of gravity attains its maximum distance from the axis twice and also its minimum distance twice. We shall show later (§ 38) that the electric centre of gravity executes an harmonic oscillation about the axis of the field.

We still have the two limiting cases of the perihelion motion to consider. If the representative curve in the (w_2^0, J_2^0)-plane has contracted to a point (the libration centre), then $J_2=0$ and $J_3=J_1+J_e$ is an integral multiple of h. The orbital ellipse has a constant eccentricity, and constant inclination, and is spatially quantised. The major axis is perpendicular to the line of nodes (since $w_2=\frac{1}{4}$), and the latter revolves uniformly about the direction of the field. To our approximation it is not a special state of motion singled out by the quantum theory, since J_2 is not fixed by a quantum condition. The necessity for fixing J_2 would be arrived at only by a closer approximation in calculating the energy.

In the other limiting case, $W_1=0$ or $J_2=\frac{1}{2}(J_1-J_3)$, where the curve in the (J_2^0, w_2^0)-plane coincides with the perimeter of the rectangle, the motion is rather complicated. The line of nodes revolves uniformly. In a certain phase of the motion the orbit is a circle ($J_2^0=J_1$), whose configuration is determined by J_3 and J_1. This circle changes gradually into an ellipse, whose perihelion lies in the line of nodes; the orbital plane is orientated perpendicular to the field during this process. Certainly in this configuration the direction of the line of nodes is indeterminate; but if we define it by continuing the uniform motion which it had previously, the perihelion lags behind the line of nodes until the separation is π. At this stage the orbital plane changes its orientation once more and the orbit gradually becomes a circle again. When it is a circle, the position of the perihelion is indeterminate. We can deduce, however, from the representative curve that it lies once again in the line of nodes when the eccentricity again increases and the path once more becomes orientated. During one revolution of the line of nodes the orbit twice becomes a circle.

The range of values of J_e or n_e is found by the following consideration. $J_3^0=J_3$ is positive and at the most equal to J_1. J_3 can never become zero, for otherwise J_2^0 would execute a libration between J_1^0 and $-J_1^0$, as can be seen from (4); this would give a limiting case in which the orbital ellipse would have to traverse a straight line (Pendelbahn, *cf.* § 21 and § 35) and, on account of the incommensurability of the periods of revolution in the ellipse and of the libration, would approach indefinitely close to the nucleus. From

$$0<J_3\leqq J_1$$

and the relation

$$0\leqq J_2\leqq \tfrac{1}{2}(J_1-J_3),$$

evident from fig. 32, since $J_2=\oint J_2^0 dw_2^0$ by (4′), which is at most equal to the area of the rectangle in the figure, we find for J_e

$$-J_1 < J_e < J_1$$

and

$$-(n-1) \leqq n_e \leqq n-1.$$

In place of the single quantum state characterised by a single n, as in the case of the Kepler motion in the absence of a field, we have the $2n-1$ states already mentioned in § 35.

§ 38.—The Motion of a Hydrogen Atom in Crossed Electric and Magnetic Fields

Bohr has given another and more illuminating method of calculating the secular motions of the hydrogen atom in an electric field.[1] Using a similar method, Lenz and Klein [2] succeeded in deducing the effect of the simultaneous influence of a magnetic field and of an electric field arbitrarily orientated with respect to it.

We reproduce the calculation for the case of an electric field **E** and a magnetic field **H**. The unperturbed motion ($\mathbf{E}=\mathbf{H}=0$) has six independent integration constants; as such constants we first choose the components of the angular momentum vector **P** and of the position vector $\bar{\mathbf{r}}$ of the electric centre of gravity of the orbit. Since **P** and $\bar{\mathbf{r}}$ are always perpendicular to one another, this provides only five independent quantities; as the sixth we can choose a magnitude which determines the phase of the motion; for this problem, however, it is unimportant. **P** and $\bar{\mathbf{r}}$ suffer variations under the influence of the fields **E** and **H**, and we commence by writing down the differential equations for **P** and $\bar{\mathbf{r}}$.

Both the electric field and the magnetic field exert couples on the electron orbit, and these determine the time-rate of variation of the angular momentum **P**. On multiplying the equation of motion of the electron, viz.:

$$(1) \qquad m\ddot{\mathbf{r}} = Ze^2 \operatorname{grad} \frac{1}{|\mathbf{r}|} - e\mathbf{E} + \frac{e}{c}[\mathbf{H}\dot{\mathbf{r}}]$$

vectorially by **r** we get the time-rate of variation of the angular momentum

$$\dot{\mathbf{P}} = m[\mathbf{r}\ddot{\mathbf{r}}] = e[\mathbf{E}\mathbf{r}] + \frac{e}{c}[\mathbf{r}[\mathbf{H}\dot{\mathbf{r}}]].$$

---

[1] N. Bohr, *Quantum Theory of Line Spectra* (Copenhagen, 1918), p. 72.

[2] The problem was first solved by P. Epstein, *Physical. Rev.*, vol. xxii, p. 202, 1923; O. Halpern gave another solution, *Zeitschr. f. Physik*, vol. xviii, p. 287, 1923. The method given here was originally given by W. Lenz (Lecture in Brunswick, 1924, and in more detailed form, *Zeitschr. f. Physik*, vol. xxiv, p. 197, 1924), and O. Klein, *ibid.*, vol. xxii, p. 109, 1924.

The secular component of this motion is found by taking the mean value over a period of the undisturbed motion; the electric contribution is

$$e[\mathbf{E}\bar{\mathbf{r}}].$$

The magnetic contribution can likewise be simply expressed, if we introduce the angular momentum **P** by means of the well-known vector relation

$$\begin{aligned}[\mathbf{r}[\mathbf{H}\dot{\mathbf{r}}]] &= [\mathbf{H}[\mathbf{r}\dot{\mathbf{r}}]]+[\dot{\mathbf{r}}[\mathbf{H}\mathbf{r}]]\\ &= \frac{1}{m}[\mathbf{HP}]+[\dot{\mathbf{r}}[\mathbf{H}\mathbf{r}]],\end{aligned}$$

and remember that the time average of

$$[\mathbf{r}[\mathbf{H}\dot{\mathbf{r}}]]+[\dot{\mathbf{r}}[\mathbf{H}\mathbf{r}]]=\frac{d}{dt}[\mathbf{r}[\mathbf{H}\mathbf{r}]]$$

is zero. We find in this way

$$2\overline{[\mathbf{r}[\mathbf{H}\dot{\mathbf{r}}]]}=\frac{1}{m}[\mathbf{HP}]$$

and

(2) $$\dot{\mathbf{P}}=e[\mathbf{E}\bar{\mathbf{r}}]+\frac{e}{2mc}[\mathbf{HP}].$$

The first term represents the couple due to the electric field acting on an electron situated at the centre of gravity of the orbit; the second term corresponds to Larmor's theorem, and signifies an additional rotation of the vector **P** about **H** with the angular velocity $\frac{e|\mathbf{H}|}{2mc}$.

In addition to the three equations included in (2), we will now find three others. In the first place the mean value of the perturbation energy, taken over a period of the undisturbed motion, is a constant

(3) $$W_1=e\mathbf{E}\bar{\mathbf{r}}+\frac{e}{2mc}\mathbf{HP}.$$

Secondly, **P** and $\bar{\mathbf{r}}$ are perpendicular, so that

(4) $$\mathbf{P}\bar{\mathbf{r}}=0,$$

and, thirdly, **P** and $\bar{\mathbf{r}}$ are connected through the eccentricity. We have from (23′), § 22 (p. 145)

$$|\bar{\mathbf{r}}|=\tfrac{3}{2}a\epsilon$$

and from (8), § 22 (p. 141),

$$\mathbf{P}^2=(1-\epsilon^2)\left(\frac{J}{2\pi}\right)^2,$$

where J is the non-degenerate action variable of the motion in the absence of a field. Elimination of ϵ leads to

$$\bar{\mathbf{r}}^2+K^2\mathbf{P}^2=\left(\frac{3}{2}a\right)^2, \tag{5}$$

where

$$K^2=\left(\frac{2\pi}{J}\right)^2\left(\frac{3}{2}a\right)^2. \tag{6}$$

From (3), (4), and (5) it is possible, with the help of (2), to derive an equation for $\dot{\bar{\mathbf{r}}}$ of the same form as (2). If (3), (4), and (5) be differentiated with respect to the time and the value of $\dot{\mathbf{P}}$ substituted from (2), we obtain

$$0=e\mathbf{E}\dot{\bar{\mathbf{r}}}+\frac{e^2}{2mc}\mathbf{H}[\mathbf{E}\bar{\mathbf{r}}]=e\mathbf{E}\left(\dot{\bar{\mathbf{r}}}+\frac{e}{2mc}[\bar{\mathbf{r}}\mathbf{H}]\right)$$

$$0=\mathbf{P}\dot{\bar{\mathbf{r}}}+\frac{e}{2mc}\bar{\mathbf{r}}[\mathbf{H}\mathbf{P}]=\mathbf{P}\left(\dot{\bar{\mathbf{r}}}+\frac{e}{2mc}[\bar{\mathbf{r}}\mathbf{H}]\right)$$

$$0=\bar{\mathbf{r}}\dot{\bar{\mathbf{r}}}+eK^2\mathbf{P}[\mathbf{E}\bar{\mathbf{r}}]=\bar{\mathbf{r}}(\dot{\bar{\mathbf{r}}}+eK^2[\mathbf{P}\mathbf{E}]).$$

This implies, however, that the scalar products of the vector

$$\dot{\bar{\mathbf{r}}}+eK^2[\mathbf{P}\mathbf{E}]+\frac{e}{2mc}[\bar{\mathbf{r}}\mathbf{H}] \tag{7}$$

with **E**, **P**, and $\bar{\mathbf{r}}$ vanish. Since in general these three vectors do not all vanish nor do they all lie in one plane, the vector (7) must itself be zero. Consequently

$$\dot{\bar{\mathbf{r}}}=eK^2[\mathbf{E}\mathbf{P}]+\frac{e}{2mc}[\mathbf{H}\bar{\mathbf{r}}]. \tag{8}$$

Our problem is solved when we can solve the system of equations (2), (8). This is best accomplished by introducing the new vectors

$$\begin{aligned}\bar{\mathbf{r}}_1&=\bar{\mathbf{r}}+K\mathbf{P}\\ \bar{\mathbf{r}}_2&=\bar{\mathbf{r}}-K\mathbf{P},\end{aligned} \tag{9}$$

instead of the unknowns **P** and $\bar{\mathbf{r}}$. Since $\bar{\mathbf{r}}$ and $K\mathbf{P}$ are perpendicular to one another, the two vectors (9) have the same magnitude which, by (5), is

$$|\bar{\mathbf{r}}_1|=|\bar{\mathbf{r}}_2|=\sqrt{\bar{\mathbf{r}}^2+K^2\mathbf{P}^2}=\tfrac{3}{2}a. \tag{10}$$

Further, in terms of $\bar{\mathbf{r}}$ and **P** the variables $\bar{\mathbf{r}}_1$ and $\bar{\mathbf{r}}_2$ are given by the equations

$$\begin{aligned}\bar{\mathbf{r}}&=\tfrac{1}{2}(\bar{\mathbf{r}}_1+\bar{\mathbf{r}}_2)\\ K\mathbf{P}&=\tfrac{1}{2}(\bar{\mathbf{r}}_1-\bar{\mathbf{r}}_2).\end{aligned} \tag{11}$$

(2) and (8) now become

$$\dot{\bar{\mathbf{r}}}_1 = e\mathrm{K}[\mathbf{E}\bar{\mathbf{r}}_1] + \frac{e}{2mc}[\mathbf{H}\bar{\mathbf{r}}_1]$$

(12)

$$\dot{\bar{\mathbf{r}}}_2 = -e\mathrm{K}[\mathbf{E}\bar{\mathbf{r}}_2] + \frac{e}{2mc}[\mathbf{H}\bar{\mathbf{r}}_2].$$

Writing for shortness

$$e\mathrm{K}\mathbf{E} = \mathbf{w}_e$$

(13)

$$\frac{e}{2mc}\mathbf{H} = \mathbf{w}_m,$$

the system of equations becomes

(14)

$$\dot{\bar{\mathbf{r}}}_1 = [\mathbf{w}_e + \mathbf{w}_m, \bar{\mathbf{r}}_1]$$
$$\dot{\bar{\mathbf{r}}}_2 = [-\mathbf{w}_e + \mathbf{w}_m, \bar{\mathbf{r}}_2].$$

This denotes simply that the vectors $\bar{\mathbf{r}}_1$ and $\bar{\mathbf{r}}_2$ rotate uniformly about the axes defined by $\mathbf{w}_e + \mathbf{w}_m = (\mathbf{H}/2mc) + \mathrm{K}\mathbf{E}$ and $-\mathbf{w}_e + \mathbf{w}_m = (\mathbf{H}/2mc) - \mathrm{K}\mathbf{E}$ respectively with the respective angular velocities $|\mathbf{w}_m + \mathbf{w}_e|$ and $|\mathbf{w}_m - \mathbf{w}_e|$. At each instant the separation of the end points of the two vectors is proportional (by (11)) to the angular momentum of the motion, and half their sum gives the radius vector of the electrical centre of gravity.

We consider first the case in which only an electric field $\mathbf{E}$ acts. $\bar{\mathbf{r}}_1$ and $\bar{\mathbf{r}}_2$ both rotate with the same velocity about the direction of the field, but in opposite directions. In the course of a complete rotation of each of the vectors they come twice into a configuration in which $\mathbf{E}$ is coplanar with them and they both lie on the same side of $\mathbf{E}$. In this position their difference, and therefore the resultant angular momentum $\mathbf{P}$, is a minimum, the eccentricity attains its maximum and the plane of the orbit deviates least from the equatorial plane of the field. Between these positions there are two others where $\bar{\mathbf{r}}_1$, $\bar{\mathbf{r}}_2$, and $\mathbf{E}$ likewise lie in a plane, but with $\bar{\mathbf{r}}_1$ and $\bar{\mathbf{r}}_2$ on opposite sides of $\mathbf{E}$. $\mathbf{P}$ is then a maximum and the eccentricity a minimum, while the plane of the orbit has its greatest inclination with the equatorial plane. While the magnitude of $\mathbf{P}$ goes through two librations during such a revolution, the direction $\mathbf{P}$ completes only one rotation, *i.e.* the line of nodes of the orbital plane completes one revolution.

If the motion of the electrical centre of gravity be alone considered, it may be found directly from the equations (2) and (8) (for $\mathbf{H}=0$). If (8) be differentiated with respect to the time and $\dot{\mathbf{P}}$ substituted from (2), we get

$$\ddot{\bar{\mathbf{r}}} = e^2\mathrm{K}^2[\mathbf{E}[\mathbf{E}\bar{\mathbf{r}}]].$$

This expresses the fact that $\ddot{\mathbf{r}}$ is directed perpendicularly to the direction of the field and that $|\ddot{\mathbf{r}}|$ is proportional to the distance of the electric centre of gravity from the axis of the field, $|[\bar{\mathbf{r}}\mathbf{E}]|\,/\,|\mathbf{E}|$. The electric centre of gravity performs, in other words, an harmonic oscillation about the axis of the field (*cf.* § 37, p. 233).

If only a magnetic field is acting, $\bar{\mathbf{r}}_1$ and $\bar{\mathbf{r}}_2$ rotate in the same sense about the axis of the field with the same velocity

$$|\mathbf{w}_m| = \frac{e}{2mc}|\mathbf{H}|,$$

i.e. the whole system performs a uniform precession (the Larmor precession) about the axis of the field.

When both fields are acting, the rotations of $\bar{\mathbf{r}}_1$ and $\bar{\mathbf{r}}_2$ occur about different axes. Thus the simple phase relation, which we had in the case of an electric field only, between the rotation of the line of nodes on the one hand and the orbital eccentricity and inclination on the other, will be destroyed and a much more complex motion sets in. Special difficulties arise when the two cones described by the vectors $\bar{\mathbf{r}}_1$ and $\bar{\mathbf{r}}_2$ intersect. If the rotation frequencies are incommensurable, the vectors $\bar{\mathbf{r}}_1$ and $\bar{\mathbf{r}}_2$ will then approach indefinitely close to one another, and, therefore, the angular momentum becomes indefinitely small. If now the frequency of rotation in the ellipse is incommensurable with the other two frequencies, the electron approaches indefinitely close to the nucleus. On the basis of the fundamental principles we have previously used, we should have to exclude such motions. We shall see later, however, when fixing the quantum conditions, that such orbits may be transformed adiabatically into those of the pure Stark or Zeeman effect which we must allow.

We turn now to the energy of the perturbed motion and the fixing of the stationary states.

Under the influence of the two fields $\mathbf{E}$ and $\mathbf{H}$, an additional term W_1 is added to the energy W_0 of the unperturbed motion, where (*cf.* (3))

$$W_1 = e\bar{\mathbf{r}}\mathbf{E} + \frac{e}{2mc}\mathbf{P}\mathbf{H}. \tag{15}$$

If we express here $\bar{\mathbf{r}}$ and $\mathbf{P}$ in terms of $\bar{\mathbf{r}}_1$ and $\bar{\mathbf{r}}_2$ by (11), we get

$$W_1 = \frac{e}{2}(\bar{\mathbf{r}}_1 + \bar{\mathbf{r}}_2)\mathbf{E} + \frac{e}{4mcK}(\bar{\mathbf{r}}_1 - \bar{\mathbf{r}}_2)\mathbf{H},$$

and, introducing the vectors $\mathbf{w}_e$ and $\mathbf{w}_m$ from (13),

$$\text{(16)} \qquad W_1 = \frac{1}{2K}\{\bar{\mathbf{r}}_1(\mathbf{w}_e + \mathbf{w}_m) + \bar{\mathbf{r}}_2(\mathbf{w}_e - \mathbf{w}_m)\}.$$

If we define the frequencies ν' and ν'' by

$$\text{(17)} \qquad \begin{aligned} \nu' &= \frac{1}{2\pi}|\mathbf{w}_e + \mathbf{w}_m| \\ \nu'' &= \frac{1}{2\pi}|\mathbf{w}_e - \mathbf{w}_m|, \end{aligned}$$

the energy can be expressed in the form

$$\text{(18)} \qquad W_1 = \nu' J' + \nu'' J'',$$

where

$$J' = \frac{1}{2} \cdot \frac{2\pi}{K}|\bar{\mathbf{r}}_1| \cos(\bar{\mathbf{r}}_1, \mathbf{w}_e + \mathbf{w}_m)$$

$$J'' = \frac{1}{2} \cdot \frac{2\pi}{K}|\bar{\mathbf{r}}_2| \cos(\bar{\mathbf{r}}_2, \mathbf{w}_e - \mathbf{w}_m).$$

By (6) and (10) we can write this

$$\text{(19)} \qquad \begin{aligned} J' &= \tfrac{1}{2}J \cos(\bar{\mathbf{r}}_1, \mathbf{w}_e + \mathbf{w}_m) \\ J'' &= \tfrac{1}{2}J \cos(\bar{\mathbf{r}}_2, \mathbf{w}_e - \mathbf{w}_m). \end{aligned}$$

Since ν' and ν'' in equation (18) are constant, it follows from the form of this equation that J' and J'' are the action variables conjugated to the angle variables

$$w' = \nu' t + \delta'$$
$$w'' = \nu'' t + \delta''.$$

The periodicity conditions of § 15 are all satisfied. The quantities J' and J'' are therefore to be determined by the quantum conditions

$$J' = n'h$$
$$J'' = n''h.$$

This implies a somewhat modified type of space quantisation, since by (19):

$$\cos(\bar{\mathbf{r}}_1, \mathbf{w}_e + \mathbf{w}_m) = 2\frac{n'}{n}$$

$$\cos(\bar{\mathbf{r}}_1, \mathbf{w}_e - \mathbf{w}_m) = 2\frac{n''}{n}.$$

The quantum numbers n' and n'' are thus restricted in this case to the range $\left(-\frac{n}{2}, \frac{n}{2}\right)$.

If the magnetic field **H** vanishes we have a case of degeneration, for then

$$\nu' = \nu'' = \nu_e.$$

The old action variable $J_e = J' + J''$ is then to be introduced in place of J' and J'' and we get

$$W_1 = \nu_e J_e,$$

in agreement with the previous results. In a similar way we have, for a pure magnetic field,

$$J_m = J' - J''$$

and

$$W_1 = \nu_m J_m.$$

If we have only a weak magnetic field in addition to a finite electric field, the axes of rotation of the vectors $\bar{\mathbf{r}}_1$ and $\bar{\mathbf{r}}_2$ have almost opposite directions. Since the cones generated by these vectors may not coincide in the case of a vanishing magnetic field (for this would give $\mathbf{P}=0$ in the Stark effect), they do not intersect in the case of a weak magnetic field. If, however, we allow **H** to increase adiabatically, the angles of the cones remain constant and, finally, a point is reached where the cones meet. A similar thing takes place when we start with a weak electric field and a finite magnetic field. The axes of rotation have then very nearly the same direction, and the cones do not intersect. Nevertheless, by an adiabatic increase of **E**, a point is again reached when the cones meet.

It is possible, therefore, to transform orbits which we have hitherto permitted, and which have been confirmed empirically, into orbits in which the electron approaches indefinitely close to the nucleus. At present no explanation of this difficulty can be given. There is a possibility that the J's need not be strictly invariant for the adiabatic changes considered in this connection, since states are continually traversed where (non-identical) commensurabilities exist between the frequencies ("accidental degeneration," see § 15, p. 89, and § 16, p. 97).

§ 39.—Problem of Two Centres

The parabolic co-ordinates used in the separation method to determine the motion of an electron in the hydrogen atom under the influence of an electric field are a special case of elliptic co-ordinates. The latter are the appropriate separation variables for the more general problem of the motion of a particle attracted to two fixed centres of force by forces obeying Coulomb's law. If one centre of force be displaced to an infinite distance, with an appropriate simultaneous increase in the intensity of its field, we get the case of the Stark effect; at the same time the elliptic co-ordinates become parabolic.

If the distance apart of the fixed points F_1 and F_2 is $2c$, the elliptic co-ordinates of a point ξ, η, distant r_1 and r_2 from the fixed points, are given by the equations

$$(1)\qquad \begin{aligned} \xi&=\frac{r_1+r_2}{2c} \qquad & r_1&=c(\xi+\eta) \\ \eta&=\frac{r_1-r_2}{2c} \qquad & r_2&=c(\xi-\eta). \end{aligned}$$

It is evident from these equations that

$$(2)\qquad \xi\geqq 1, \qquad -1\leqq\eta\leqq 1,$$

and, moreover, that the surfaces ξ=const. are ellipsoids of revolution with semi-major axis $c\xi$ and foci F_1 and F_2, whilst the surfaces η=const. are hyperboloids of revolution of two sheets with a distance $2c\eta$ between their vertices, and the same focal points. To determine a point uniquely a third co-ordinate is required, *e.g.* the azimuth ϕ about the line F_1F_2.

Taking cylindrical co-ordinates (r, ϕ, z) with F_1F_2 as z-axis, and its mid-point as origin, we can write the equations of these surfaces of revolution

$$\frac{z^2}{\xi^2}+\frac{r^2}{\xi^2-1}=c^2$$

$$\frac{z^2}{\eta^2}-\frac{r^2}{1-\eta^2}=c^2.$$

These give the equations of transformation

$$(3)\qquad \begin{aligned} z^2&=c^2\xi^2\eta^2 \\ r^2&=c^2(\xi^2-1)(1-\eta^2). \end{aligned}$$

We shall show that the "problem of two centres" referred to above is separable in the co-ordinates ξ, η, ϕ. The potential energy of an electric charge $-e$ attracted by two positively charged points is

$$U=-e^2\left(\frac{Z_1}{r_1}+\frac{Z_2}{r_2}\right),$$

or, in elliptic co-ordinates :

$$(4)\qquad U=-\frac{e^2}{c(\xi^2-\eta^2)}[(Z_1+Z_2)\xi-(Z_1-Z_2)\eta].$$

The kinetic energy is

$$T=\frac{m}{2}(\dot{r}^2+r^2\dot{\phi}^2+\dot{z}^2),$$

and by the relations (*cf.* (3))

$$\dot{z}=c(\xi\dot{\eta}+\dot{\xi}\eta)$$

$$\dot{r}=r\left(\frac{\xi\dot{\xi}}{\xi^2-1}-\frac{\eta\dot{\eta}}{1-\eta^2}\right)$$

this takes the form

$$\text{(5)}\qquad T=\frac{mc^2}{2}\left[(\xi^2-\eta^2)\left(\frac{\dot{\xi}^2}{\xi^2-1}+\frac{\dot{\eta}^2}{1-\eta^2}\right)+(\xi^2-1)(1-\eta^2)\dot{\phi}^2\right].$$

This gives for the momenta conjugate to ξ, η, ϕ,

$$\text{(6)}\qquad \begin{aligned} p_\xi&=mc^2\dot{\xi}\,\frac{\xi^2-\eta^2}{\xi^2-1}\\ p_\eta&=mc^2\dot{\eta}\,\frac{\xi^2-\eta^2}{1-\eta^2}\\ p_\phi&=mc^2\dot{\phi}(\xi^2-1)(1-\eta^2). \end{aligned}$$

If we express T in terms of the co-ordinates and momenta, and add the potential energy, we obtain the Hamiltonian function

$$\text{(7)}\quad H=\frac{1}{\xi^2-\eta^2}\left\{\frac{1}{2mc^2}\left[(\xi^2-1)p_\xi^{\ 2}+(1-\eta^2)p_\eta^{\ 2}+\left(\frac{1}{\xi^2-1}+\frac{1}{1-\eta^2}\right)p_\phi^{\ 2}\right]-\frac{e^2}{c}[(Z_1+Z_2)\xi-(Z_1-Z_2)\eta]\right\}=W.$$

It will be seen at once that our problem may be solved by separation of the variables. The three momenta are found to be

$$\text{(8)}\qquad \begin{aligned} p_\xi&=\sqrt{2mc^2(-W)}\frac{1}{\xi^2-1}\sqrt{-A-B_1\xi+C\xi^2+B_1\xi^3-\xi^4}\\ p_\eta&=\sqrt{2mc^2(-W)}\frac{1}{1-\eta^2}\sqrt{-A-B_2\eta+C\eta^2+B_2\eta^3-\eta^4}\\ p_\phi&=\text{const.}, \end{aligned}$$

where C is an arbitrary constant and

$$\text{(9)}\qquad \begin{aligned} A-C+1&=\frac{p_\phi^{\ 2}}{2mc^2(-W)}\\ B_1&=\frac{e^2(Z_1+Z_2)}{-cW}\\ B_2&=\frac{e^2(Z_1-Z_2)}{-cW}. \end{aligned}$$

We may now proceed to investigate the possible types of orbit, leaving out of consideration individual limiting cases, and restricting ourselves to the case of a negative W. We shall not give the method of proof in detail.

I. Orbits which are Coplanar with the Centres.[1]

In this case $p_\phi=0$, therefore $A-C+1=0$ and $\xi=1$, $\eta=\pm 1$ are roots of the expressions under the square root sign (radicand) in (8). We distinguish the following cases :—

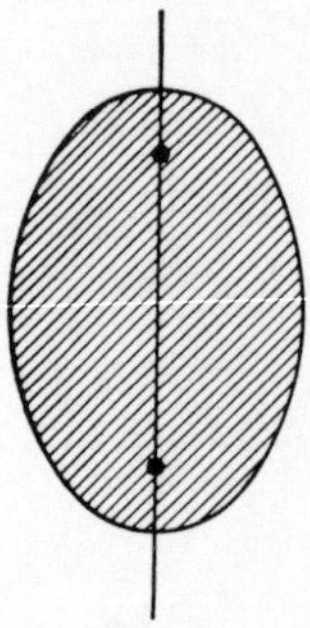

Fig. 33.

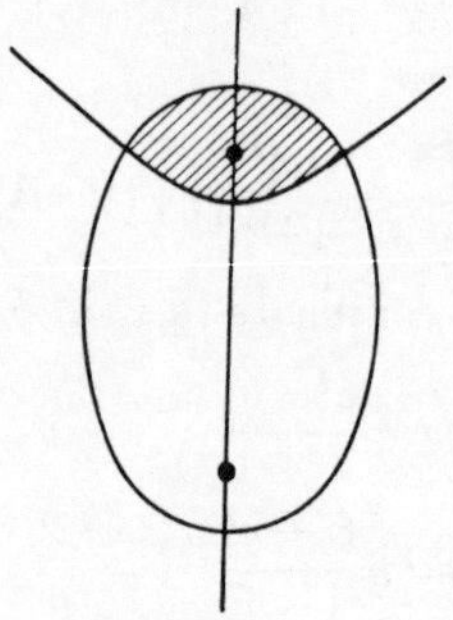

Fig. 34.

1. The radicand of p_ξ is positive for $\xi>1$; ξ then performs a libration between $\xi=1$ and a value $\xi=\xi_{max}$.

(*a*) The radicand of p_η is positive throughout the whole interval $-1<\eta<1$. The orbit lies within the ellipse $\xi=\xi_{max}$ (fig. 33).

(*b*) The radicand of p_η has a root in the interval $-1<\eta<1$ in addition to the roots $\eta=\pm 1$. The orbit is then contained within a region bounded by the ellipse $\xi=\xi_{max}$ and a hyperbola η=const. (fig. 34). The case in which two roots occur in the interval $-1<\eta<1$ does not arise.

2. The radicand of p_ξ is negative for $\xi>1$ and later assumes positive values in the interval (ξ_{min}, ξ_{max}); ξ then performs a libration in this interval. In this case, the radicand of p_η must be positive throughout the whole interval $-1<\eta<1$. The curve is then confined between the two ellipses $\xi=\xi_{min}$ and $\xi=\xi_{max}$ (fig. 35).

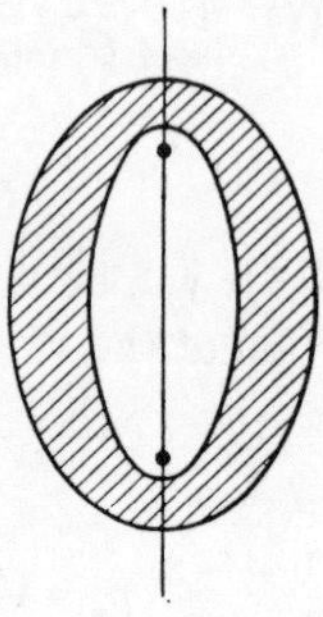

Fig. 35.

II. Orbits which are not Coplanar with the Centres.[2]

The radicand of p_ξ is at most positive in an interval (ξ_{min}, ξ_{max}), which does not extend to $\xi=1$: the radicand of p_η is likewise negative for $\eta=\pm 1$ and can have two or four roots in the interval $-1<\eta<1$. Finally, p_ϕ is not zero and ϕ performs a rotation about the line of centres. In all cases where motions are possible at all, they are confined to a ring bounded by two hyperboloids of rotation and

[1] For a detailed discussion of these orbits, see C. L. Charlier, *Die Mechanik des Himmels*, vol. i, Leipzig, 1902, iii, § 1 (p. 122).

[2] Detailed discussion by W. Pauli, jr., *Ann. d. Physik*, vol. lxviii, p. 177, 1922, ii, § 6, and K. F. Niessen, *Zur Quantentheorie des Wasserstoffmolokül-Ions* (Diss., Utrecht, 1922), section 1.

two ellipsoids of rotation, whose axes pass through the centres (figs. 36 and 37). In the case of double roots two of the ellipsoids or hyperboloids can coincide ; limitation motions can also occur.

The regions mentioned here will be completely filled if the motion is not strictly periodic. In the two cases I, 1 (*a*) and (*b*), this would involve an infinitely close approach of the moving point to the centres of force.

Pauli [1] and Niessen [2] have endeavoured to treat the quantum theory of the problem of two centres, and to apply it to the hydrogen molecule positive ion, which consists of two nuclei with charges $+e$ (*i.e.* $Z_1=Z_2=1$), and one electron. To a first approximation, the motion of the nuclei can be neglected on account of their large mass. The first step is to calculate the motion of the electrons when the

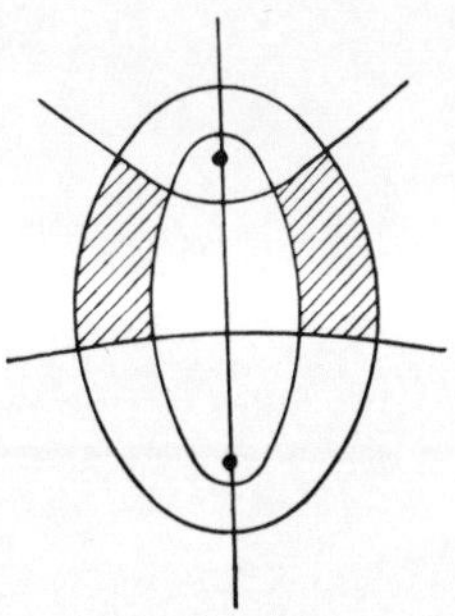

FIG. 36.

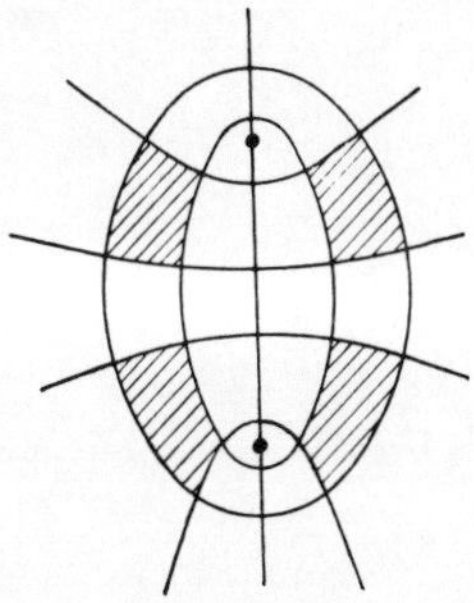

FIG. 37.

nuclei are an arbitrary distance apart ; the nuclear separation has then to be determined so that the nuclei are in stable equilibrium for definite values of the action variables of the electron motion. It has been found in this way that a configuration of minimum energy (the normal state) is uniquely determined by these conditions (it is of the type in fig. 36, the figure being symmetrical for nuclei with equal charges). Not only can the value of the energy be found in this case, but the small oscillations of the nuclei, which are brought about by small perturbations, can also be calculated.

It has been found, however, that the numbers obtained in this way do not agree with experimental determinations of the ionisation and excitation potentials. On this account we shall refrain from discussing more fully this model for H_2^+. At present the reason for the failure of the theory is by no means clear. We shall see later that the treatment of atomic problems with the help of classical mechanics

[1] W. Pauli, *loc. cit.*

[2] K. F. Niessen, *loc. cit.*

leads to false results immediately several electrons are present; in other words, whenever we have to deal with a problem involving three or more bodies. The artificial reduction of a multiple-body problem to a one-body problem, on the basis of the small ratio of electron to nuclear mass, is, perhaps, not permissible.

FOURTH CHAPTER

THEORY OF PERTURBATIONS

§ 40.—The Significance of the Theory of Perturbations for the Mechanics of the Atom

If we glance back at the atomic models dealt with in the previous chapter, we see that they are all characterised by the fact that the motion of only one electron is taken into consideration. The results tend to show that, in such cases, our method of procedure is legitimate or, in other words, that we are justified in first calculating the motions in accordance with classical mechanics, and subsequently singling out certain stationary states by means of quantum conditions. The problem now arises of how to treat atoms with several electrons.

At first glance a similar method would appear applicable to this case, the mechanical many-body problem being first solved, and the quantum conditions introduced subsequently. It is well known, however, what difficulties arise even in the three-body problem of astronomy; and in the present case things are still more unfavourable, the reason being that whereas the perturbing forces which two planets exert on one another in the problems of celestial mechanics are extremely small in comparison with the attraction of the sun for either of them, the repulsive force between two electrons in an atom is of the same order of magnitude as the force of attraction between each and the nucleus. Moreover, in astronomical problems it suffices to calculate the motions in advance for periods of a few hundred or thousand years; in atomic theory, on the other hand, only those multiply-periodic motions can be employed whose course can be represented for all time by one and the same Fourier series. It appears, then, that all progress in this direction is barred by insurmountable analytical difficulties, and so it might be concluded that it is impossible from a purely theoretical basis to arrive at an explanation of the structures of the atoms right up to uranium.

The object of the investigations of this chapter is to show that this is not the decisive difficulty. It would, indeed, be remarkable if Nature fortified herself against further advance in knowledge behind the analytical difficulties of the many-body problem. Atomic mechanics overcomes the above-mentioned difficulties arising from the like order of magnitude of all the forces acting, by precisely those characteristics which distinguish it from celestial mechanics, namely, the quantum restrictions on the possible types of motion. We shall show, by a systematic development of the perturbation theory, that it is only the simplest types of orbits which are of importance in the quantum theory, and in astronomy these occur only as exceptional cases and so receive no attention. These quantum orbits admit of relatively simple analytical description. One might, therefore, proceed in this way to compute the atoms of the periodic system one after another.

An attempt has actually been made to subject to the theory of perturbations the second simplest atom, that of helium, with its one nucleus and two electrons. The result, however, was entirely negative; the discrepancies between theory and observation were much too large to be accounted for by the inaccuracy of the calculations. This indicates that there is some basic error in the principles of our atomic mechanics.

When we set forth these fundamental principles (§ 16) we called attention to their provisional nature; this is shown in particular by the fact that the theory introduces magnitudes such as frequencies of rotation, distances of separation, etc., which, in all probability, are by nature incapable of being observed. Again, the phenomena of dispersion show that the system is not in resonance with an external alternating electric field of the frequency ($\tau\nu$) calculated by classical mechanics, but of the quantum frequencies ν which are associated with the quantum transitions. Finally, in the course of our investigations we have come across several cases where the failure of our hypothesis has been indubitably established by experiment, *e.g.* the appearance of "half" quantum numbers, the multiplets and anomalous Zeeman effects, etc. The presentation of atomic mechanics given here must therefore be regarded as only a first step towards a final theory, which can be approached only by gradually eliminating all false trails.

In order to set about this thoroughly, it is necessary to follow through the method suggested, and to examine the consequences to which we are led by the application of classical mechanics in conjunction with the quantum restrictions. We shall therefore give in this chapter a detailed account of the theory of perturbations, including all cases permitted by the quantum theory; finally, we shall demonstrate the failure of this theory in the case of helium.

We are of opinion that this will not be labour spent in vain, but that this broad development of the theory of perturbations will, together with the negative results, form the foundation for the true quantum theory of the interaction of several electrons.[1]

§ 41.—Perturbations of a Non-degenerate System

Even the three-body problem, to say nothing of those involving more bodies, belongs to that class of mechanical problems which have not been solved by the method of separation of the variables, and, indeed, are hardly likely to be. In all such cases one is compelled to fall back on methods which give the motion to successive degrees of approximation. These methods are applicable if a parameter λ can be introduced into the Hamiltonian function in such a way that for $\lambda=0$ it degenerates into the Hamiltonian function H_0 of a problem soluble by the method of separation, provided also that it may be expanded in a series

$$(1) \qquad H=H_0+\lambda H_1+\lambda^2 H_2+\ldots,$$

which converges for a sufficiently large range of values of the co-ordinates and momenta.

Problems of this kind are dealt with in celestial mechanics, and the various methods adopted for their solution are referred to under the heading "Theory of Perturbations." The additional terms $\lambda H_1+\lambda^2 H_2+\ldots$ are in fact regarded as a "perturbation" of the "unperturbed" motion characterised by H_0.

It is only the multiply-periodic solutions which are of importance for the quantum theory. The methods which we shall employ for their deduction in what follows are essentially the same as those which Poincaré has treated in detail in his *Méthodes nouvelles de la Mécanique céleste*.[2] By a solution we mean, as usual, the discovery of a principal function S which generates a canonical transformation,

$$p_k=\frac{\partial S}{\partial q_k}, \qquad w_k=\frac{\partial S}{\partial J_k},$$

as a result of which the original co-ordinates and momenta are transformed into angle and action variables.

---

[1] The first applications of the theory of perturbations to atomic mechanics will be found in the following works: N. Bohr, *Quantum Theory of Line Spectra*, parts i, ii, iii, Copenhagen, 1918 and 1922; M. Born and E. Brody, *Zeitschr. f. Physik*, vol. vi, p. 140, 1921; P. S. Epstein, *Zeitschr. f. Physik*, vol. viii, pp. 211, 305, 1922; vol. ix, p. 92, 1922.

[2] Three vols., Paris, 1892–99.

Let us suppose that the unperturbed motion is already known and assume, for the time being, that this motion is non-degenerate. In other words, we suppose that there exists no integral relation of the form

$$(2) \qquad (\tau\nu^0)=\tau_1\nu_1{}^0+\ldots+\tau_f\nu_f{}^0=0$$

between the frequencies $\nu_k{}^0$ of the unperturbed motion, either identically in the action variables $J_k{}^0$ or for the special values of the $J_k{}^0$'s which characterise the initial state of motion.

We now introduce the angle and action variables $w_k{}^0$, $J_k{}^0$ of the undisturbed motion, and consider the Hamiltonian function of the perturbed motion defined in terms of them. They are still canonical co-ordinates, but, in general, they are no longer angle and action variables ; in fact, it is evident from the canonical equations

$$\dot{J}_k{}^0=-\frac{\partial H}{\partial w_k{}^0}, \qquad \dot{w}_k{}^0=\frac{\partial H}{\partial J_k{}^0},$$

that $J_k{}^0$ depends on time and that $w_k{}^0$ is no longer a linear function of time. For $\lambda=0$, H becomes the Hamiltonian function H_0 of the unperturbed system, which depends only on the $J_k{}^0$'s :

$$H_0(J_1{}^0, J_2{}^0 \ldots).$$

Similarly, the angle and action variables of the perturbed system become those of the unperturbed system for $\lambda=0$.

To find them, we have to look for the generator $S(w^0, J)$ of a canonical transformation

$$(3) \qquad J_k{}^0=\frac{\partial S}{\partial w_k{}^0}, \qquad w_k=\frac{\partial S}{\partial J_k},$$

which transforms the variables w^0, J^0 into fresh variables w, J, in such a way as to satisfy the following three conditions (*cf.* § 15) :—

(A) The position co-ordinates of the system are periodic functions of the w_k's with the fundamental period 1.

(B) H is transformed into a function W depending only on the J_k's.

(C) $S^*=S-\sum_k w_kJ_k$ is periodic in the w_k's with the period 1.

The rectangular co-ordinates of the system are thus periodic functions of the $w_k{}^0$'s, as well as of the w_k's : in other words, a periodicity parallelepiped in the $w_k{}^0$-space will be transformed into another in the w_k-space. Apart from an arbitrary integral linear transformation of the w_k's among themselves with the determinant ± 1, we have, therefore,

(4) $w_k = w_k^0 +$ a periodic function of the w_k^0's (period 1).

From this and from (C) we conclude that $S - \sum_k w_k^0 J_k$ is also periodic in the w_k^0's with period 1. Or conversely, taking $S - \sum_k w_k^0 J_k$ to be periodic in the w_k^0's with the fundamental period 1, equation (4), and with it the periodicity of S*, follows from the relation

$$w_k = \frac{\partial S}{\partial J_k},$$

and further, since from the beginning we have assumed that the position co-ordinates are periodic functions of the w_k^0's, they must also be periodic functions of the w_k's. The conditions (A) and (C) are thus satisfied.

The function S which we require is now supposed to be capable of expansion as a power series in λ, of the form

(5) $$S = S_0 + \lambda S_1 + \lambda^2 S_2 + \cdots.$$

S_0 is here the generator of the identical transformation and has therefore (*cf.* § 7, p. 31) the form

(6) $$S_0 = \sum_k w_k^0 J_k,$$

and S_1, S_2 . . . are periodic in the w_k^0's. Conversely, every function S possessing these properties leads to variables which satisfy the conditions (A) and (C).

We now substitute the series (5) for S in the Hamiltonian-Jacobi equation for the perturbed motion

(7) $$H_0\left(\frac{\partial S}{\partial w^0}\right) + \lambda H_1\left(w^0, \frac{\partial S}{\partial w^0}\right) + \lambda^2 H_2\left(w^0, \frac{\partial S}{\partial w^0}\right) + \ldots = W(J)$$

and expand W in turn in powers of λ:

$$W = W_0(J) + \lambda W_1(J) + \lambda^2 W_2(J) + \cdots.$$

A number of differential equations then result on equating the coefficients of like powers of λ.

First of all we have

(8) $$H_0(J) = W_0(J),$$

i.e. W_0 is found by replacing J_k^0 by J_k in the energy of the unperturbed motion. We shall refer to W_0 as the zero approximation to the energy.

We find the equation for the first approximation by equating the coefficients of λ, viz.:

(9) $$\sum_k \frac{\partial H^0}{\partial J_k} \frac{\partial S_1}{\partial w_k^0} + H_1(w^0, J) = W_1(J);$$

in which $H_0(J)$ and $H_1(w^0, J)$ mean that in $H_0(J^0)$ and $H_1(w^0, J^0)$ the J^0's are simply replaced by the J's, the form of the function remaining unaltered. The two unknown functions W_1 and S_1 may be determined by means of this equation. Since S_1 is to be periodic in the w_k^0's, the mean value of the sum in (9), taken over the unit cube of the w^0-space, or over the time variation of the unperturbed motion, is zero. It follows, then, from (9) that

(10) $$W_1(J) = \overline{H_1(w^0, J)},$$

where H_1 is likewise to be averaged over the time variation of the unperturbed motion. Hence we obtain for W_1 the same expression as in the calculation of the secular perturbations, although in this case we have started out from the totally different hypothesis that the unperturbed motion is not degenerate. Here again we have the theorem :

The energy of the perturbed motion is, to a first approximation, equal to the energy of the unperturbed motion increased by the time average of the first term of the perturbation function taken over the unperturbed motion. Apart, then, from the determination of the unperturbed motion, no new integration is involved in the calculation of the energy to this degree of approximation.

After calculation of $W_1(J)$, we have for S_1 the equation

(11) $$\sum_k \frac{\partial H^0}{\partial J_k} \frac{\partial S_1}{\partial w_k^0} = -\tilde{H}_1,$$

where the sign ~ over H_1 denotes the difference of the function H_1 from its mean value :

$$\tilde{H}_1 = H_1 - \overline{H}_1.$$

We may conveniently refer to $\tilde{H}_1$ as the " periodic component " of H_1. It may be represented as a Fourier series

$$\tilde{H}_1 = \sum_\tau{}' A_\tau(J) e^{2\pi i(\tau w^0)}$$

without a constant term (this being denoted by the accent on the summation sign). If we imagine S_1 expressed as a Fourier series

$$S_1 = \sum_\tau B_\tau(J) e^{2\pi i(\tau w^0)},$$

the unknown coefficients $B_\tau(J)$ may be expressed in terms of the known $A_\tau(J)$ with the help of (11). It is found that

$$2\pi i(\tau\nu^0) B_\tau(J) = A_\tau(J),$$

if we write

$$\frac{\partial \mathrm{H}^0}{\partial \mathrm{J}_k}=\nu_k{}^0(\mathrm{J}) \tag{12}$$

so that $\nu_k{}^0(\mathrm{J})$ can be derived from the frequencies $\nu_k{}^0(\mathrm{J}^0)$ of the unperturbed motion by replacing $\mathrm{J}_k{}^0$ by J_k. In this way we find as a solution of (11)

$$\mathrm{S}_1=\sum_\tau{}' \frac{1}{2\pi i}\frac{\mathrm{A}_\tau}{(\tau\nu^0)}e^{2\pi i(\tau w^0)}. \tag{13}$$

In addition to this there can occur an arbitrary function which depends only on the J_k's. We are now in a position to calculate the influence of the perturbation on the motion to a first approximation.

To this degree of approximation we have for the angle variables of the motion

$$w_k=w_k{}^0+\lambda\frac{\partial \mathrm{S}_1(w^0, \mathrm{J})}{\partial \mathrm{J}_k}, \tag{14}$$

from which the $w_k{}^0$'s are given as functions of the time. Superposed on the unperturbed motion are small periodic oscillations, the amplitudes of which are of the order of magnitude λ, and are therefore proportional to the perturbing forces, while the frequencies

$$\nu_k=\nu_k{}^0+\lambda\frac{\partial \overline{\overline{\mathrm{H}}}_1}{\partial \mathrm{J}_k}, \tag{15}$$

deviate but slightly from those of the unperturbed motion.

For the $\mathrm{J}_k{}^0$'s we have

$$\mathrm{J}_k{}^0=\mathrm{J}_k+\lambda\frac{\partial \mathrm{S}_1(w^0, \mathrm{J})}{\partial w_k{}^0}, \tag{16}$$

which implies that the $\mathrm{J}_k{}^0$'s, which in the unperturbed motion are constant, are likewise subject to small oscillations with amplitudes of the order of λ. So-called secular perturbations do not occur, *i.e.* quantities constant in the unperturbed motion do not undergo changes of their own order of magnitude, such as occur in the case of a degenerate unperturbed motion (*cf.* § 18).

The necessity for the hypothesis of the non-degenerate character of the unperturbed motion is evident from (13), since, if this were not the case, the expression (13) would be meaningless, owing to certain of the denominators vanishing. We see further, however, that, even if such degeneration be absent, the denominators can be made arbitrarily small by a suitable choice of the numbers $\tau_1 \ldots \tau_f$, and, moreover, this may happen for an infinite number of terms if the τ_k's vary from $-\infty$ to $+\infty$. In view of this, the convergence of the

Fourier series (13) appears questionable. We shall return to this at the end of the paragraph and meanwhile continue the formal development of the method of approximation.

By comparison of the coefficients, more differential equations may be deduced from (7), the second (coefficients of λ^2) and n^{th} (coefficients of λ^n) of which we give below :

$$(17)\quad \sum_k \frac{\partial H_0}{\partial J_k}\frac{\partial S_2}{\partial w_k^0}+\sum_{k,j}\frac{1}{2!}\frac{\partial^2 H_0}{\partial J_k \partial J_j}\frac{\partial S_1}{\partial w_k^0}\frac{\partial S_1}{\partial w_j^0} +\sum_k \frac{\partial H_1}{\partial J_k}\frac{\partial S_1}{\partial w_k^0}+H_2=W_2(J),$$

$$(18)\quad \begin{aligned} &\sum_k \frac{\partial H_0}{\partial J_k}\frac{\partial S_n}{\partial w_k^0}+\sum_{k,j}\frac{1}{2!}\frac{\partial^2 H_0}{\partial J_k \partial J_j}\sum_{p+q=n}\frac{\partial S_p}{\partial w_k^0}\frac{\partial S_q}{\partial w_j^0}\\ &+\sum_{k,j,l}\frac{1}{3!}\frac{\partial^3 H_0}{\partial J_k \partial J_j \partial J_l}\sum_{p+q+r=n}\frac{\partial S_p}{\partial w_k^0}\frac{\partial S_q}{\partial w_j^0}\frac{\partial S_r}{\partial w_l^0}\\ &+\ldots+\sum_{k_1\ldots k_n}\frac{1}{n!}\frac{\partial^n H_0}{\partial J_{k_1}\ldots\partial J_{k_n}}\frac{\partial S_1}{\partial w_{k_1}^0}\cdots\frac{\partial S_1}{\partial w_{k_n}^0}\\ &+\sum_k \frac{\partial H_1}{\partial J_k}\frac{\partial S_{n-1}}{\partial w_k^0}+\ldots\\ &+\sum_{k_1\ldots k_{n-1}}\frac{1}{(n-1)!}\frac{\partial^{n-1} H_1}{\partial J_{k_1}\ldots\partial J_{k_{n-1}}}\frac{\partial S_1}{\partial w_{k_1}^0}\cdots\frac{\partial S_1}{\partial w_{k_{n-1}}^0}\\ &+\ldots+\sum_k \frac{\partial H_{n-1}}{\partial J_k}\frac{\partial S_1}{\partial w_k^0}+H_n=W_n(J). \end{aligned}$$

All the equations have the form

$$(19)\quad \sum_k \frac{\partial H_0}{\partial J_k}\frac{\partial S_n}{\partial w_k^0}=W_n(J)-\Phi_n(w^0, J),$$

where Φ_n is a function, involving only the results of previous stages of approximation, and so known at the stage to which (19) refers, and periodic in the w^0's, and S_n and W_n are the required functions. By forming the time average over the unperturbed motion we find, in exactly the same manner as in the first stage of the process,

$$(20)\quad W_n(J)=\overline{\Phi_n(w^0, J)}$$

and

$$(21)\quad \sum_k \nu_k^0(J)\frac{\partial S_n}{\partial w_k^0}=-\tilde{\Phi}_n,$$

where $\tilde{\Phi}_n$ again denotes the "periodic component" of the function Φ_n.

If now we again express the right-hand side in the form of a Fourier series

$$\tilde{\Phi}_n = \sum_\tau{}' A_\tau(J) e^{2\pi i(\tau w^0)},$$

in which no constant term appears, integration of (21) gives

$$\text{(22)} \qquad S_n = \sum_\tau{}' \frac{1}{2\pi i} \frac{A_\tau}{(\tau\nu^0)} e^{2\pi i(\tau w^0)}.$$

This is a formal solution of the proposed problem.

As an illustration of the method of procedure, we shall carry out the calculation as far as the expression for W_2 in terms of the Fourier coefficients of the perturbation function. By (13)

$$S_1 = \sum_\tau{}' \frac{1}{2\pi i} \frac{A_\tau}{(\tau\nu^0)} e^{2\pi i(\tau w^0)},$$

where the A_τ's are the Fourier coefficients of H_1, and the term for which $\tau_1 = \tau_2 = \ldots = \tau_f = 0$ is absent. The equation (17) for W_2 we now rewrite as

$$\sum_k \nu_k{}^0 \frac{\partial S_2}{\partial w_k{}^0} + \sum_{k,j} \frac{1}{2!} \frac{\partial \nu_j{}^0}{\partial J_k} \sum_\tau{}' \sum_\sigma{}' \frac{\tau_k \sigma_j A_\tau A_\sigma}{(\tau\nu^0)(\sigma\nu^0)} e^{2\pi i(\tau+\sigma,\, w^0)}$$
$$+ \sum_k \sum_\tau{}' \sum_\sigma{}' \frac{\partial A_\tau}{\partial J_k} \frac{\sigma_k A_\sigma}{(\sigma\nu^0)} e^{2\pi i(\tau+\sigma,\, w^0)} + H_2 = W_2.$$

W_2 is obtained by averaging

$$\frac{1}{2} \sum_{k,j} \frac{\partial \nu_j{}^0}{\partial J_k} \sum_\tau{}' \tau_k \tau_j \frac{A_\tau A_{-\tau}}{(\tau\nu^0)^2} - \sum_k \sum_\tau{}' \frac{\partial A_\tau}{\partial J_k} \frac{\tau_k A_{-\tau}}{(\tau\nu^0)} + \overline{H}_2 = W_2.$$

This can be written

$$\text{(23)} \qquad W_2 = \overline{H}_2 - \frac{1}{2} \sum_\tau{}' \sum_k \tau_k \frac{\partial}{\partial J_k} \left(\frac{|A_\tau|^2}{(\tau\nu^0)} \right)$$

or (what comes to the same thing, the case $(\tau\nu^0) = 0$ being excluded)

$$\text{(24)} \qquad W_2 = \overline{H}_2 - \sum_{(\tau\nu^0)>0} \sum_k \tau_k \frac{\partial}{\partial J_k} \left(\frac{|A_\tau|^2}{(\tau\nu^0)} \right).$$

We shall now consider briefly the question of the convergence of the series so obtained. The point to be decided is whether the small values of the denominators $(\tau\nu^0)$ which must continually recur in the higher terms of the series, will prevent the series being convergent, or whether the convergence can be maintained by correspondingly small values of the numerators. Bruns [1] has shown

[1] H. Bruns, *Astr. Nachr.*, vol. cix, p. 215, 1884; C. L. Charlier, *Mechanik des Himmels*, vol. ii, p. 307, Leipzig, 1907.

that this depends entirely on the character of the frequency ratios $\nu_1^0 : \nu_2^0 : \ldots : \nu_f^0$. He deduced the following theorem : Those values of the periods ν_k^0 for which the series are absolutely convergent and those for which even the individual terms of the series do not converge to zero, lie indefinitely close to one another. Since the ν_k^0's are functions of the J_k's, it follows that the function S, derived according to the above procedure, is not a continuous function of the J_k's. Since, on the other hand, this continuity must be presumed, in order that the Hamiltonian equations should be satisfied on the basis of (3) and the equations

$$J_k = \text{const.}, \quad w_k = \frac{\partial H}{\partial J_k} t + \text{const.},$$

it follows that our series do not necessarily represent the motion to any required degree of accuracy, even when they happen to converge.

These results of Bruns have been supplemented by Poincaré's investigations ;[1] these lead to the following conditions : Apart from special cases, it is not possible to represent strictly the motion of the perturbed system by means of convergent f-fold Fourier series in the time and magnitudes J_k constant in time, which could serve for the fixation of the quantum states. For this reason it has hitherto been impossible to carry out the long-sought-for proof of the stability of the planetary system, *i.e.* to prove that the distances of the planets from one another and from the sun remain always within definite finite limits, even in the course of infinitely long periods of time.

Although the method of approximation under consideration is not, in the strict sense of the word, convergent, it has proved very useful in celestial mechanics. It may in fact be shown that the series possess a kind of semi-convergence.[2] If they are discontinued at certain points they give a very accurate representation of the motion of the perturbed system, not indeed for arbitrarily long periods of time, but still over what are for practical purposes long intervals. This shows that the absolute stability of atoms cannot be established purely theoretically in this way. We may, however, ignore these fundamental difficulties for the time being and carry out the calculation of the energy, in order to see if our results are in agreement with observation, as is the case in celestial mechanics.

---

[1] H. Poincaré, *Méthodes nouvelles de la Mécanique céleste*, Paris, 1892–99, vol. i, chap. v.

[2] H. Poincaré, *loc. cit.*, vol. ii, chap. viii.

§ 42.—Application to the Non-harmonic Oscillator

In the case of one degree of freedom the motion may always be found by a quadrature (*cf.* § 9); the desired result, however, is often obtained more simply by adopting the method of approximation described in § 41.

Let us take as an example a linear oscillator whose motion is slightly non-harmonic, a case already treated by a simple method (§ 12). Here we will consider an oscillator for which the potential energy contains a small term proportional to the cube of the displacement q, and a term in q^4 which is of the second order of small quantities. The Hamiltonian function has the form (*cf.* (3), § 12):

(1) $$H = H_0 + \lambda H_1 + \lambda^2 H_2 + \dots,$$

where

(2) $$H_0 = \frac{1}{2m} p^2 + \frac{m}{2} (\omega^0)^2 q^2$$
$$H_1 = a q^3$$
$$H_2 = b q^4.$$

The angle and action variables of the unperturbed motion, in this case that of the harmonic oscillator, are given by the canonical transformation with the generator (*cf.* (16), § 7)

$$V(q, w^0) = \frac{m}{2} \omega^0 q^2 \cot 2\pi w^0,$$

or by

$$q = \sqrt{\frac{J^0}{\pi \omega^0 m}} \sin 2\pi w^0$$
$$p = \sqrt{\frac{\omega^0 m J^0}{\pi}} \cos 2\pi w^0.$$

If we express H in terms of w^0 and J^0 we obtain

$$H_0 = \nu^0 J^0, \qquad (2\pi\nu^0 = \omega^0)$$

(3) $$H_1 = a \left(\frac{J^0}{\pi \omega^0 m} \right)^{\frac{3}{2}} \sin^3 2\pi w^0,$$
$$H_2 = b \left(\frac{J^0}{\pi \omega^0 m} \right)^2 \sin^4 2\pi w^0,$$
$$\dots\dots\dots\dots$$

We now find $W_1(J)$ and $\frac{\partial S_1}{\partial w^0}$ from equation (9), § 41; this gives

(4) $$W_1 = \overline{H}_1 = 0,$$

(5) $$\frac{\partial S_1}{\partial w^0} = -\frac{a}{\nu^0}\left(\frac{J}{\pi\omega^0 m}\right)^{\frac{3}{2}} \sin^3 2\pi w^0.$$

From (4) it follows that in this case the deviation from a linear restoring force does not give rise to terms in the energy which are proportional to the deviation. On the other hand, to this approximation, the motion does contain an additional term, which arises from S_1.

In order to find an additional term in the expression for energy, we must make a second approximation. From equation (17), § 41, we deduce

$$\nu^0 \frac{\partial S_2}{\partial w^0} + \frac{\partial H_1}{\partial J}\frac{\partial S_1}{\partial w^0} + H_2 = W_2$$

and

$$W_2 = \overline{\frac{\partial H_1}{\partial J}\frac{\partial S_1}{\partial w^0}} + \overline{H}_2.$$

The calculation gives

(6) $$W_2 = -\frac{15}{4}a^2 \frac{J^2}{(2\pi)^6(\nu^0)^4 m^3} + \frac{3}{2}b\frac{J^2}{(2\pi)^4(\nu^0)^2 m^2}.$$

The term proportional to a^2 is in agreement with our previous result (9), § 12.

Finally, we can deduce from (5) the effect on the oscillation of the deviation from a linear restoring force. We find that

(7) $$S_1 = \frac{a}{(2\pi)^4\nu^0}\left(\frac{2J}{\nu^0 m}\right)^{\frac{3}{2}}\left(\frac{1}{3}\sin^2 2\pi w^0 \cos 2\pi w^0 + \frac{2}{3}\cos 2\pi w^0\right)$$

and

$$w = \frac{\partial S}{\partial J}$$

$$= w^0 + \frac{\lambda a}{(2\pi)^4 2J\nu^0}\left(\frac{2J}{\nu^0 m}\right)^{\frac{3}{2}}(\sin^3 2\pi w^0 \cos 2\pi w^0 + 2\cos 2\pi w^0),$$

$$J^0 = \frac{\partial S}{\partial w^0} = J - \frac{\lambda a}{\nu^0}\left(\frac{J}{2\pi^2\nu^0 m}\right)^{\frac{3}{2}}\sin^3 2\pi w^0.$$

By solving the first equation for w^0 and substituting the values of w^0, J^0 in

$$q = \sqrt{\frac{J^0}{2\pi^2\nu^0 m}}\sin 2\pi w^0,$$

the result (11) of § 12 is arrived at by a simple calculation :

(8) $$q = \sqrt{\frac{J}{2\pi^2\nu^0 m}}\sin 2\pi w - \lambda a \frac{J}{(2\pi)^4(\nu^0)^3 m^2}(3 + \cos 4\pi w).$$

As an example of a more complicated case, we may indicate the method of calculation applicable to a spatial non-harmonic oscillator consisting of any number f of coupled linear non-harmonic oscillators.[1] Its Hamiltonian function is

$$\text{(9)} \qquad H=H_0+\lambda H_1+\lambda^2 H_2+\ldots,$$

where

$$H_0=\sum_{k=1}^{f}\left(\frac{1}{2m}p_k^2+\frac{m}{2}(\omega_k^0)^2 q_k^2,\right)$$

$$\text{(10)} \qquad H_1=\sum_k a_k q_k^3+\sum_{kj} a_{kj} q_k^2 q_j+\sum_{kjl} a_{kjl} q_k q_j q_l$$

$$H_2=\sum_k b_k q_k^4+\sum_{kj}(b_{kj} q_k^2 q_j^2+b'_{kj} q_k^3 q_j)$$
$$+\sum_{kjl} b_{kjl} q_k^2 q_j q_l+\sum_{kjlm} b_{kjlm} q_k q_j q_l q_m;$$

here we make the convention that different suffixes $j, k, l \ldots$ in the same product always signify different numbers of the set $1, 2, \ldots f$. The coefficients have, of course, the same symmetrical properties as the products of the q's which they multiply.

We shall assume that the ν_k^0's are incommensurable. Introducing the angle and action variables w^0, J^0 of the unperturbed motion, we have

$$H_0=\sum_{k=1}^{f}\nu_k^0 J_k^0,$$

and in H_1, H_2 we have to substitute

$$q_k=Q_k \sin\phi_k \qquad \left(Q_k=\sqrt{\frac{J_k^0}{\pi\omega_k^0 m}},\ \phi_k=2\pi w_k^0\right).$$

Since H_1 is a polynomial of odd degree in the q_k's, it follows at once that

$$\text{(11)} \qquad W_1=\overline{H}_1=0.$$

To calculate W_2 we have only to find the Fourier coefficients A_τ of H_1.

In order to obtain H_1 in the form of a Fourier series we make use of the identity

$$4\sin\alpha\sin\beta\sin\gamma=-\sin(\alpha+\beta+\gamma)+\sin(-\alpha+\beta+\gamma)$$
$$+\sin(\alpha-\beta+\gamma)+\sin(\alpha+\beta-\gamma),$$

---

[1] M. Born and E. Brody, *Zeitschr. f. Physik*, vol. vi, p. 140, 1921.

we find :

$$\text{(12)}\quad H_1=\tfrac{1}{4}\sum_k a_k Q_k^3(-\sin 3\phi_k+3\sin\phi_k)$$
$$+\tfrac{1}{4}\sum_{kj} a_{kj}Q_k^2Q_j[-\sin(2\phi_k+\phi_j)+2\sin\phi_j+\sin(2\phi_k-\phi_j)]$$
$$+\tfrac{1}{4}\sum_{kjl} a_{kjl}Q_kQ_jQ_l[-\sin(\phi_k+\phi_j+\phi_l)+3\sin(\phi_k+\phi_j+\phi_l)].$$

If this be arranged as a Fourier series

$$\text{(13)}\qquad H_1=\sum B_\tau \sin(\tau\phi)=\sum A_\tau e^{i(\tau\phi)},$$

where

$$\text{(14)}\qquad A_\tau=\frac{1}{2i}(B_\tau-B_{-\tau})$$

the following values are found for the coefficients :

$$B_\tau=\begin{cases} \tfrac{3}{4}a_kQ_k^3+\tfrac{1}{2}\sum_j a_{jk}Q_j^2Q_k & (\tau_k=1,\text{ all other }\tau\text{'s zero}),\\ -\tfrac{1}{4}a_kQ_k^3 & (\tau_k=3,\text{ all other }\tau\text{'s zero}),\\ -\tfrac{1}{4}a_{kj}Q_k^2Q_j & (\tau_k=2,\ \tau_j=1,\text{ all other }\tau\text{'s zero}),\\ \tfrac{1}{4}a_{kj}Q_k^2Q_j & (\tau_k=2,\ \tau_j=-1,\text{ all other }\tau\text{'s zero}),\\ -\tfrac{3}{2}a_{kjl}Q_kQ_jQ_l & (\tau_k=\tau_j=\tau_l=1,\text{ all other }\tau\text{'s zero}),\\ \tfrac{3}{2}a_{kjl}Q_kQ_jQ_l & (\tau_k=\tau_j=1,\tau_l=-1,\text{ all other }\tau\text{'s zero}),\\ 0 & (\text{in all other cases}).\end{cases}$$

The terms with like combinations of the τ's (*e.g.* $\tau_k=\tau_j=\tau_l=1$ for $(k, j, l)=(1, 2, 3)$ and $(1, 3, 2)$ and $(2, 1, 3)$, etc.), are already grouped together here.

From $|A_\tau|^2=A_\tau A_{-\tau}=\tfrac{1}{4}(B_\tau-B_{-\tau})^2$ it follows that :

$$\text{(15)}\qquad |A_\tau|^2=\begin{cases} \mathsf{A}_k=\tfrac{1}{64}(3a_kQ_k^3+2\sum_j a_{jk}Q_j^2Q_k)^2 & (|\tau_k|=1,\ \text{all other }\tau\text{'s zero}),\\ \mathsf{A}_k'=\tfrac{1}{64}a_k^2Q_k^6 & (|\tau_k|=3,\ \text{all other }\tau\text{'s zero}),\\ \mathsf{A}_{kj}=\tfrac{1}{64}a_{kj}^2Q_k^4Q_j^2 & (|\tau_k|=2,\ |\tau_j|=1,\ \text{all other }\tau\text{'s zero}),\\ \mathsf{A}_{kjl}=\tfrac{9}{16}a_{kjl}^2Q_k^2Q_j^2Q_l^2 & (|\tau_k|=|\tau_j|=|\tau_l|=1,\ \text{all other }\tau\text{'s zero}),\\ 0 & (\text{in all other cases}).\end{cases}$$

By (23), § 41, we have :

$$(16)\qquad W_2=\tfrac{3}{8}\sum_k b_k Q_k^4+\tfrac{1}{4}\sum_{kj} b_{kj}Q_k^2Q_j^2-\sum_k \frac{1}{\nu_k^0}\left(\frac{\partial A_k}{\partial J_k}+\frac{\partial A_k'}{\partial J_k}\right)$$

$$-\sum_{kj}\frac{2}{4(\nu_k^0)^2-(\nu_j^0)^2}\left(4\nu_k^0\frac{\partial A_{kj}}{\partial J_k}-\nu_j^0\frac{\partial A_{kj}}{\partial J_j}\right)$$

$$-\sum_{kjl}\left[\frac{1}{\nu_k^0+\nu_j^0+\nu_l^0}\frac{\partial A_{kjl}}{\partial J_k}+\frac{1}{\nu_k^0+\nu_j^0-\nu_l^0}\left(\frac{\partial A_{kjl}}{\partial J_k}+\frac{\partial A_{kjl}}{\partial J_j}-\frac{\partial A_{kjl}}{\partial J_l}\right)\right].$$

The quantities Q_k^2 are of the first order in the J's, the quantities A are of the third order, and so W_2 is quadratic in the J_k's. The total energy may therefore be written

$$(17)\qquad W=\sum_k \nu_k^0 J_k+\tfrac{1}{2}\sum_{kj}\nu_{kj}^0 J_k J_j.$$

The ν_{kj}^0 may be calculated from (16).

It will be seen that the method fails even to this degree of approximation if one of the following commensurabilities occur:

$$2\nu_k^0=\nu_j^0,\qquad \nu_k^0+\nu_j^0=\nu_l^0,$$

that is, if one frequency of the unperturbed system is twice one of the others, or is equal to the sum of two others.

The formula (17) finds an application in the theory of the thermal expansion of solid bodies [1] and in the theory of the band spectra of polyatomic molecules.[2]

§ 43.—Perturbations of an Intrinsically Degenerate System

As we have seen, certain denominators in the terms of the series of § 41 will be zero if an integral linear relation exists between the frequencies ν^0 of the unperturbed system, and so the method is not applicable.

We consider next the case of "intrinsic" degeneration, *i.e.* we assume that a relation

$$(\tau\nu^0)=0$$

between frequencies ν^0 of the unperturbed motion is true identically in the J^0's. In this case the angle and action variables w_k^0, J_k^0 can be transformed in such a way that they can be separated into non-degenerate w_α^0's and J_α^0's, and degenerate w_ρ^0's and J_ρ^0's ($\nu_\rho^0=0$)

[1] For literature on this subject, see M. Born, *Atomtheorie des festen Zustandes*, Leipzig, 1923; also *Encykl. d. math. Wiss.*, v, 25, § 29f.

[2] M. Born and E. Hückel, *Physikal. Zeitschr.*, vol. xxiv, p. 1, 1923; M. Born and W. Heisenberg, *Ann. d. Physik*, vol. lxxiv, p. 1, 1924.

($\alpha=1, 2 \ldots s$; $\rho=s+1 \ldots f$). H_0 depends then only on the J_α^0's (§ 15, p. 91).

We might now try

$$S=\sum_k w_k^0 J_k+\lambda S_1+\lambda^2 S_2+\cdots.$$

On substituting in the Hamilton-Jacobi equation (7), § 41, equation (9) would again result; but in averaging subsequently over the unperturbed motion, $H_1(w^0, J)$ would remain dependent on w_ρ^0. We cannot therefore apply the method without further consideration. The deeper physical reason for this is that the variables w^0, J^0, with which the angle and action variables w, J of the perturbed motion are correlated, are not determined by the unperturbed motion; on account of its degenerate character, other degenerate action variables, connected with the J_ρ^0's by linear non-integral relations, could be introduced in place of the J_ρ^0's, by a suitable choice of co-ordinates.

Our first problem will therefore be to find the proper variables $\bar{w}_\rho^0$, $\bar{J}_\rho^0$ in place of the w_ρ^0's, J_ρ^0's, to serve as the limiting values in an approximation to w_ρ, J_ρ. For this purpose we make use of the method of secular perturbations already discussed (*cf.* § 18). It consists in finding a transformation $w^0 J^0 \rightarrow \bar{w}^0 \bar{J}^0$ such that the first term of the perturbation function, when averaged over the unperturbed motion, depends only on the $\bar{J}^0$'s. We assume at the start that $\overline{H}_1$ is not identically zero; we shall return later to the case where it vanishes identically. We have now, as before, to solve a Hamiltonian-Jacobi equation

$$\overline{H}_1(J_\alpha^0;\ w_\rho^0, J_\rho^0)=W_1(\bar{J}^0). \tag{1}$$

We have considered this problem in detail in § 18. If the equation (1) is soluble by separation of the variables, we obtain new angle and action variables $\bar{w}_k^0$, $\bar{J}_k^0$. If the generator of the transformation is

$$V=\sum_k w_k^0 \bar{J}_k^0+V_1(w_\rho^0 \bar{J}_k^0)$$

we have

$$J_\alpha^0=\bar{J}_\alpha^0; \qquad J_\rho^0=\bar{J}_\rho^0+\frac{\partial V_1}{\partial w_\rho^0}$$

$$\bar{w}_\alpha^0=w_\alpha^0+\frac{\partial V_1}{\partial \bar{J}_\alpha^0}; \qquad \bar{w}_\rho^0=w_\rho^0+\frac{\partial V_1}{\partial \bar{J}_\rho^0}.$$

We now introduce $\bar{w}_k^0 \bar{J}_k^0$ into the Hamiltonian function of the motion:

(2) $$H=H_0(\bar{J}_\alpha{}^0)+\lambda H_1(\bar{w}_k{}^0, \bar{J}_k{}^0)+\lambda^2 H_2(\bar{w}_k{}^0, \bar{J}_k{}^0)+\dots$$

and, as in § 41, try to find the generator $S(\bar{w}_k{}^0, J_k)$

$$S=S_0+\lambda S_1+\lambda^2 S_2+\dots$$

of a canonical transformation, which transforms the $\bar{w}_k{}^0$'s and $\bar{J}_k{}^0$'s into angle and action variables w_k, J_k of the perturbed motion. This again leads to the equations (9), (17), and generally (18) of § 41, if, instead of $\bar{w}_k{}^0$, $\bar{J}_k{}^0$ we again write $w_k{}^0$, $J_k{}^0$.

The solution takes a somewhat different form, since the quantities $\frac{\partial H_0}{\partial J_\rho}$ vanish. If we solve equation (11) of § 41:

(3) $$\sum_\alpha \frac{\partial H_0}{\partial J_\alpha}\frac{\partial S_1}{\partial w_\alpha{}^0}=-\tilde{H}_1,$$

where $\tilde{H}_1=H_1-\bar{H}_1$ is the periodic component of H_1, there remains in S_1 an indeterminate additive function R_1 which depends on the J_k's and also on the $w_\rho{}^0$'s but not on the $w_\alpha{}^0$'s. We shall determine this in the course of the next approximation. S_1 now takes the form

(4) $$S_1=S_1{}^0+R_1,$$

where $S_1{}^0$ can be found by solving (3).

If this be substituted in equation (17), § 41, for the next approximation

(5) $$\sum_\alpha \frac{\partial H^0}{\partial J_\alpha}\frac{\partial S_2}{\partial w_\alpha{}^0}+\sum_{kj}\frac{1}{2}\frac{\partial^2 H^0}{\partial J_k \partial J_j}\frac{\partial S_1}{\partial w_k{}^0}\frac{\partial S_1}{\partial w_j{}^0}+\sum_k \frac{\partial H_1}{\partial J_k}\frac{\partial S_1}{\partial w_k{}^0}+H_2=W_2(J)$$

all the terms containing $S_1{}^0$ can be taken as known; the terms in R_1 are not yet known, so that (17), § 41, takes the form

(6) $$\sum_\alpha \frac{\partial H^0}{\partial J_\alpha}\frac{\partial S_2}{\partial w_\alpha{}^0}+\Phi(w_k{}^0, J_k)+\sum_\rho \frac{\partial H_1}{\partial J_\rho}\frac{\partial R_1}{\partial w_\rho{}^0}=W_2(J),$$

Φ being a known function. It should be noticed that the coefficients $\frac{\partial^2 H_0}{\partial J_k \partial J_j}$ of the quadratic terms in the differential equation differ from zero only if both J_k and J_j belong to the J_α's.

From equation (6), $W_2(J)$, R_1 and a part $S_2{}^0$ of S_2 may be determined. Indicating mean values over a unit cube of the $w_\alpha{}^0$-space by a single bar as before, and mean values over a unit cube of the whole $w_k{}^0$-space by a double bar, we have

(7) $$W_2(J)=\bar{\bar{\Phi}};$$

further

(8) $$\sum_\rho \frac{\partial H_1}{\partial J_\rho}\frac{\partial R_1}{\partial w_\rho^0} = -\tilde{\bar{\Phi}},$$

where $\tilde{\bar{\Phi}} = \bar{\Phi} - \bar{\bar{\Phi}}$. This equation is of the same type as (3) and may be solved in an analogous manner. Finally we have also

(9) $$\sum_\alpha \frac{\partial H^0}{\partial J_\alpha}\frac{\partial S_2}{\partial w_\alpha^0} = -\tilde{\Phi}.$$

We can now write

(10) $$S_2 = S_2^0 + R_2$$

and determine S_2^0 as a function of w_k^0, J_k from (9); R_2 is a function of w_ρ^0, J_k, which so far remains undetermined.

The process may be continued; the next step determines $W_3(J)$, $R_2(w_\rho^0, J_k)$ and a part S_3^0 of S_3, etc. The final result is again a series for the energy

(11) $$W = W_0(J_\alpha) + \lambda W_1(J_k) + \lambda^2 W_2(J_k) + \cdots.$$

These considerations provide a justification for our previous method of determining the secular perturbations (§ 18) by regarding them as first approximations in a method of successive approximations. The higher approximations lead to periodic variations of the w_k^0's and J_k^0's, whose amplitudes are at most of the order of magnitude of λ. Secular motions of w_α^0, J_α^0 do not occur; also in addition to the secular motions of w_ρ^0, J_ρ^0 which we recalculated in the first stage of the process, only periodic variations occur having frequencies of the same order of magnitude and amplitudes proportional to λ.

We see further that the terms $\tilde{H}_1 = H_1 - \bar{H}_1$ merely contribute to the energy an amount of the second order in λ, although they produce effects of the first order in the motion of the system.

The method hitherto discussed fails if

$$\bar{H}_1 = 0$$

identically (in the w_ρ^0's, J_k^0's), a case which very frequently occurs. A more rigorous investigation shows that the secular motion of w_ρ^0, J_ρ^0 and the additional energy W_2 follow from the Hamilton-Jacobi equation, if we substitute in (5) the expression for S_1 given by (3), and average the equation over the unperturbed motion. The procedure can be continued, the main object being to eliminate H_1 altogether from the perturbation function by means of a suitable canonical substitution.[1]

Further special cases can occur, *e.g.* when the secular motion de-

---

[1] See M. Born and W. Heisenberg, *Ann. d. Physik*, vol. lxxiv, p. 1, 1924.

termined by (1) is itself degenerate, inasmuch as commensurabilities exist between the quantities $\frac{\partial W_1}{\partial J_\rho}$. The secular motions of the variables which are still degenerate to a first approximation would then have to be found from the second approximation.

§ 44.—An Example of Accidental Degeneration

The method of approximation described in § 41 can also fail when the unperturbed system is not intrinsically degenerate, if there exist relations of the form

$$\sum \tau_k \nu_k^0 = 0 \tag{1}$$

for the unperturbed motion with those values of the J_k^0's which are fixed by quantum conditions. In such cases we speak of accidental degeneration. The w_k^0's may then be chosen so that for those particular values of J_k^0 the frequencies ν_ρ^0 vanish ($\rho = s+1 \ldots f$) and the frequencies $\nu_\alpha (\alpha = 1, 2 \ldots s)$ are incommensurable. In the unperturbed motion, however, the J_ρ's are also to be determined by quantum conditions, as already mentioned. Accidentally degenerate degrees of freedom are therefore subject to quantum conditions, intrinsically degenerate are not.

Accidental degeneration is a rare and remarkable exception in astronomy; the odds against (1) being exactly fulfilled are infinite. A close approach to it is found in the case of perturbations of some minor planets (Achilles, Patroclus, Hector, Nestor) which have very nearly the same period of revolution as Jupiter. In atomic theory, on the other hand, where the J_k^0's can only have discrete values, accidental degeneration is very common.

We may illustrate the most important properties of accidentally degenerate systems by a simple example.[1]

Consider two similar rotating bodies of moment of inertia A, with a common axis, their positions being defined by the angles ϕ_1 and ϕ_2. As long as they do not interact they rotate uniformly. The angle and action variables are given by

$$w_1^0 = \frac{\phi_1}{2\pi}, \qquad J_1^0 = 2\pi p_1,$$

$$w_2^0 = \frac{\phi_2}{2\pi}, \qquad J_2^0 = 2\pi p_2,$$

[1] M. Born and W. Heisenberg, *Zeitschr. f. Physik*, vol. xiv, p. 44, 1923.

where p_1, p_2 are the angular momenta. The energy is

$$H_0 = \frac{1}{8\pi^2 A}[(J_1^0)^2 + (J_2^0)^2] = W_0. \tag{2}$$

If we fix J_1^0 and J_2^0 by means of quantum conditions, the two frequencies of rotation are always commensurable; in particular, they are equal when $J_1^0 = J_2^0$.

Let us now suppose the motion to be perturbed by an interaction between the two rotators, consisting of a couple proportional to $\sin(\phi_1 - \phi_2)$; the energy is then

$$H = H_0 + \lambda H_1 \tag{3}$$

where

$$H_1 = 1 - \cos 2\pi(w_1^0 - w_2^0) \tag{4}$$

and λ measures the strength of coupling. In this case we can give a rigorous solution of the problem of the perturbed motion. If we carry out the canonical transformation

$$\begin{aligned} \tfrac{1}{2}(w_1^0 + w_2^0) &= w^0, \qquad & J_1^0 + J_2^0 &= J^0, \\ \tfrac{1}{2}(w_1^0 - w_2^0) &= w'^0, \qquad & J_1^0 - J_2^0 &= J'^0, \end{aligned} \tag{5}$$

then

$$H = \frac{(J^0)^2 + (J'^0)^2}{16\pi^2 A} + \lambda(1 - \cos 4\pi w'^0), \tag{6}$$

and this expression involves only one co-ordinate w'^0. w^0 is cyclic, and consequently J^0 is constant; suppose its value is J. Since the determinant of the transformation (5) of the J_k^0's is not ± 1, it follows that J^0 and J'^0 are not action variables of the unperturbed system. J can therefore only be fixed by quantum conditions in such a way that, in passing over to the unperturbed system, $J + J'^0$ is an integral multiple of h. Instead of J'^0 we have, in the case of the perturbed motion, the action integral

$$J' = \oint J'^0 dw'^0 = \oint \sqrt{16\pi^2 A[W - \lambda(1 - \cos 4\pi w'^0)] - J^2}\, dw'^0,$$

$$J' = \oint \frac{\sqrt{8\lambda A}}{k} \sqrt{1 - k^2 \sin^2 2\pi w'^0}\, d(2\pi w'^0), \tag{7}$$

where

$$\frac{2\lambda}{W - \dfrac{J^2}{16\pi^2 A}} = k^2. \tag{8}$$

If we put

$$\oint \sqrt{1 - k^2 \sin^2 \psi}\, d\psi = 4E(k),$$

then

$$\text{(9)} \qquad J' = 8\frac{\sqrt{2\lambda A}}{k}E(k).$$

In order to obtain the energy as a function of the action variables, the equation (9) must be solved for k and the solution substituted in the equation

$$\text{(10)} \qquad W = \frac{J^2}{16\pi^2 A} + \frac{2\lambda}{k^2},$$

derived from (8). For $k>1$, w'^0 executes a motion of libration within the libration limits

$$\sin 2\pi w'^0 = \pm\frac{1}{k},$$

and the integral $E(k)$ has to be evaluated over a complete period between limits $\sin\psi = \pm 1/k$. For $k<1$, w'^0 performs a rotational motion; the limits of the integral are 0 and 2π, and $E(k)$ denotes the complete elliptic integral of the second kind.

For the purposes of further calculation we have to distinguish between two different cases:

I. $J_1{}^0 \neq J_2{}^0$; $J'^0 \neq 0$; the unperturbed motion has two unequal frequencies. $W_0 - \frac{J^2}{16\pi^2 A}$ is not zero, and k vanishes with λ. For sufficiently small values of λ, the motion of w'^0 is clearly a rotation, and for $E(k)$ we can make use of the expansion

$$\text{(11)} \qquad E(k) = \frac{\pi}{2}\left(1 - \frac{k^2}{4} + \ldots\right).$$

We find then from (9):

$$\frac{2\lambda}{k^2} = \frac{J'^2}{16\pi^2 A} + \lambda,$$

and from (10):

$$\text{(12)} \qquad W = \frac{1}{16\pi^2 A}(J^2 + J'^2) + \lambda.$$

II. $J_1{}^0 = J_2{}^0$, $J'^0 = 0$, *i.e.* the frequencies of the unperturbed motion are equal. We shall then have $W_0 - \frac{J^2}{16\pi^2 A} = 0$, the denominator in equation (8) will be of the same order as λ, and for finite values of W_1, k^2 is of the order of magnitude 1. Both libration and rotation of w'^0 can occur, and the expansion (11) is no longer valid. For the larger values of W_1, we have $k<1$, and therefore a rotation;

for the smaller values of W_1 we have $k>1$, and hence libration (*cf.* fig. 38). The libration limits approach one another as W_1 diminishes; for $W_1=0$ the curve representing the motion in the (w'^0, J'^0)-plane contracts to the libration centre $w'^0=0$, $J'^0=0$, or $w'^0=\frac{1}{2}$, $J'^0=0$; negative values of W_1 do not occur since, by (7), J′ would then be imaginary. Disregarding the limitations imposed

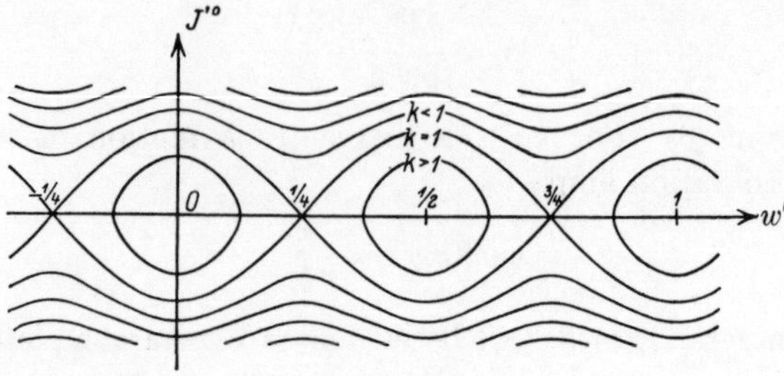

FIG. 38.

by quantum conditions, all these motions are possible, since W_1 can assume a continuous set of values.

The quantum theory requires, however, that J′ should be an integral multiple of h; moreover, J′ is proportional to $\sqrt{\lambda}$ (by (7)) and must, therefore, be capable of becoming arbitrarily small for small values of λ. These two conditions are fulfilled only by the value

$$J'=0.$$

In the case of a rotation of w'^0 this is not possible, and for a libration it can hold only in the limiting cases $w'^0=0$, $J'^0=0$, and $w'^0=\frac{1}{2}$, $J'^0=0$. Hence in the perturbed motion the two rotating bodies are exactly in phase. We have only one frequency, but two quantum conditions.

If all that is required is that the equations of motions shall be satisfied without the state necessarily being stable, the cases $w'^0=\frac{1}{4}$, $J'^0=0$, and $w'^0=\frac{3}{4}$, $J'^0=0$ are also possible.

In any neighbourhood of each of the motions defined by $w'^0=\frac{1}{4}$ and $\frac{3}{4}$ there are, however, motions of rotation and libration for which w'^0 takes values widely different from $\frac{1}{4}$ or $\frac{3}{4}$. For $w'^0=\frac{1}{4}$ or $\frac{3}{4}$ the motion with a definite phase relation is therefore unstable, in the mechanical sense of the word. In this case the motions $w'^0=\frac{1}{4}$ and $\frac{3}{4}$ are also energetically unstable, inasmuch as H is then a maximum. We shall also meet with cases, however, where the mechanically stable motion is energetically unstable.

These special motions can be very simply characterised by the fact that they are the only solutions of the equations of motion

$$(13) \qquad \frac{dw'^0}{dt} = \frac{\partial H}{\partial J'^0}, \qquad \frac{dJ'^0}{dt} = -\frac{\partial H}{\partial w'^0}$$

for which w'^0 is constant and hence for which the bodies rotate with a constant difference of phase. It then follows from the conservation of energy

$$H(J^0, J'^0, w'^0) = W,$$

that since J^0 is constant, J'^0 must likewise be constant ; consequently

$$\frac{\partial H}{\partial w'^0} = 0.$$

According to (6) this equation has the solutions

$$w'^0 = 0, \tfrac{1}{4}, \tfrac{1}{2}, \tfrac{3}{4}.$$

Putting (6) into the first of equations (13) it then follows that

$$J'^0 = 0.$$

This is our first example of a case in which the selection of a particularly simple motion as a stationary state, from the mass of complex mechanical motions, is due entirely to the quantum conditions. We shall see quite generally that the simple motions with phase relations have a special significance.

§ 45.—Phase Relations in the Case of Bohr Atoms and Molecules

As already mentioned, the accidental degeneration of the unperturbed system is a very exceptional case in astronomy. In atomic physics, on the other hand, it plays an important rôle, for firstly, according to Bohr's ideas, a whole set of equivalent orbits occur in the higher atoms ; and again according to the quantum theory the periods of rotation of the Kepler motions with different principal quantum numbers are always commensurable, since they vary as the cubes of whole numbers.

After the discussion of the example in the foregoing paragraph, we should expect quite generally, in such cases of accidental degeneration, that the quantum conditions would enforce exact phase relations, and consequently particularly simple types of motion. Since the proof of this for any degree of approximation is somewhat complicated, and since the necessary mathematical method can only be given later, we shall indicate here a simpler method by means of which the phase relations can be found to a first approximation only.

In this section we shall therefore neglect all expressions involving higher power of λ than the first, even, for example, $\lambda^{\frac{3}{2}}$.

If for the moment we disregard the presence of intrinsic degenerations, but assume the existence of several accidental degenerations, we can choose the angle and action variables w_k^0, J_k^0 ($k=1, 2 \ldots f$) of the unperturbed system so that the ν_α^0's ($\alpha=1, 2 \ldots s$) differ from zero and are incommensurable, while $\nu_\rho^0 (\rho=s+1 \ldots f)$ vanish for the particular values which the J_k^0's have in the case of the unperturbed motion. We assume therefore that an $(f-s)$-fold accidental degeneration exists.

We may write (with an alteration of suffixes from those used previously) the Hamiltonian function in the form

(1) $$H=H_0(J_k^0)+\lambda H_2(w_k^0, J_k^0)$$

and endeavour to represent the energy constant as a series of the form

(2) $$W=W_0(J_k)+\lambda W_2(J_k).$$

If, as before, we made the assumption

$$S=S_0(w_k^0, J_k)+\lambda S_2(w_k^0, J_k),$$

we should obtain for S_2 expressions in which denominators occur which vanish for $\lambda=0$, *i.e.* S is no longer an analytic function of λ at $\lambda=0$. Now Bohlin [1] has shown that a series in increasing powers of $\sqrt{\lambda}$ of the form

(3) $$S=S_0+\sqrt{\lambda}S_1+\lambda S_2+\ldots$$

is what is required. Here again (*cf.* § 41)

$$S_0=\sum_k w_k^0 J_k,$$

and S_1, S_2 are periodic in the w_k^0's (period 1). If $\frac{\partial S}{\partial w_k^0}$ be substituted for J_k^0 in the Hamiltonian function (1), we obtain an expression of the form (2) if the equations

(4_0) $$H_0(J)=W_0(J)$$

(4_1) $$\sum_\alpha \frac{\partial H_0}{\partial J_\alpha}\frac{\partial S_1}{\partial w_\alpha^0}=0$$

(4_2) $$\sum_\alpha \frac{\partial H^0}{\partial J}\frac{\partial S_2}{\partial w_\alpha^0}+\frac{1}{2!}\sum_{kj}\frac{\partial^2 H_0}{\partial J_k \partial J_j}\frac{\partial S_1}{\partial w_k^0}\frac{\partial S_1}{\partial w_j^0}+H_2=W_2(J)$$

are satisfied.

[1] K. Bohlin, "Über eine neue Annäherungsmethode in der Störungstheorie," *Bihang till K. Svenska Vet. Akad. Handl.*, vol. xiv, Afd. i, Nr. 5, 1888; see also, for example, H. Poincaré, *Méthodes nouvelles*, vol. ii, chap. xix, and C. L. Charlier, *Mechanik des Himmels*, vol. ii, p. 446. The application to the quantum theory is due to L. Nordheim, *Zeitschr. f. Physik*, vol. xvii, p. 316, 1923; vol. xxi, p. 242, 1924.

W_0 is found from (4_0). Since S_1 is to be a periodic function of the w_k^0's, it follows from (4_1) that

$$\frac{\partial S_1}{\partial w_\alpha^0}=0;$$

the quantities $\frac{\partial S_1}{\partial w_\rho^0}$ remain, however, indeterminate. By averaging over the unperturbed motion (that is, over the w_α^0's only) we obtain from (4):

$$(5)\qquad \frac{1}{2!}\sum_{\rho,\sigma}\frac{\partial^2 H_0}{\partial J_\rho \partial J_\sigma}\frac{\partial S_1}{\partial w_\rho^0}\frac{\partial S_1}{\partial w_\sigma^0}+\overline{H}_2(w_\rho^0)=W_2 \qquad (\rho,\sigma=s+1\ldots f).$$

(Suffixes ρ and σ both refer to accidentally degenerate variables.) This is a partial differential equation of the Hamilton-Jacobi type. It does not admit of integration in all cases, and the method fails, therefore, for the determination of the motion for arbitrary values of the J_k's. We can show, however, as in the example of § 44, that the motions for which the w_ρ^0's are constant to zero approximation, and remain constant also to a first approximation, are stationary motions in the sense of quantum theory.

We shall now demonstrate this for one accidentally degenerate degree of freedom, the last (f). In this case equation (5) has the form

$$(5')\qquad \frac{1}{2!}\frac{\partial^2 H_0}{\partial J_f^2}\left(\frac{\partial S_1}{\partial w_f^0}\right)^2+\overline{H}_2(w_f^0)=W_2.$$

This differential equation of the Hamilton-Jacobi type for one degree of freedom can always be solved by the method of quadratures and we find

$$(6)\qquad S_1=\int\frac{\partial S_1}{\partial w_f^0}dw_f^0=\int\sqrt{\frac{W_2-\overline{H}_2(w_f^0)}{\frac{1}{2!}\frac{\partial^2 H_0}{\partial J_f^2}}}\,dw_f^0.$$

The constant of integration must satisfy the condition that

$$(7)\qquad \begin{aligned} J_f=\oint J_f^0 dw_f^0 &=\oint\frac{\partial S_0}{\partial w_f^0}dw_f^0+\sqrt{\lambda}\oint\frac{\partial S_1}{\partial w_f^0}dw_f^0\\ &=J_f\oint dw_f^0+\sqrt{\lambda}\oint\frac{\partial S_1}{\partial w_f^0}dw_f^0\end{aligned}$$

is an integral multiple of h. From this it follows, according to whether w_f^0 performs a rotation ($\oint dw_f^0=1$) or a libration ($\oint dw_f^0=0$),

$$\sqrt{\lambda}\oint\frac{\partial S_1}{\partial w_f^0}dw_f^0=0$$

or

(8) $$\sqrt{\lambda}\oint\frac{\partial S_1}{\partial w_f^0}dw_f^0=J_f=n_f h.$$

The integrand $\frac{\partial S_1}{\partial w_f^0}$ is never negative along the path of integration. Hence in the case of rotation we must have

$$\frac{\partial S_1}{\partial w_f^0}=0$$

for all values of w_f^0, *i.e.* $\overline{H}_2$ is totally independent of w_f^0. It follows, of course, that with this approximation, nothing is known about w_f^0. In the case of libration, J_f must decrease to zero with $\sqrt{\lambda}$, but since on the quantum theory J_f must be an integral multiple of h, it follows that $J_f=0$, *i.e.* the integral is to be taken over an infinitely short section of the (w_f^0, J_f^0)-plane; the libration contracts therefore to a point. Since w_f^0 is now constant during the motion, the perturbed motion has only $f-1$ frequencies, and has therefore no higher degree of periodicity than the unperturbed motion.

The value which w_f^0 has for the motion must be a double root of $W_2-\overline{H}_2(w_f^0)$; it must therefore satisfy the equations

(9) $$W_2=\overline{H}_2(w_f^0)$$

and

(10) $$\frac{\partial\overline{H}_2}{\partial w_f^0}=0.$$

The fact that w_f^0 can only have certain definite values, namely, the roots of (10), signifies a phase relation in the motion of the system.

If the motion determined in this way is to be actually the limiting case of a libration—and only if this is the case will it be stable—the radicand of (6) must be negative in the neighbourhood of the root w_f^0, *i.e.*

$$\frac{\overline{H}_2(w_f^0)}{\frac{1}{2!}\frac{\partial^2 H_0}{\partial J_f^0}}$$

must have a minimum. If the latter condition is not fulfilled the equations of motion

$$\dot{w}_f^0=\frac{\partial\overline{H}_2}{\partial J_f^0},\qquad \dot{J}_f^0=-\frac{\partial\overline{H}_2}{\partial w_f^0}$$

will still be satisfied, but in any immediate neighbourhood of the solution with constant values of w_f^0 and J_f^0 there will be solutions of the equations of motion for which the co-ordinates differ widely from these constant values. The motions determined by (9) and (10) are thus mechanically unstable.

In the case where $\frac{\partial^2 H_0}{\partial J_f^2}$ is positive (as in the example of the two rotators, § 44), the mechanically stable motion has the smallest value of $\overline{H}_2$. If, however, $\frac{\partial^2 H_0}{\partial J_f^2}$ is negative (this case occurs in atomic mechanics), the mechanically stable motion has the largest value of $\overline{H}_2$, and the mechanically unstable the smallest. As yet we are unable to decide whether only the mechanically stable motions are permissible for stationary states. If only the stable motions are permitted it can so happen that the perturbation energy $\overline{H}_2$ is a maximum, as opposed to static models where the energy is always a minimum. If mechanically unstable motions be also allowed (on the quantum theory their neighbouring motions are not allowed as they do not satisfy quantum conditions) it may happen that the normal state (state of minimum energy) is included among them.

In order to illustrate this behaviour, consider two electrons revolving in circular Kepler orbits (it is immaterial whether they revolve about the same nucleus or about different nuclei) and at the same time exercising small perturbations on one another. Suppose the position and form of the orbits are fixed, and let us consider only the variation of the phase of the motion under the influence of the perturbing forces. The energy of the unperturbed motion is

$$H = -A\left(\frac{1}{J_1^2} + \frac{1}{J_2^2}\right),$$

the unperturbed frequencies are

$$\nu_1 = \frac{2A}{J_1^3}, \qquad \nu_2 = \frac{2A}{J_2^3}.$$

They are therefore commensurable for each quantum state ($J_1 = n_1 h$; $J_2 = n_2 h$), since $\tau_1\nu_1 + \tau_2\nu_2 = 0$ if $\tau_1 = n_1^3$, $\tau_2 = -n_2^3$, and these τ_1, τ_2 are both integral. If now, by means of a canonical substitution, we separate the angle and action variables into those which are degenerate and those which are not, we have to put

$$\bar{w}_1 = \frac{1}{2}(\tau_1 w_1 - \tau_2 w_2), \qquad J_1 = \frac{\tau_1}{2}\left(\bar{J}_2 + \bar{J}_1\right),$$

$$\bar{w}_2 = \frac{1}{2}(\tau_1 w_1 + \tau_2 w_2), \qquad J_2 = \frac{\tau_2}{2}\left(\bar{J}_2 - \bar{J}_1\right),$$

we find

$$\mathrm{H}_0=-4\mathrm{A}\left[\frac{1}{\tau_1^2(\bar{\mathrm{J}}_2+\bar{\mathrm{J}}_1)^2}+\frac{1}{\tau_2^2(\bar{\mathrm{J}}_2-\bar{\mathrm{J}}_1)^2}\right];$$

$\bar{\mathrm{J}}_2$ is the degenerate action variable. If we now evaluate

$$\frac{\partial^2\mathrm{H}_0}{\partial\bar{\mathrm{J}}_2^{\,2}}=-24\ \mathrm{A}\left[\frac{1}{\tau_1^2(\bar{\mathrm{J}}_2+\bar{\mathrm{J}}_1)^4}+\frac{1}{\tau_2^2(\bar{\mathrm{J}}_2-\bar{\mathrm{J}}_1)^4}\right],$$

it will be seen that this expression is negative for all values of $\bar{\mathrm{J}}$. Hence in this case the minimum of the perturbation energy $\bar{\mathrm{H}}_2$ corresponds to the unstable motion.

It will be seen that this result is due to the fact that

$$\frac{\partial^2\mathrm{H}_0}{\partial\mathrm{J}^2}<0,$$

where H_0 denotes the energy of the unperturbed Kepler motion. It will therefore be true generally when electronic orbits in atoms or molecules exert a mutual influence on one another.

Our considerations show that in the case of one degree of freedom the motions for which phase relations hold are the only ones possible according to the quantum theory. The same is true if the equation (5) is soluble by separation of the variables or can be made so by a transformation of the w_ρ^0's. Equations of the form (6) are then obtained for the individual terms of S_1, and all conclusions which follow from this equation can be arrived at in the same manner.

In the general case, it is true, the necessity for phase relations cannot be proved; it can, however, be shown that there are perturbed motions with the same degree of periodicity s as the unperturbed, for which phase relations exist and which are of significance from the point of view of the quantum theory.

The differential equation (5) is equivalent to a system of canonical equations

$$\dot{q}_\rho=\frac{\partial\mathrm{K}}{\partial p_\rho},\qquad \dot{p}_\rho=-\frac{\partial\mathrm{K}}{\partial q_\rho},$$

in which K is the expression obtained by replacing the w_ρ^0's in the left-hand side of (5) by "co-ordinates" q_ρ, and the $\frac{\partial\mathrm{S}_1}{\partial w_\rho^0}$'s by the conjugate "momenta" p_ρ, *i.e.*:

(11) $$\mathrm{K}=\tfrac{1}{2}\sum_{\rho\sigma}\nu_{\rho\sigma}p_\rho p_\sigma+\bar{\mathrm{H}}_2(q_\rho),$$

the quantities $\nu_{\rho\sigma}=\frac{\partial^2\mathrm{H}_0}{\partial\mathrm{J}_\rho\partial\mathrm{J}_\sigma}$ being treated as constants. The mechanical system defined by (11) has, in general, several equilibrium configurations : for if the values of $q_\rho = q_\rho^0$ be determined from

$$\frac{\partial K}{\partial q_\rho} = \frac{\partial \bar{H}_2}{\partial q_\rho} = 0,$$

$q_\rho = q_\rho^0$, $p_\rho = 0$ will be solutions of the canonical equations. Also

(12) $$\frac{\partial S_1}{\partial w_\rho^0} = 0, \qquad S_1 = \text{const.}$$

is a particular integral of the differential equation (5), if the constant value of w_ρ^0 be calculated from the equations

(13) $$\frac{\partial \bar{H}_2}{\partial w_\rho^0} = 0$$

and

$$W_2 = \bar{H}_2(w_\rho^0).$$

This method fails only if the system of equations (13) is not soluble for the w_ρ^0's, *i.e.* if the " Hessian determinant "

$$\left| \frac{\partial^2 \bar{H}_2}{\partial w_\rho^0 \partial w_\sigma^0} \right|$$

vanishes.

The motion of the perturbed system found in this way has the same degree of periodicity s as the unperturbed motion. The fact that the constants w_ρ^0 can have only certain definite values indicates the existence of phase relations in the perturbed motion.

The motion is stable only if the auxiliary variables q_ρ of equation (11) have a stable equilibrium for $q_\rho = q_\rho^0$. The neighbouring motions then consist of small oscillations about the particular motion under consideration.

The fact that the motions found here satisfy the quantum conditions can be seen as follows. J_ρ^0 is constant and equal to the value which it has in the case of the unperturbed motion ; in addition,

$$J_\rho^0 = J_\rho + \sqrt{\lambda} \frac{\partial S_1}{\partial w_\rho^0},$$

and so, by (12),

$$J_\rho^0 = J_\rho \, ;$$

so that J_ρ is also quantised.

§ 46.—Limiting Degeneration

A common characteristic of the two cases of degeneration which have been considered is the fact that the trajectory occupies a region of less than f dimensions in the co-ordinate space. A third possibility, characterised by the same property, occurs in the case of multiply periodic systems; it arises in a number of atomic problems and leads to typical difficulties in the application of the quantum theory. It is therefore advisable to generalise somewhat the conception of degeneration and to regard a multiply periodic motion as degenerate whenever the trajectory occupies a region of less dimensions than the number of degrees of freedom.

Generalising our previous terminology (§ 15, p. 92), we shall refer to the number of dimensions of the region of the q-space filled by the trajectory of the motion as the degree of periodicity of the motion. A motion is thus always degenerate when its degree of periodicity is less than f.

We shall consider a system whose motion may be found by the method of separation of the variables when unperturbed. As we have seen (§ 14), in separable systems the trajectory in the q-space is bounded by a series of surfaces, each of the separation co-ordinates oscillating backwards and forwards between two surfaces of such a series. In certain cases these surfaces may coincide. The number of dimensions of the region filled by the path is then decreased by 1.

This coincidence of two libration limits characterises the third and, it appears, last possibility of a degeneration.

An example will at once make clear what is meant. Let us take the relativistic Kepler motion, or, in other words, motion in an ellipse with a perihelion rotation. In general, the path fills a circular ring and, therefore, a two-dimensional region, densely everywhere. The boundaries for the libration of the radius vector are here concentric circles.

If now we suppose the eccentricity of the initial orbit to decrease, the two limiting circles approach one another until finally they coalesce and the orbit becomes a one-dimensional circular orbit. This does not involve any degeneration in the previous sense of the word. Actually, however, one angle variable (in this case the longitude of the perihelion) will be indeterminate owing to its geometrical definition, whilst one of the action variables assumes a limiting value consistent with being real. For the relativistic Kepler motion, for instance, we always have $J_2 \leq J_1$, while here $J_2 = J_1$. We may therefore call this appropriately "limiting degeneration."

Other examples are provided by an orbit perpendicular to the direction of the field in the case of the Zeeman effect and, in the case of the problem of two centres (§ 39), by one which is confined to the surface of an ellipsoid of rotation, etc. For the purpose of illustration we shall continue to speak of circular orbits, eccentricities, etc., although our considerations will have a much more general significance.

Let the degree of freedom subject to limiting degeneration be denoted by the separation co-ordinate q_f, whose libration limits coincide. The action variable corresponding to it,

$$J_f^0 = \oint p_f dq_f,$$

has, obviously, the value 0. If we allow perturbing forces to act on such a motion with $J_f^0=0$, the degree of freedom q_f will in general be excited (quite apart from the quantum theory) and the phase integral J_f will differ from zero (in our example the path would not remain circular).

According to the principles of the quantum theory, J_f must be an integral multiple of h; since it must be equivalent to J_f^0 for a vanishingly small perturbation, it can have only the value zero. We shall see that the only solution which satisfies this condition is that for which J_f^0 also remains zero during the perturbed motion. The perturbed motion has therefore (as in the case of accidental degeneration) the same degree of periodicity as the unperturbed motion.

The problem of finding this solution involves a mathematical difficulty. Returning to our example, the perturbation function contains in general terms which are linear in the eccentricity, that is in terms in $\sqrt{J_f^0}$.[1] Now this can occur quite generally if the unperturbed system has limiting degeneration. Terms in $1/\sqrt{J_f^0}$ then occur in

$$\frac{dw_f^0}{dt} = \frac{\partial H}{\partial J_f^0},$$

i.e. in passing over in the limit to the unperturbed motion, the co-ordinate w_f^0 (perihelion longitude) will vary very rapidly and will have no finite limiting value. The expansions of § 41 are now no longer applicable.

The behaviour of the variables $J_f^0 w_f^0$ resembles that of polar co-ordinates: w_f^0 is indeterminate when $J_f^0=0$. We can, as a matter of fact, overcome the difficulty which has been mentioned by replacing them by the Poincaré "rectangular" canonical co-ordinates:[2]

---

[1] In our previous notation the eccentricity is

$$\varepsilon = \sqrt{1 - \frac{J_2^2}{J_1^2}},$$

the degree of freedom subject to limiting degeneration corresponds to the radial action integral

$$J_r = J_1 - J_2.$$

It is seen at once that, for small J_r, the eccentricity is proportional to $\sqrt{J_r}$.

[2] *Cf.* H. Poincaré, *Méthodes nouvelles*, vol. ii, chap. xii.

$$(1) \qquad \xi^0 = \sqrt{\frac{J^0}{\pi}} \sin 2\pi w_f^0, \qquad \eta^0 = \sqrt{\frac{J^0}{\pi}} \cos 2\pi w_f^0$$

(the generator of the transformation is $\frac{1}{2}(\eta^0)^2 \tan 2\pi w_f^0$). w_f^0 can then be varied in the neighbourhood of $J_f^0=0$ without ξ^0 and η^0 being at the same time subject to rapid variations.

Since in the perturbed motion J_f^0 can deviate but slightly from the corresponding action variable $J_f=0$, we can consider ξ^0 and η^0 to be small. If we substitute the new variables in the Hamiltonian function, we can expand this in terms of ξ^0 and η^0 in such a way that each coefficient of the powers of λ will itself be a series in increasing powers of ξ^0 and η^0.

On account of (1) the expansion of H_0, and therefore of the energy function of the unperturbed motion, proceeds in even powers of ξ^0 and η^0 only, since it depends only on J_f^0 and not on w_f^0. In the perturbation function, on the other hand, linear terms will also occur. The difficulty previously mentioned may now be formulated analytically.

The circular orbit $\xi^0=0$, $\eta^0=0$ is indeed an exact solution of the equations of motion for the unperturbed system, since

$$\frac{d\xi^0}{dt} = \frac{\partial H_0}{\partial \eta^0}\Bigg|_{\xi^0=0,\,\eta^0=0} = 0, \qquad \frac{d\eta^0}{dt} = -\frac{\partial H_0}{\partial \xi^0}\Bigg|_{\xi^0=0,\,\eta^0=0} = 0,$$

but it is no longer so in the case of the perturbed motion, since the perturbation function contains in general terms which are linear in the ξ^0's and η^0's.

This consideration indicates a method of solution. If, by a suitable transformation, variables ξ, η can be introduced, such that all linear terms in the development of the Hamiltonian function are absent, we have in $\xi=0$, $\eta=0$ a rigorous solution of the equations of motion for the perturbed system as well. This transformation may be found by means of a recurrence method, the integration of the remaining equations of motion being accomplished at the same time.

We postulate then a mechanical problem with the Hamiltonian function

$$(2) \quad H = H_1 + \lambda H_1 + \lambda^2 H_2 + \dots$$

$$H_0 = H_{00}(J_\alpha^0) + c_0(\xi^0)^2 + d_0(\eta^0)^2 + \dots$$

$$H_1 = H_{10}(J_\alpha^0, w_\alpha^0) + a_1\xi^0 + b_1\eta^0 + c_1(\xi^0)^2 + d_1(\eta^0)^2 + e_1\xi^0\eta^0 + \dots$$

$$H_2 = H_{20}(J_\alpha^0, w_\alpha^0) + a_2\xi^0 + b_2\eta^0 + c_2(\xi^0)^2 + d_2(\eta^0)^2 + e_2\xi^0\eta^0 + \dots.$$

The H_{n0}, a_n, b_n . . .'s ($n=1, 2$ . . .) are here periodic functions of the

w_α^0's (period 1). When transformed, the expression (2) must take the form

(3) $$H=W_0+\lambda W_1+\lambda^2 W_2+\ldots,$$

where

(4) $$W_n=V_n(J_\alpha)+R_n$$

and the R_n's denote power series in ξ, η commencing with quadratic terms.

We assume for the generating function of the transformation

(5) $$S=\sum_1^{f-1} J_\alpha w_\alpha^0+T+\xi^0\eta+B\xi^0-A\eta,$$

where

(6) $$\begin{aligned} T&=\lambda T_1+\lambda^2 T_2+\ldots \\ A&=\lambda A_1+\lambda^2 A_2+\ldots \\ B&=\lambda B_1+\lambda^2 B_2+\ldots \end{aligned}$$

are to be power series in λ, whose coefficients T_n, A_n, B_n are periodic functions of the quantities $w_1^0 \ldots w_{f-1}^0$.

We find in this way for the transformation formulæ for ξ^0 and η^0:

(7) $$\begin{aligned} \xi&=\frac{\partial S}{\partial \eta}=\xi^0-A\,; \qquad \xi^0=\xi+\lambda A_1+\lambda^2 A_2+\ldots \\ \eta^0&=\frac{\partial S}{\partial \xi^0}=\eta+\lambda B_1+\lambda^2 B_2+\ldots\,; \qquad \eta=\eta^0-B, \end{aligned}$$

and employing these in turn:

(8) $$\begin{aligned} J_\alpha^0=\frac{\partial S}{\partial w_\alpha}=J_\alpha&+\lambda\left(\frac{\partial T_1}{\partial w_\alpha^0}+\xi\frac{\partial B_1}{\partial w_\alpha^0}-\eta\frac{\partial A_1}{\partial w_\alpha^0}\right) \\ &+\lambda^2\left(\frac{\partial T_2}{\partial w_\alpha^0}+\xi\frac{\partial B_2}{\partial w_\alpha^0}-\eta\frac{\partial A_2}{\partial w_\alpha^0}+A_1\frac{\partial B_1}{\partial w_\alpha^0}\right)+\cdots. \end{aligned}$$

The new variables differ therefore from the old only by terms of the order of λ, so that for $\lambda=0$ we have once again the unperturbed circular orbits $\xi^0=\eta^0=0$.

If now we carry out the transformation and expand everything in powers of λ, then, to each approximation, there are three, and only three, functions available—T_n, A_n, B_n—which are so far undetermined and can be chosen so as to satisfy our conditions. Comparison of the coefficients of λ in (2) and (3) gives

(9) $$\begin{aligned} \sum_\alpha \frac{\partial H_{00}}{\partial J_\alpha}\left(\frac{\partial T_1}{\partial w_\alpha^0}+\xi\frac{\partial B_1}{\partial w_\alpha^0}-\eta\frac{\partial A_1}{\partial w_\alpha^0}\right)&+2c_0A_1\xi+2d_0B_1\eta \\ &+H_{10}+a_1\xi+b_1\eta+\ldots=V_1+R_1. \end{aligned}$$

On making the coefficients of ξ and η zero, equations for A_1 and B_1 are obtained, viz.:

$$(10)\qquad \begin{aligned} &\sum_\alpha \frac{\partial H_{00}}{\partial J_\alpha}\frac{\partial B_1}{\partial w_\alpha^0}+2c_0A_1+a_1=0\\ -&\sum_\alpha \frac{\partial H_{00}}{\partial J_\alpha}\frac{\partial A_1}{\partial w_\alpha^0}+2d_0B_1+b_1=0. \end{aligned}$$

Equations of the same type occur very frequently in the theory of perturbations. To integrate them, A and B are each separated into a constant part, depending only on the J's, and a purely periodic component:

$$A_1=\bar{A}_1+\tilde{A}_1, \qquad B_1=\bar{B}_1+\tilde{B}_1.$$

The former is found from the equations which result on averaging (10), viz:

$$(11)\qquad \bar{A}_1=-\frac{\bar{a}_1}{2c_0}, \qquad \bar{B}_1=-\frac{\bar{b}_1}{2d_0},$$

and the latter is then found directly from (10), as in the case of equation (11), § 41. As usual, V_1 and T_1 may be calculated as functions of the J_α's and w_α^0's, from the terms in (9) independent of ξ and η.

The higher approximations can be obtained in exactly the same way. Since in the case of even the second approximation the formulæ are already very involved, we shall not write them down. Finally, it should be noticed that to the first approximation no new terms occur in the energy W_1, but that this is again obtained by simply averaging H_{10} over $w_1 \ldots w_{f-1}$; in the second approximation, however, a whole series of new terms appears.

The final result is an expression for the Hamiltonian function in the form

$$(12)\qquad H=V(J_\alpha)+c(J_\alpha)\xi^2+d(J_\alpha)\eta^2+e(J_\alpha)\xi\eta+\cdots.$$

It is the Hamiltonian function of a system in which all co-ordinates but one are cyclic. The motion may be found in the usual way by solving a Hamilton-Jacobi differential equation for one degree of freedom. Since ξ and η (like ξ^0 and η^0) must vanish with λ, we need only consider small motions, that is, those belonging to a system whose Hamiltonian function is

$$(13)\qquad c\xi^2+d\eta^2+e\xi\eta.$$

By means of a suitable homogeneous linear transformation from ξ, η to new variables X, Y it takes the form

$$(14)\qquad CX^2+DY^2.$$

If the quadratic form (13) is "definite," *i.e.* C and D have the same sign in (14), the motions in the neighbourhood of $X=Y=0$ or $\xi=\eta=0$ are small oscillations of X and Y about this point. The only motion compatible with the quantum condition

$$J_f=\oint X dY=0$$

is one in which ξ and η remain zero. The energy of this particular state is a minimum, if the quadratic form is positive definite; it is a maximum if the form is negative definite.

If the quadratic form (13) is indefinite there are motions in each neighbourhood of $\xi=\eta=0$, for which ξ and η do not remain small. The only values which satisfy the equations of motion and the quantum condition are again $\xi=\eta=0$: the motion is, however, mechanically unstable.

In every case the perturbed motion has the same degree of periodicity $f-1$, whilst its energy is

$$W=V(J_\alpha). \tag{15}$$

The restriction to simple limiting degeneration is not necessary. The corresponding considerations and calculations are also valid for limiting degeneration of arbitrary multiplicity. The appropriate expression for the generator S is

$$S=\sum_{\alpha=1}^{s} w_\alpha^0 J_\alpha+T+\sum_{\rho=s+1}^{f}(\xi_\rho^0\eta_\rho+B^\rho\xi_\rho^0-A^\rho\eta_\rho). \tag{16}$$

The result of the transformation is an expression for H in the form

$$H=V(J_\alpha)+\sum_{\rho,\sigma}c_{\rho\sigma}\xi_\rho\xi_\sigma+\sum_{\rho,\sigma}d_{\rho\sigma}\eta_\rho\eta_\sigma+\sum_{\rho,\sigma}e_{\rho\sigma}\xi_\rho\eta_\sigma+\ldots, \tag{17}$$

to which must be added terms of the third and higher orders in ξ_ρ, η_ρ. The Hamilton-Jacobi equation to which this function leads is not, in general, separable for finite values of ξ_ρ, η_ρ. We need examine, however, only those motions for which ξ_ρ and η_ρ remain small. By means of a suitable homogeneous linear transformation, the quadratic terms in (17) may be written in the form

$$H=V(J_\alpha)+\sum_\rho(C_\rho X_\rho^2+D_\rho Y_\rho^2). \tag{18}$$

H is now separable. The only motions compatible with the quantum conditions are those for which X_ρ, Y_ρ and consequently ξ_ρ, η_ρ are always zero.

The conditions for stability are analogous to those in the case of one degree of freedom. The particular motion $\xi_\rho=\eta_\rho=0$ is stable when, and only when, the quadratic form in (17) is definite. The energy is a minimum if it is positive definite.

To summarise, we may state : For an initial motion possessing limiting degeneration, the perturbed motion, selected in accordance with the quantum theory, has the same degree of periodicity s as the unperturbed motion. Its energy is

$$W=V(J_\alpha). \tag{19}$$

§ 47.—Phase Relations to any Degree of Approximation

In § 45 we had to leave unanswered the question whether, in the case of an accidentally degenerate initial motion, the motions singled out by the quantum theory have the same degree of periodicity as the initial one, when the work is carried to any degree of approximation. The method developed for limiting degeneration now enables us to answer this question. At the same time the restriction on the w_ρ^0's given in § 45 will be established by an independent method.

Let us again state the problem : we wish to study those motions of the mechanical system with the Hamiltonian function

$$H=H_0(J_k^0)+\lambda H_1(J_k^0, w_k^0)+\ldots \qquad (k=1\ldots f) \tag{1}$$

which are connected with the accidentally degenerate motions of the unperturbed system ($\lambda=0$), *i.e.* those for which, as a result of the choice of integration constants, certain frequencies vanish :

$$\nu_\rho^0=\frac{\partial H_0}{\partial J_\rho^0}=0 \qquad (\rho=s+1\ldots f). \tag{2}$$

The path fills a region of only s dimensions ($s<f$) in the case of the unperturbed system, since the w_ρ^0's are constant.

Let us assume that the perturbed motion is connected with a certain unperturbed motion for which

$$J_\rho^0=J_\rho^*, \qquad w_\rho^0=w_\rho^*.$$

It follows from the assumption of accidental degeneration that the J_ρ^0's must have perfectly definite values in the initial motion. The J_ρ^*'s may be determined if equation (2) be solved for the J_ρ^0's ; they appear as functions of the J_α^0's. That w_ρ^0 must necessarily have definite discrete values in the initial motion is certainly an assumption; it is also conceivable that the perturbed motion could be associated with every system of values w_ρ^0 of a continuum, but our argument cannot be applied to this case.

If we assume, therefore, that only certain initial motions are possible, the J_ρ^*'s and w_ρ^*'s are perfectly definite functions of the J_α^0's ; so far we do not know $w_\rho^*(J_\alpha)$, but this will be found in the course of the investigations. We now introduce new variables

(3) $$\xi_\rho^0=J_\rho^0-J_\rho^*(J_\alpha^0), \qquad \eta_\rho^0=w_\rho^0-w_\rho^*(J_\alpha^0).$$

This may be accomplished by means of a canonical transformation with the generator

(4) $$\sum_\alpha w_\alpha^0\bar{J}_\alpha^0+\sum_\rho[w_\rho^0 J_\rho^*+\xi_\rho^0(w_\rho^0-w_\rho^*)];$$

the transformation equations are

(5) $$\begin{aligned} J_\alpha^0&=\bar{J}_\alpha^0\\ J_\rho^0&=J_\rho^*+\xi_\rho^0\\ \bar{w}_\alpha^0&=w_\alpha^0+\sum_\rho\left(\frac{\partial J_\rho^*}{\partial J_\alpha^0}w_\rho^0-\xi_\rho^0\frac{\partial w_\rho^*}{\partial J_\alpha^0}\right)\\ \eta_\rho^0&=w_\rho^0-w_\rho^*.\end{aligned}$$

The new $\bar{J}_\alpha^0$'s will be equal to the original J_α^0's, while the $\bar{w}_\alpha^0$'s will differ from the w_α^0's only by quantities which are constant in the unperturbed motion; they retain their character of action and angle variables respectively. The ξ_ρ^0's and η_ρ^0's tend to zero with vanishing perturbation.

We can now develop the Hamiltonian function with respect to ξ_ρ^0, η_ρ^0, thus obtaining

(6) $$H=H_0'+\lambda H_1'+\lambda^2 H_2'+\ldots;$$

where (omitting the bar in $\bar{w}_\alpha^0$)

(7) $$\begin{aligned} H_0'&=H_{00}(J_\alpha^0, J_\rho^*)+\sum_{\rho\sigma}c_0^{\rho\sigma}\xi_\rho^0\xi_\sigma^0+\ldots\\ H_1'&=H_{10}(w_\alpha^0, w_\rho^*, J_\alpha^0, J_\rho^*)+\sum_\rho(a_1^\rho\xi_\rho^0+b_1^\rho\eta_\rho^0)+\ldots\end{aligned}$$

. . . .

From (5)

(8) $$\begin{aligned} c_0^{\rho\sigma}&=\frac{1}{2!}\frac{\partial^2 H_{00}}{\partial J_\rho^*\partial J_\sigma^*}\\ a_1^\rho&=-\frac{\partial H_{10}}{\partial J_\rho^*}+\sum_\alpha\frac{\partial H_{10}}{\partial w_\alpha^0}\frac{\partial w_\rho^*}{\partial J_\alpha^0}\\ b_1^\rho&=-\frac{\partial H_{10}}{\partial w_\rho^*}-\sum_\alpha\frac{\partial H_{10}}{\partial w_\alpha^0}\frac{\partial J_\rho^*}{\partial J_\alpha^0},\end{aligned}$$

while the expressions H_{00}, H_{10} . . . are obtained from H_0, H_1 . . . in (1) simply by writing J_ρ^*, w_ρ^* instead of J_ρ^0, w_ρ^0. (6) has now a form analogous to that of (2) in § 46, and may in consequence be dealt with, to any degree of approximation, by the method employed there.

There is the one difference, that the η_ρ's do not appear at all in H_0'. If, therefore, we make the transformation given by (16), § 46, the equations for determining the A_1^ρ's and B_1^ρ's (*cf.* (10), § 46) become :

$$\sum_\alpha \frac{\partial H_{00}}{\partial J_\alpha} \frac{\partial B_1^\rho}{\partial w_\alpha^0} + a_1^\rho + 2\sum_\sigma c_0^{\rho\sigma} A_1^\rho = 0$$

$$-\sum_\alpha \frac{\partial H_{00}}{\partial J_\alpha} \frac{\partial A_1^\rho}{\partial w_\alpha^0} + b_1^\rho \qquad = 0.$$

It follows from the second of these equations that the mean value $\overline{b_1^\rho}$ vanishes.

Finally, the Hamiltonian function is obtained in the form

$$H = V(J_\alpha) + R(J_\alpha, \xi_\rho, \eta_\rho), \tag{9}$$

where the expansion of R in terms of ξ_ρ, η_ρ commences with quadratic terms. For small values of ξ_ρ, η_ρ, which are all that we need consider, H is separable and gives, as the only solution satisfying the quantum conditions,

$$\xi_\rho = \eta_\rho = 0.$$

The perturbed motion has therefore the same degree of periodicity as the unperturbed motion. It is stable (in the ordinary mechanical sense) when, and only when, the quadratic form in ξ_ρ, η_ρ in (9) is definite.

The condition

$$\overline{b_1^\rho} = 0 \tag{10}$$

implies a determination of the w_ρ^*'s. For since the mean values of the $\frac{\partial H_{10}}{\partial w_\alpha^0}$'s, which are pure periodic functions without a constant term, vanish, it follows from (8) that

$$\frac{\partial \overline{H}_{10}}{\partial w_\rho^*} = 0. \tag{11}$$

This equation implies, however, phase relations for the w_ρ^*'s. It is, in fact, equation (13), § 45, since H_{10} in the present notation is identical with H_2 in § 45.

In § 45 we considered in great detail the case of one accidentally degenerate degree of freedom ; we may show finally how it fits in with our general considerations of stability. Equation (5′), § 45 (H_2 there is equivalent to H_{10} here),

$$\frac{1}{2\,!} \frac{\partial^2 H_0}{\partial J_f^2} \left(\frac{\partial S_1}{\partial w_f^0} \right)^2 + \overline{H}_2(w_f^0) = W_2,$$

is, to a first approximation, equivalent to

$$\frac{1}{2!}\frac{\partial^2 H_0}{\partial J_f^2}\xi^2+d.\eta^2=\text{const.},$$

for motions in the neighbourhood of solutions of the equation

$$\frac{\partial \overline{H}_2}{\partial w_f^0}=0.$$

If $\frac{\partial^2 H_0}{\partial J_f^2}$ is positive, we have in the neighbourhood of the stable solution ($\overline{H}_2$ is a minimum) a positive definite quadratic form, whilst in the neighbourhood of the unstable solution ($\overline{H}_2$ a maximum) the form is indefinite. If $\frac{\partial^2 H_0}{\partial J_f^2}$ is negative, the form is negative definite ($\overline{H}_2$ is a maximum) in the neighbourhood of the stable solution, indefinite ($\overline{H}_2$ a minimum) in the neighbourhood of the unstable solution.

It remains to consider the cases of combinations of different kinds of degeneration. It has been shown that accidental degeneration and limiting degeneration can be treated in the same way, and so it is obvious that they do not interfere with one another. In this case the number of the ξ, η variables is simply increased. In addition the sole remaining possibility, a combination of intrinsic degeneration with limiting degeneration, does not, as a rule, involve any difficulty. In such a case the secular motions of the intrinsically degenerate variables are first of all calculated and then the procedure of § 46 adopted.[1]

Special cases, in which, for example, by averaging over the non-degenerate variables, their dependence on the degenerate variables disappear (*e.g.* $\overline{H}_1=0$), must of course be examined separately.

We have now justified the statement made in § 40, that the stationary states are to be found chiefly among the particularly simple types of motion, which can be calculated by comparatively easy approximate methods.

With this mathematical tool at hand we shall now proceed to the calculation of the next simplest atom to hydrogen, that of helium. We shall show (as mentioned in § 40) that the results are not in agreement with observation; but quite apart from this, we consider

---

[1] The case in which the degrees of freedom exhibiting limiting degeneration are at the same time intrinsically degenerate is dealt with by L. Nordheim, *Zeitschr. f. Physik*, vol. xvii, p. 316, 1923.

that working out this example is a necessary preliminary to any attempt to discover the true principles of quantum mechanics.

§ 48.—The Normal State of the Helium Atom

According to § 32, two one-quantum electron orbits are present in helium in its normal state. Our problem is to investigate their possible arrangements in the atom.

We shall take the unperturbed motion to be one in which the electrons are only subject to the action of the nucleus, of charge Ze. Let the angle and action variables of the first electron be w_1, w_2, w_3, J_1, J_2, J_3, and let us distinguish by a dash the corresponding quantities for the second electron. The energy of the unperturbed motion is then

$$H_0 = -A\left(\frac{1}{J_1^2} + \frac{1}{J_1'^2}\right), \tag{1}$$

where

$$A = 2\pi^2 e^4 m Z^2.$$

The perturbation function is the mutual potential energy of the electrons

$$\lambda H_1 = \frac{e^2}{R} = \frac{e^2}{\sqrt{(x-x')^2+(y-y')^2+(z-z')^2}}, \tag{2}$$

where R denotes the distance between the electrons and (x, y, z), (x', y', z'), their respective cartesian co-ordinates in any co-ordinate system with the nucleus as origin.

The expansions of the cartesian co-ordinates as functions of the angle variables (to be calculated from (26), § 22) must now be introduced, to provide a starting-point for the calculation of the perturbations. In this connection, however, there is one point to be borne in mind. In the unperturbed Kepler motion (without taking account of the variation in mass) only J_1 is fixed by the quantum theory, whilst J_2, *i.e.* the eccentricity, remains arbitrary; in the relativistic Kepler motion, J_2 is also to be quantised and, for a one-quantum orbit, $J_2 = J_1 = h$. We shall not take account quantitatively of the relativistic variation of mass, but we shall assume that the initial orbit of each electron is circular with limiting degeneration $J_1 = h$, $J_2 = h$.

The unperturbed system consists therefore of two circular orbits of the same size. In addition to the double limiting degeneration due to the circular orbits, we have also a double intrinsic degeneration, arising from the fact that the planes of the two orbits are fixed, and in addition we have an accidental degeneration, since the rotation frequencies of the two electrons are equal.

By the principle of conservation of angular momentum, the interaction of the two electrons must leave still one intrinsic degeneration (the difference of the longitudes of the nodes of the two orbits on the invariable plane remains zero). The line of nodes, however, precesses uniformly about the axis of the resultant angular momentum ; as long as we confine our attention to secular perturbations, the latter makes the same angle with the angular momentum vectors of the two electron orbits. Limiting degeneration also persists in the perturbed motion (by the argument of § 46). The same is true (§ 47) of the accidental degeneration. The perturbed motion will, however, only be related to those unperturbed motions for which the two electrons have some quite definite phase relations.

In this special state the mutual energy of the electrons will have a stationary value. It is evident, on visualising the motion, that this will be the case only if the electrons are as far apart as possible at every instant, that is, if they are always in the same meridional plane passing through the axis of the angular momentum.

This almost self-evident result may be arrived at analytically. In this connection we must first of all choose the variables of the unperturbed motion, so that they can be separated into those which are degenerate and those which are non-degenerate.

The limiting degeneration

$$J_1 - J_2 = 0, \qquad J_1' - J_2' = 0$$

necessitates the transformation (which we shall only give for the first electron)

$$\bar{J}_1 = J_1, \qquad \bar{w}_1 = w_1 + w_2,$$

$$\xi = -\sqrt{\frac{J_1 - J_2}{\pi}}\sin 2\pi w_2, \qquad \eta = \sqrt{\frac{J_1 - J_2}{\pi}}\cos 2\pi w_2.$$

In what follows we shall again omit the bars over w_1 and J_1 : $2\pi w_1$ is then the angular distance of the electron in its orbit from the line of nodes ; ξ and η are zero in the unperturbed motion.

The accidental degeneration requires the following canonical transformation :

$$(3) \qquad \begin{aligned} w_1 &= \mathfrak{w}_1 + \mathfrak{w}_1', & J_1 &= \tfrac{1}{2}(\mathfrak{J}_1 + \mathfrak{J}_1'), \\ w_1' &= \mathfrak{w}_1 - \mathfrak{w}_1', & J_1' &= \tfrac{1}{2}(\mathfrak{J}_1 - \mathfrak{J}_1'), \end{aligned}$$

or, solved for the new variables,

$$(3')\qquad \begin{aligned} \mathfrak{w}_1&=\tfrac{1}{2}(w_1+w_1'), & \mathfrak{J}_1&=J_1+J_1',\\ \mathfrak{w}_1'&=\tfrac{1}{2}(w_1-w_1'), & \mathfrak{J}_1'&=J_1-J_1'. \end{aligned}$$

The geometrical significance of w_3, w_3', J_3, and J_3' depends on the position of the co-ordinate system. If we take the (x, y)- and (x', y')-planes in the invariable plane of the system (elimination of the lines of nodes), J_3+J_3' is the total angular momentum and $w_3-w_3'=\frac{1}{2}$. Since the energy of the perturbed motion can depend only on the combination J_3+J_3', we may write

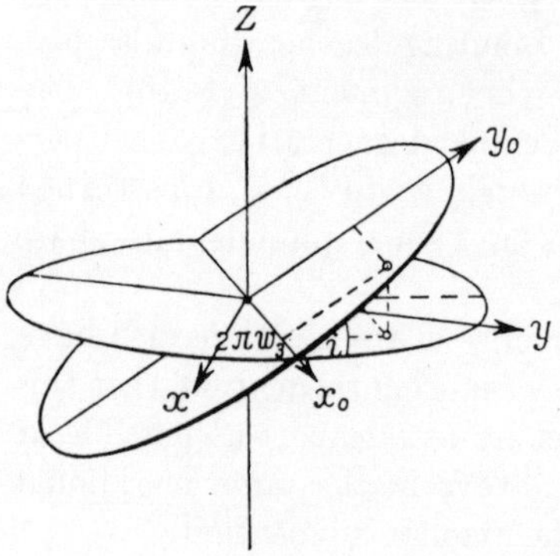

Fig. 39.

$$(4)\qquad \begin{aligned} w_3&=\mathfrak{w}_3+\mathfrak{w}_3',\\ w_3'&=\mathfrak{w}_3-\mathfrak{w}_3',\\ J_3&=\tfrac{1}{2}(\mathfrak{J}_3+\mathfrak{J}_3'),\\ J_3'&=\tfrac{1}{2}(\mathfrak{J}_3-\mathfrak{J}_3'), \end{aligned}$$

so that $\mathfrak{w}_3'=\frac{1}{4}$.

In order to calculate the phase relations in the initial motion we have to express the perturbation function (2) in terms of the variables $\mathfrak{w}_1$, $\mathfrak{w}_1'$, $\mathfrak{w}_3$, $\mathfrak{J}_1$, $\mathfrak{J}_1'$, $\mathfrak{J}_3$. A simple geometrical treatment gives (fig. 39)

$$(5)\qquad \begin{aligned} x&=x_0\cos 2\pi w_3-y_0\sin 2\pi w_3\cos i\\ y&=x_0\sin 2\pi w_3+y_0\cos 2\pi w_3\cos i\\ z&=y_0\sin i, \end{aligned}$$

where x_0 and y_0 are the rectangular co-ordinates of the electron in its orbit (the nodal line is the x_0-axis) and i is the inclination of the orbital plane to the (xy)-plane. We have

$$(6)\qquad \cos i=\frac{J_3}{J_1}=p=p'.$$

For x_0, y_0, we have

$$(7)\qquad \begin{aligned} x_0&=a\cos 2\pi w_1\\ y_0&=a\sin 2\pi w_1,\\ a&=\frac{J_1^2}{4\pi^2e^2mZ}=\frac{\mathfrak{J}_1^2}{16\pi^2e^2mZ.} \end{aligned}$$

The perturbation function is now

$$(8)\qquad \lambda H_1=\frac{e^2}{a\sqrt{2(1-k^2)}},$$

where

$$k^2 = \frac{1}{a^2}(xx' + yy' + zz')$$

(9) $$= -\cos 2\pi(\mathfrak{w}_1 + \mathfrak{w}_1') \cos 2\pi(\mathfrak{w}_1 - \mathfrak{w}_1') + \sin 2\pi(\mathfrak{w}_1 + \mathfrak{w}_1') \sin 2\pi(\mathfrak{w}_1 - \mathfrak{w}_1')(1 - 2p^2)$$
$$= -(1 - p^2)\cos 4\pi\mathfrak{w}_1 - p^2 \cos 4\pi\mathfrak{w}_1'.$$

$\mathfrak{w}_3$ does not appear; it is a cyclic variable, and $\mathfrak{J}_3$, the resultant angular momentum, is constant.

We must now average the perturbation function over the unperturbed motion:

(10) $$\lambda\bar{H}_1 = \frac{e^2}{a\sqrt{2}} \int_0^1 \frac{d\mathfrak{w}_1}{\sqrt{1 - k^2}}$$

and determine the constant value which $\mathfrak{w}_1'$ has in the case of the unperturbed motion from

$$\frac{\partial \bar{H}_1}{\partial \mathfrak{w}_1'} = 0.$$

This equation takes the form

$$\int_0^1 \frac{d\mathfrak{w}_1}{(1 - k^2)^{\frac{3}{2}}} p^2 \, . \, \sin 4\pi\mathfrak{w}_1' = 0$$

and is satisfied only if $p = 0$, or if $\mathfrak{w}_1' = \frac{1}{2}(w_1 - w_1')$ has one of the values 0 or $\frac{1}{4}$ (0 and $\frac{1}{2}$ are equivalent, as they give the same configuration). $p = 0$ would lead to $J_3 = 0$; the two electrons would revolve in the same circle in opposite directions, and this case must be excluded. In the case $\mathfrak{w}_1' = \frac{1}{4}$ the electrons will collide on the nodal line each period. The only remaining possibility is $\mathfrak{w}_1' = 0$, for which the two electrons pass simultaneously through their ascending nodes. They then lie at each instant in the same meridian plane through the axis of angular momentum.

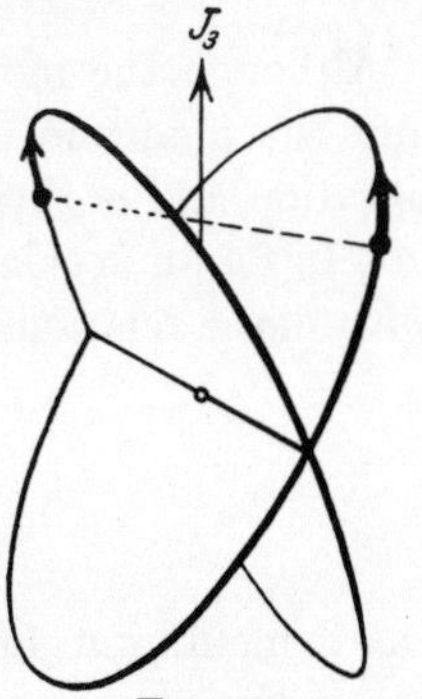

FIG. 40.

Let us now introduce the quantum conditions. In the perturbed motion $\mathfrak{J}'$ remains zero; $\mathfrak{J}_1$ is to be put equal to $2h$, and for $\mathfrak{J}_3$ we have the values $2h$, h, or 0; correspondingly, p will be equal to 1, $\frac{1}{2}$, or 0. As already mentioned, the case $p = 0$ can be rejected; $p = 1$ gives a plane model of the helium atom; $p = \frac{1}{2}$ gives a spatial model, in which the normals to the electron orbits are inclined to one another at an angle of 120° (fig. 40 shows this case).

The plane model is the He-model first proposed by Bohr.[1] The

[1] N. Bohr, *Phil. Mag.*, vol. xxvi, p. 476, 1913.

two electrons are situated at the extremities of a diameter of the orbit. The problem reduces to a one-body problem ; each electron moves in a field of force with potential

$$\frac{e^2 Z}{r} - \frac{e^2}{4r} = \frac{e^2(Z-\frac{1}{4})}{r}.$$

It describes a Kepler motion of energy

$$-cRh(Z-\tfrac{1}{4})^2,$$

so that the energy of the whole atom becomes

$$W = -2cRh(Z-\tfrac{1}{4})^2. \tag{11}$$

In the special case of helium (Z=2)

$$W = -\tfrac{49}{8} cRh. \tag{12}$$

This enables the energy to be calculated which is necessary for removal of the first electron, since after its separation the atom must have the normal state of ionised helium with energy

$$W = -4cRh.$$

The energy difference

$$W_{ion.} = \tfrac{17}{8} cRh \tag{13}$$

gives the work done in separating the first electron, or the ionisation energy of the neutral helium atom.

To calculate the ionisation potential 13·53 volts has to be substituted for the energy cRh of the hydrogen atom ; it follows that

$$V_{ion.} = 28{\cdot}75 \text{ volts}.$$

This value is not in agreement with observation, the method of electron impact giving the value

$$V_{ion.} = 24{\cdot}6 \text{ volts}.\tag{14}$$ [1]

Although the motion so found satisfies the equations of motion and the quantum conditions, yet it is not the limiting case of a libration and is therefore not stable. Applying the result obtained in § 45 for an accidentally degenerate degree of freedom, the motion with phase relations is only stable if

$$\frac{W_1 - \overline{H}_1(\mathfrak{w}_1')}{\dfrac{\partial^2 H_0}{\partial \mathfrak{J}_1'^2}}$$

has a maximum for it. Here $\overline{H}_1$ has obviously a minimum and hence the numerator a maximum, whilst the denominator (as we have shown in § 45) is negative.

---

[1] J. Franck, *Zeitschr. f. Physik*, vol. xi, p. 155, 1922.

This last difficulty alone would not definitely point to the incorrectness of our model, since it is not known if the ordinary stability conditions are valid in the quantum theory. The discrepancy between the calculated and observed values of the ionisation potential shows, however, that the model is not correct.

The spatial model was likewise proposed by Bohr and investigated in detail by Kramers.[1] Here we shall merely calculate the energy to a first approximation. The energy of the unperturbed motion is

$$W_0 = -2Z^2Rh,$$

where R is the Rydberg frequency. The first approximation to the perturbation energy is, by (10),

$$W_1 = \lambda\bar{H}_1 = \frac{e^2}{a}\frac{1}{\sqrt{2}}\int_0^1 \frac{d\mathfrak{w}_1}{\sqrt{(1+p^2)+(1-p^2)\cos 4\pi\mathfrak{w}_1}}$$

or

$$W_1 = \frac{e^2}{a}\frac{1}{4\pi}\int_0^{2\pi} \frac{d\psi}{\sqrt{1-\sin^2 i \sin^2 \psi}} = \frac{e^2}{a}\frac{1}{\pi}K,$$

where K is the complete elliptic integral of the first kind:

$$K = \int_0^{\pi/2} \frac{d\psi}{\sqrt{1-\sin^2 i \sin^2 \psi}}.$$

In our case $i = \frac{\pi}{3}$ and $K = 2{\cdot}157$.[2] It follows that

$$W_1 = 0{\cdot}687 \cdot \frac{e^2}{a} = 1{\cdot}373cRhZ.$$

and to this approximation the total energy is given by

$$W = -cRh(2Z^2 - 1{\cdot}373Z):$$

for $Z=2$,

(15) $$W = -5{\cdot}254cRh.$$

We cannot expect this first approximation to be very accurate, since at times the perturbing force attains half the value of the force due to the nucleus. Kramers has carried out the calculation with greater accuracy and finds

(16) $$W = -5{\cdot}525cRh.$$

Energy equivalent to $1{\cdot}525cRh$ must therefore be expended to liberate the electron, and the ionisation potential is 20·63 volts. This is almost 4 volts too small.

---

[1] H. A. Kramers, *Zeitschr. f. Physik*, vol. xiii, p. 312, 1923; also J. H. van Vleck, *Phys. Rev.*, vol. xxi, p. 372, 1923.

[2] Jahnke-Emde, *Funktionentafeln*, p. 57, Leipzig and Berlin, 1909.

In addition, the motion of this molecule is unstable, as may be shown in the same way as for the plane model.

We find, then, that a systematic application of the theory of perturbations does not lead to a satisfactory model of the normal helium atom. It might be supposed that the failure of our method was due to the fact that we are dealing here with the normal state, where several electrons move in equivalent orbits, and that a better result would be anticipated in the case of the excited states, where the main characteristics of the spectra are reproduced by the quantum theory in the form used here. We shall now show that this again is not the case.

§ 49.—The Excited Helium Atom

Before proceeding to calculate the excited states of the helium atom we may mention a few facts about the helium spectrum. The terms consist of two partial systems which do not combine with one another. Both are approximately hydrogen-like; one consists of singlets, and gives rise to the so-called parhelium spectrum; this also includes the normal state. The other component system yields the orthohelium spectrum, and consists (apart from the simple *s*-terms) of very close doublets. The lowest orthohelium term is (according to its effective quantum number) a 2_1-term. Since the corresponding state cannot pass into the normal state with emission of radiation, it has a particularly long life, or, to use Franck's expression, it is metastable. The transition from the normal atom to this metastable state can be brought about by electron impact.[1]

We shall now investigate the highly excited orbits of the helium atom on the basis of the theory of perturbations, by which we mean the external orbits which can be occupied by an electron when added to a helium ion. We shall assume that the orbit of the first electron in the ion is circular. Our problem is to investigate those types of orbits for which the inner electron, if unperturbed, would move in a one-quantum circle.

In this connection it is convenient to choose the reciprocal radius of the outer electron, or some quantity connected with it, as the

[1] J. Franck and F. Reiche, *Zeitschr. f. Physik*, vol. i, p. 154, 1920. According to measurements of H. Schüler, *Naturwissenschaften*, vol. xii, p. 579, 1924, the spectrum of Li^+ likewise shows the two corresponding systems of terms (see further Y. Sugiura, *Jour. de Physique*, Ser. 6, vol. vi, p. 323, 1925; S. Werner, *Nature*, vol. cxv, p. 191; vol. cxvi, p. 574, 1925; vol. cxviii, p. 154, 1926; H. Schüler, *Zeitschr. f. Physik*, vol. xxxvii, p. 568, 1926). Moreover, M. Morand (*Comptes Rendus*, vol. clxxviii, p. 1897, 1925) has found a new spectrum of neutral Li which he ascribes to the metastable state of the Li^+ core (corresponding to the lowest level of orthohelium).

small " parameter " λ in calculating the perturbation, for the farther away the " outer " electron, the more will the motion of the inner electron resemble the " unperturbed motion." We shall take into account the relativistic variation of mass.

If we denote the polar co-ordinates of the outer electron by r, θ, ϕ, those of the inner electron by r', θ', ϕ', and the conjugated momenta by $p_r \ldots p_{\phi'}$, the Hamiltonian function of the three-body problem of the helium type has the form

$$\text{(1)} \quad \mathrm{H}=\frac{1}{2m}\left(p_r^2+\frac{p_\theta^2}{r^2}+\frac{p_\phi^2}{r^2\sin^2\theta}\right)+\frac{1}{2m}\left(p_{r'}^2+\frac{p_{\theta'}^2}{r'^2}+\frac{p_{\phi'}^2}{r'^2\sin^2\theta'}\right)$$

$$-\frac{e^2\mathrm{Z}}{r}-\frac{e^2\mathrm{Z}}{r'}$$

$$+\frac{e^2}{\sqrt{r^2+r'^2-2rr'[\cos\theta\cos\theta'+\sin\theta\sin\theta'\cos(\phi-\phi')]}}$$

$$+\text{relativity terms.}$$

Let us resolve this function into H_0 and H_1, where H_0 is the Hamiltonian function of the (non-relativistic) Kepler motion of the inner electron and H_1 the remaining part of the above expression.

After calculating the unperturbed motion of the inner electron, we can find the secular motions of the remaining variables by introducing a new Hamiltonian function, the mean value of H_1 taken over the unperturbed motion of the inner electron. The integration of the corresponding Hamilton-Jacobi equation is again performed by the methods of the theory of perturbations.

We can decrease the number of degrees of freedom in the problem by an application of the theorem of the conservation of angular momentum (elimination of the nodes).

If the polar axis of the co-ordinate system be taken in the direction of the resultant angular momentum $\mathrm{P}=\mathfrak{J}_3/2\pi$, the angular separation of the line of nodes from a fixed line in the invariable plane is a cyclic variable conjugate to P. For the other co-ordinates let us take the radius vector r of the outer electron and the conjugate momentum p_r, together with the angular separation ψ of the outer electron from the line of nodes and the conjugate momentum

$$p_\psi=\sqrt{\frac{p_\phi^2}{\sin^2\theta}+p_\theta^2}=\frac{\mathrm{J}_2}{2\pi};$$

finally we also require the variables w_1', w_2', J_1', J_2' of the inner electron, where (as before) w_1', J_1' correspond to the principal quantum number, w_2', J_2' to the subsidiary quantum number.

Since the initial motion of the inner electron exhibits limiting degeneration, it is convenient to replace the variables w_1', w_2', J_1', J_2' by other variables. We therefore perform the canonical transformation

$$\bar{J}_1' = J_1' \qquad \bar{w}_1' = w_1' + w_2'$$

(2)
$$\xi = -\sqrt{\frac{J_1' - J_2'}{\pi}} \sin 2\pi w_2'$$

$$\eta = \sqrt{\frac{J_1' - J_2'}{\pi}} \cos 2\pi w_2',$$

and then omit the bars once again.

We shall now calculate the mean value of H_1 in these new variables. At the same time we shall develop H_1 in terms of spherical harmonics, *i.e.* in powers of $1/r$, and powers of ξ and η. We shall stop after terms in $1/r^3$: it appears that this approximation is equivalent to taking into account terms linear in ξ and η.

We have now

(3)
$$W_0 = -\frac{cRh^3Z^2}{J_1'^2}$$

and

(4)
$$W_1 = \bar{H}_1 = \frac{1}{2m}\left(p_r^2 + \frac{p_\psi^2}{r^2}\right) - \frac{e^2(Z-1)}{r} + \Delta_1 \frac{e^2 a_H}{r^2} + \Delta_2 \frac{e^2 a_H^2}{r^3} + \text{relativity terms},$$

where a_H stands for the hydrogen radius, and evaluation gives for Δ_1 and Δ_2:

(5)
$$\Delta_1 = -\frac{3}{2Z}\frac{J_1'}{h^2}\sqrt{2\pi J_1'}\left\{\eta\cos\psi - \xi\sin\psi\,\frac{\mathfrak{J}_3^2 - J_2^2 - J_1'^2}{2J_2J_1'}\right\}$$

$$\Delta_2 = \frac{1}{4Z^2}\frac{J_1'^4}{h^4}\left\{1 - 3\sin^2\psi\left[1 - \left(\frac{\mathfrak{J}_3^2 - J_2^2 - J_1'^2}{2J_2J_1'}\right)^2\right]\right\}.$$

We have neglected terms of degree higher than the first in ξ and η.

The partial differential equation $\bar{\bar{H}}_1 = \text{const.}$ is not separable. Since, however, it may be resolved into terms of different orders of magnitude, it can be dealt with by the methods of the theory of perturbations. Let us put

(6) $$\overline{H}_1 = \mathfrak{H}_0 + \mathfrak{H}_1 + \mathfrak{H}_2,$$

where

$$\mathfrak{H}_0 = \frac{1}{2m}\left(p_r^2 + \frac{p_\psi^2}{r^2}\right) - \frac{e^2(Z-1)}{r}$$

(7) $$\mathfrak{H}_1 = \Delta_1 \frac{e^2 a_H}{r^2}$$

$$\mathfrak{H}_2 = \Delta_2 \frac{e^2 a_H^2}{r^3} + \text{relativity terms.}$$

It is easy to see that the relativistic terms are small compared with $\mathfrak{H}_2$, so that our expansion is legitimate.

We must now introduce into $\overline{H}_1$ the angle and action variables w_1, w_2, J_1, J_2 of the unperturbed Kepler motion of the outer electron, represented by the term $\mathfrak{H}_0$. We shall, however, replace w_1 by the true anomaly ϕ_1 which is connected with w_1 by the equation

(8) $$d(2\pi w_1) = \frac{J_2^3}{J_1^3} \frac{d\phi_1}{(1-\epsilon\cos\phi_1)^2}, \qquad \epsilon = \sqrt{1 - \frac{J_2^2}{J_1^2}}$$

(*cf.* (18), (7′), and (8)–(11), § 22; ϕ_1 here $= \pi + \psi$ of (18), § 22); let us also put $\phi_2 = 2\pi w_2$. If we take $J_1' = h$, which is the only case of interest, we obtain:

$$\mathfrak{H}_0 = -\frac{cRh^3(Z-1)^2}{J_1^2},$$

$$\mathfrak{H}_1 = -\frac{3\sqrt{2\pi}(Z-1)^2}{Z} \cdot \frac{cRh^4\sqrt{h}}{J_2^4}(1-\epsilon\cos\phi_1)^2$$

$$\cdot\left\{\eta\cos(\phi_1+\phi_2) - \xi\sin(\phi_1+\phi_2)\frac{\mathfrak{J}_3^2 - J_2^2 - h^2}{2J_2}\right\} + \cdots,$$

(9) $$\mathfrak{H}_2 = \frac{(Z-1)^3}{2Z^2} \cdot cRh \cdot \frac{h^6}{J_2^6}(1-\epsilon\cos\phi_1)^3$$

$$\cdot\left\{1 - 3\sin^2(\phi_1-\phi_2)\left[1 - \left(\frac{\mathfrak{J}_3^2 - J_2^2 - h^2}{2J_2}\right)^2\right]\right\}$$

$$-\alpha^2\left[\frac{Z^4 cRh}{4} + \frac{(Z-1)^4 cRh^5}{4} \cdot \frac{4(J_1/J_2) - 3}{J_1^4}\right] + \cdots.$$

α is the Sommerfeld fine structure constant $\alpha = \frac{2\pi e^2}{hc}$ (*cf.* § 33); the terms proportional to α^2 contain the relativity correction for the inner and outer electrons.

In order to solve our problem we have to apply the method discussed in § 46.

Let us therefore try to find a function

$$S=w_1\mathfrak{J}_1+\xi Y+B_1\xi-A_1Y, \tag{10}$$

which introduces variables $\mathfrak{w}_1$, $\mathfrak{J}_1$, X, Y, such that $\overline{H}_1$ has no linear terms in X and Y, and is quite independent of $\mathfrak{w}_1$. The terms T_1, $T_2\ldots$; A_2, $A_3\ldots$; B_2, $B_3\ldots$ of (10) are omitted, since we do not require them to this degree of approximation. The transformation generated by (10) is

$$\begin{aligned} J_1&=\mathfrak{J}_1+\xi\frac{\partial B_1}{\partial w_1}-Y\frac{\partial A_1}{\partial w_1} \\ \mathfrak{w}_1&=w_1+\xi\frac{\partial B_1}{\partial \mathfrak{J}_1}-Y\frac{\partial A_1}{\partial \mathfrak{J}_1} \\ \eta&=Y+B_1 \\ X&=\xi-A_1. \end{aligned} \tag{11}$$

The reason why we do not need the function T_1 is that $\mathfrak{H}_1$ has no term independent of ξ and η.

Writing for shortness

$$\mathfrak{H}_1=a_1\xi+b_1\eta,$$

the method leads to the following equations:

$$\mathfrak{H}_0=\mathfrak{W}_0, \tag{12}$$

$$\frac{\partial \mathfrak{H}_0}{\partial \mathfrak{J}_1}\left(-\eta\frac{\partial A_1}{\partial w_1}+\xi\frac{\partial B_1}{\partial w_1}\right)+a_1\xi+b_1\eta=\mathfrak{W}_1=0, \tag{13}$$

$$\frac{\partial \mathfrak{H}_0}{\partial \mathfrak{J}_1}A_1\frac{\partial B_1}{\partial w_1}+a_1A_1+b_1B_1+\mathfrak{H}_2=\mathfrak{W}_2. \tag{14}$$

We have neglected the terms in (14) which involve ξ and η. It follows from (13) that

$$\frac{\partial \mathfrak{H}_0}{\partial \mathfrak{J}_1}\frac{\partial A_1}{\partial w_1}=b_1; \qquad \frac{\partial \mathfrak{H}_0}{\partial \mathfrak{J}_1}\frac{\partial B_1}{\partial w_1}=-a_1 \tag{15}$$

and from this and from (14) by averaging over w_1 for $\xi=\eta=0$,

$$\overline{b_1B_1}+\overline{\mathfrak{H}_2}=\mathfrak{W}_2. \tag{16}$$

Hence we do not need to calculate A_1. The mean values may easily be found with the help of (8) (*cf.* § 22). We obtain from (9) and (15):

$$-\frac{2cRh^4(Z-1)^2}{\mathfrak{J}_1^{\,3}}\frac{\partial B_1}{\partial w_1}$$

$$=\frac{3\sqrt{2}\pi cRh^5\sqrt{\bar{h}}(Z-1)^2}{ZJ_2^{\,4}}(1-\epsilon\cos\phi_1)^2\sin(\phi_1+\phi_2)\frac{\mathfrak{J}_3^{\,2}-J_2^{\,2}-h^2}{2hJ_2}$$

whence

$$B_1 = -\int dw_1 \frac{3}{2} \frac{\sqrt{2\pi h}\sqrt{h}\mathfrak{J}_1^3}{ZJ_2^4}(1-\epsilon\cos\phi_1)^2 \sin(\phi_1+\phi_2)\frac{\mathfrak{J}_3^2 - J_2^2 - h^2}{2hJ_2}$$

i.e.

$$B_1 = \frac{3h\sqrt{h}}{2\sqrt{2\pi}ZJ_2}\cos(\phi_1+\phi_2)\frac{\mathfrak{J}_3^2 - J_2^2 - h^2}{2hJ^2}. \tag{17}$$

It follows that

$$b_1B_1 = -\frac{9cRh^6(Z-1)^2}{2Z^2J_2^5}(1-\epsilon\cos\phi_1)^2\cos^2(\phi_1+\phi_2)\frac{\mathfrak{J}_3^2 - J_2^2 - h^2}{2hJ_2}, \tag{18}$$

and finally

$$\begin{aligned}\mathfrak{W}_2 = -\frac{cRh^4(Z-1)^2}{4Z^2\mathfrak{J}_1^3}\Bigg\{&\frac{9h^2}{J_2^2}\frac{\mathfrak{J}_3^2 - J_2^2 - h^2}{2J_2h} \\ &+\frac{(Z-1)h^3}{J_2^3}\left[1-3\left(\frac{\mathfrak{J}_3^2 - J_2^2 - h^2}{2J_2h}\right)^2\right]\Bigg\} \\ &-\alpha^2\frac{cRh}{4}\left[Z^4 + \frac{(Z-1)^4h^4}{\mathfrak{J}_1^4}\left(4\frac{\mathfrak{J}_1}{J_2}-3\right)\right].\end{aligned} \tag{19}$$

We notice that in averaging over w_1 in $\mathfrak{H}_2$ and $\mathfrak{W}_2$ the dependence on w_2 has of itself vanished : w_2 is cyclic to this approximation and J_2 remains an action variable.

The quantum conditions are therefore

$$\mathfrak{J}_1 = nh, \qquad J_2 = \mathfrak{J}_2 = kh, \qquad \mathfrak{J}_3 = jh.$$

The relativistic terms are of no practical importance (we have taken them into consideration throughout only to show that they give rise to no difficulties). If we omit them, the energy $W_1 = \bar{H}_1$ may be expressed as a Rydberg series formula. It is found that

$$W_1 = -\frac{cRh(Z-1)^2}{(n+\delta)^2}, \tag{20}$$

where

$$\delta = -\frac{9}{8Z^2k^2}\cdot\frac{j^2-k^2-1}{2k} - \frac{Z-1}{8Z^2k^3}\left[1-3\left(\frac{j^2-k^2-1}{2k}\right)^2\right]. \tag{21}$$

Writing $j = k+p$, and expanding in powers of $\frac{1}{k}$, the result is

$$\delta = \frac{9}{8Z^2k^2}\left(-p+\frac{1-p^2}{2k}\right) + \frac{Z-1}{8Z^2k^3}(3p^2-1). \tag{22}$$

The total energy of the excited helium atom becomes:

$$W=-cRhZ^2-\frac{cRh(Z-1)^2}{(n+\delta)^2}, \tag{23}$$

with Z=2. This solves our problem.[1]

The formula (20) must lead to the spectrum of helium. Since p can have the values 1, 0, −1, it must give three systems of terms. Their Rydberg corrections would be (for Z=2):

$$\begin{aligned} p=1: \quad & \delta=-\frac{1}{32k^2}\left(9-\frac{2}{k}\right), \\ p=0: \quad & \delta=\frac{7}{64k^3}, \\ p=-1: \quad & \delta=\frac{1}{32k^2}\left(9+\frac{2}{k}\right). \end{aligned} \tag{24}$$

The following table gives the values of δ for k=2, 3, 4, and below them the empirical values of δ:

		k=2	k=3	k=4
Theoretical	p= 1	−0·063	−0·029	−0·017
	p= 0	+0·014	+0·004	+0·002
	p=−1	+0·078	+0·034	+0·019
Empirical	Orthohelium	−0·069	−0·003	−0·001
	Parhelium	+0·011	−0·002	−0·001

Comparison of the two shows clearly that the theoretical values do not agree with the empirical values.

We may therefore conclude that the systematic application of the principles of the quantum theory proposed in the second chapter, namely, the calculation of the motion according to the principles of classical mechanics, and the selection of the stationary states from these by determining the action variables as integral multiples of Planck's constant, gives results in agreement with experiment only in those cases where the motion of a single electron is considered; it fails even in the treatment of the motion of the two electrons in the helium atom.

This is not surprising, for the principles used are not really consistent; on the one hand the classical differential relation is replaced by a difference relation, in the shape of the Bohr frequency condition,

[1] The general solution of this problem without restriction to circular orbits of the inner electron has been obtained by M. Born and W. Heisenberg, *Zeitschr. f. Physik*, vol. xvi, p. 229, 1923.

in describing the interaction of an atom with radiation, while on the other hand the classical differential relations have hitherto been employed in dealing with the interaction of several electrons. A complete systematic transformation of the classical mechanics into a discontinuous mechanics of the atom is the goal towards which the quantum theory strives.

APPENDIX

I. Two Theorems in the Theory of Numbers

(*a*) Theorem.—If λ is an irrational number, two integers τ and τ' differing from zero can be chosen so that $(\tau+\tau'\lambda)$ is arbitrarily small.

Proof.—On the unit distance OE, imagine the distances OP_1, OP_2 . . . measured out from O, their lengths being $\lambda-[\lambda]$, $2\lambda-[2\lambda]$ . . . ($[x]$ denotes here the greatest integer which is not greater than x). It follows from the irrationality of λ that none of the points O, P_1, P_2 . . . coincide. Further, since they are all situated on the unit length they must have a point of concentration P, in the neighbourhood of which there are points P_σ and $P_{\sigma+\tau'}$ of the series, between which the distance is smaller than a given quantity δ. This separation, however, is given by

$$\sigma\lambda-[\sigma\lambda]-(\sigma+\tau')\lambda+[(\sigma+\tau')\lambda],$$

and is smaller than an integer by $\tau'\lambda$. Let this whole number be $-\tau$; then

$$|\tau+\tau'\lambda|<\delta.$$

(*b*) The trajectory in the space of the angle variables w is a straight line. Without loss of generality we can choose a point on the trajectory as origin; it will then be seen that the direction cosines of the trajectory are proportional to the frequencies ν_1, ν_2 . . . ν_f. We have then the

Theorem.—If no degeneration is present, then for any given point in the w-space it is always possible to find an equivalent point to which the trajectory approaches indefinitely close.

If we confine the trajectory to a single cube, by replacing each point of the trajectory by the equivalent point in the unit cube, we can state the theorem in the following form:

Theorem.—The trajectory approaches infinitely close to every point of the unit cube.

This corresponds to the following theorem in the theory of numbers:

If n irrational numbers $a_1 \ldots a_n$ and any number b are given, n integers $\tau_1 \ldots \tau_n$ can always be found so that

$$(\tau a)-b=\tau_1 a_1+\ldots+\tau_n a_n-b$$

differs from an integer by an arbitrarily small amount.

We can prove the theorem for the trajectory in the following way :[1]

Let O be the origin and OE_1, $OE_2 \ldots OE_f$ unit lengths along the axes of the $(w_1, w_2 \ldots w_f)$-co-ordinate system. Let $P_0, P_1, P_2 \ldots$ be the points of intersection of the path, confined to the unit cube, with the $(f-1)$-dimensional surfaces bounding the unit cube, which intersect in OE_1, $OE_2 \ldots OE_f$. Let P_0 and O be identical. Since the direction cosines are incommensurable none of these points P_n coincide ; they have at least one limit point in each of the bounding surfaces perpendicular to the axes. In each of these $(f-1)$-dimensional surfaces, there is therefore an infinite number of vectors $\overline{P_m P_{m+n}}$, whose magnitudes are less than a given number δ.

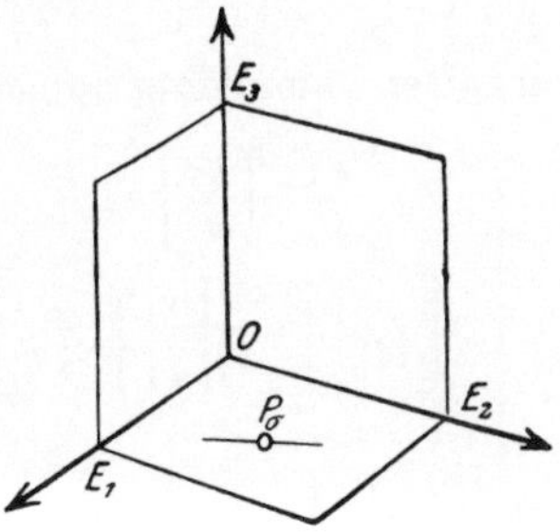

FIG. 41.

We must be quite clear as to the distribution of the points of intersection on the bounding surfaces, each of which is perpendicular to one of the axes $OE_1 \ldots$. For this purpose, let us consider any one of the surfaces, say that which is perpendicular to OE_f. Of the series of points of intersection $P_1, P_2 \ldots$, let P_σ be the first which falls in this bounding surface (σ is a finite number, since otherwise we should have degeneration). We may suppose that the vectors $\overline{P_m P_{m+n}}$ in the bounding surface are drawn from P_σ, and so we arrive at new points of our series, $Q_1, Q_2 \ldots$.

We have now to show that these do not all lie in one $(f-2)$-dimensional space passing through P_σ. We shall prove this indirectly, by first assuming it to be true, and showing that this leads to a contradiction.

The point P_σ has the co-ordinates

$$w_k=\frac{\nu_k}{\nu_f}-\left[\frac{\nu_k}{\nu_f}\right] \qquad (k=1\ldots f-1)$$

in the bounding surface under consideration. For $f-1$ other points

[1] Appended to the proof by F. Lettenmeyer (*Proc. London Math. Soc.* (2), vol. xxi, p. 306, 1923) of this theorem in the theory of numbers.

$P_{x_1}, P_{x_2} \ldots P_{x_{f-1}}$ of the Q-series we have, if P_σ and the $(f-1)$ other points all lie on a surface of $f-2$ dimensions,

$$\begin{vmatrix} \frac{\nu_1}{\nu_f}-\left[\frac{\nu_1}{\nu_f}\right] \ldots & \frac{\nu_{f-1}}{\nu_f}-\left[\frac{\nu_{f-1}}{\nu_f}\right] & 1 \\ x_1\frac{\nu_1}{\nu_f}-\left[x_1\frac{\nu_1}{\nu_f}\right] \ldots & x_1\frac{\nu_{f-1}}{\nu_f}-\left[x_1\frac{\nu_{f-1}}{\nu_f}\right] & 1 \\ \cdot \quad \cdot \quad \cdot & \cdot \quad \cdot \quad \cdot & \cdot \\ x_{f-1}\frac{\nu_1}{\nu_f}-\left[x_{f-1}\frac{\nu_1}{\nu_f}\right] \ldots & x_{f-1}\frac{\nu_{f-1}}{\nu_f}-\left[x_{f-1}\frac{\nu_{f-1}}{\nu_f}\right] & 1 \end{vmatrix}=0.$$

or, after a simple rearrangement,

$$\begin{vmatrix} \frac{\nu_1}{\nu_f}-\left[\frac{\nu_1}{\nu_f}\right] \ldots & \frac{\nu_{f-1}}{\nu_f}-\left[\frac{\nu_{f-1}}{\nu_f}\right] & 1 \\ \left[x_1\frac{\nu_1}{\nu_f}\right]-x_1\left[\frac{\nu_1}{\nu_f}\right] \ldots & \left[x_1\frac{\nu_{f-1}}{\nu_f}\right]-x_1\left[\frac{\nu_{f-1}}{\nu_f}\right] & x_1-1 \\ \cdot \quad \cdot \quad \cdot & \cdot \quad \cdot \quad \cdot & \cdot \\ \left[x_{f-1}\frac{\nu_1}{\nu_f}\right]-x_{f-1}\left[\frac{\nu_1}{\nu_f}\right] \ldots & \left[x_{f-1}\frac{\nu_{f-1}}{\nu_f}\right]-x_{f-1}\left[\frac{\nu_{f-1}}{\nu_f}\right] & x_{f-1}-1 \end{vmatrix}=0.$$

Since no integral relation

$$\tau_1\frac{\nu_1}{\nu_f}+\tau_2\frac{\nu_2}{\nu_f}+\ldots+\tau_{f-1}\frac{\nu_{f-1}}{\nu_f}+\tau_f=0$$

may exist, apart from the case when all the τ's are zero, the coefficient of $\frac{\nu_1}{\nu_f}$ must vanish :

$$\begin{vmatrix} \left[x_1\frac{\nu_2}{\nu_f}\right]-x_1\left[\frac{\nu_2}{\nu_f}\right] \ldots & \left[x_1\frac{\nu_{f-1}}{\nu_f}\right]-x_1\left[\frac{\nu_{f-1}}{\nu_f}\right] & x_1-1 \\ \cdot \quad \cdot \quad \cdot & \cdot \quad \cdot \quad \cdot & \cdot \\ \left[x_{f-1}\frac{\nu_2}{\nu_f}\right]-x_{f-1}\left[\frac{\nu_2}{\nu_f}\right] \ldots & \left[x_{f-1}\frac{\nu_{f-1}}{\nu_f}\right]-x_{f-1}\left[\frac{\nu_{f-1}}{\nu_f}\right] & x_{f-1}-1 \end{vmatrix}=0.$$

If we divide the first row by x_1-1 and proceed to the limit $x_1 \to \infty$ we obtain

$$\begin{vmatrix} \frac{\nu_2}{\nu_f}-\left[\frac{\nu_2}{\nu_f}\right] \ldots & \frac{\nu_{f-1}}{\nu_f}-\left[\frac{\nu_{f-1}}{\nu_f}\right] & 1 \\ \left[x_2\frac{\nu_2}{\nu_f}\right]-x_2\left[\frac{\nu_2}{\nu_f}\right] \ldots & \left[x_2\frac{\nu_{f-1}}{\nu_f}\right]-x_2\left[\frac{\nu_{f-1}}{\nu_f}\right] & x_2-1 \\ \cdot \quad \cdot \quad \cdot & \cdot \quad \cdot \quad \cdot & \cdot \\ \left[x_{f-1}\frac{\nu_2}{\nu_f}\right]-x_{f-1}\left[\frac{\nu_2}{\nu_f}\right] \ldots & \left[x_{f-1}\frac{\nu_{f-1}}{\nu_f}\right]-x_{f-1}\left[\frac{\nu_{f-1}}{\nu_f}\right] & x_{f-1}-1 \end{vmatrix}=0.$$

The coefficient of $\frac{\nu_2}{\nu_f}$ in this expression must vanish. If we divide first row by x_2-1, and allow x_2 to tend to ∞, it will be seen that we must have

$$\begin{vmatrix} \frac{\nu_3}{\nu_f}-\left[\frac{\nu_3}{\nu_f}\right] \cdots & \frac{\nu_{f-1}}{\nu_f}-\left[\frac{\nu_{f-1}}{\nu_f}\right] & 1 \\ \left[x_3\frac{\nu_3}{\nu_f}\right]-x_3\left[\frac{\nu_3}{\nu_f}\right] \cdots & \left[x_3\frac{\nu_{f-1}}{\nu_f}\right]-x_3\left[\frac{\nu_{f-1}}{\nu_f}\right] & x_3-1 \\ \cdots & \cdots & \cdots \end{vmatrix}=0.$$

we may continue this process until we arrive at the relation :

$$\begin{vmatrix} \frac{\nu_{f-1}}{\nu_f}-\left[\frac{\nu_{f-1}}{\nu_f}\right] & 1 \\ \left[x_{f-1}\frac{\nu_{f-1}}{\nu_f}\right]-x_{f-1}\left[\frac{\nu_{f-1}}{\nu_f}\right] & x_{f-1}-1 \end{vmatrix}=0.$$

This contradicts, however, the irrationality of $\frac{\nu_{f-1}}{\nu_f}$.

If the points of the Q-series do not all lie in one linear $(f-2)$-dimensional space passing through P_σ, we can pick out $f-1$ of the vectors $\overline{P_\sigma Q_m}$, which form an $(f-1)$-dimensional $(f-1)$-edge. If we again attach all the $f-1$ vectors to the end point of each of these vectors, and continue this process, we can cover the whole $(f-1)$-dimensional surface of the unit cube perpendicular to OE_f with a net of cells, the sides of which are smaller than δ. Evidently the same is true for those boundaries perpendicular to the other OE_i. This shows, however, that the points of intersection of the trajectory fill the bounding surfaces completely, and hence the trajectory approaches infinitely close to every point of the unit cube.

II. Elementary and Complex Integration

Integrals of the form

$$\int R(x, \sqrt{-Ax^2+2Bx-C})dx,$$

where R is a rational function of the given argument, are of frequent occurrence in our problems. We have to deal with the definite integral, taken over a libration of x, in calculating the energy as a function of the J's, and with the indefinite form in calculating, for example, the angle variables.

The indefinite integration may be performed by elementary means : if e_1 and $e_2 (e_1>e_2)$ denote the roots of the expression under the square root sign, this expression takes the form (neglecting the factor A)

$$\left(\frac{e_1-e_2}{2}\right)^2(1-\sin^2\psi)$$

on making the substitution

$$x=\frac{e_1+e_2}{2}+\frac{e_1-e_2}{2}\sin\psi,$$

$$dx=\frac{e_1-e_2}{2}\cos\psi d\psi.$$

The integral then becomes

$$J=\int R\left(\frac{e_1+e_2}{2}+\frac{e_1-e_2}{2}\sin\psi,\ \frac{e_1-e_2}{2}\cos\psi\right)\frac{e_1-e_2}{2}\cos\psi d\psi,$$

which is the integral of a rational function of $\sin\psi$ and $\cos\psi$, which in every case may be reduced to the integral of a rational function of u by the substitution $u=\tan\frac{1}{2}\psi$, or alternatively, if the integrand is an even function of its argument, by the substitution $u=\tan\psi$. Let us consider the following examples :

1. $$\int\sqrt{a^2-x^2}dx.$$

The substitution $x=a\sin\psi$ gives

(1) $$a^2\int\cos^2\psi d\psi=\frac{a^2}{4}\int(1+\cos 2\psi)d2\psi=a^2\left[\frac{\psi}{2}+\frac{1}{4}\sin 2\psi\right]$$
$$=\frac{1}{2}\left[a^2\sin^{-1}\frac{x}{a}+x\sqrt{a^2-x^2}\right].$$

The definite integral taken over one libration of x is

(2) $$\oint\sqrt{a^2-x^2}dx=a^2\int_0^{2\pi}\cos^2\psi d\psi=\pi a^2.$$

2. $$\int\frac{\sqrt{1-x^2}}{1-ax^2}dx.$$

By the substitutions $x=\sin\psi$, $u=\tan\psi$, we obtain

$$\int\frac{\cos^2\psi}{1-a\sin^2\psi}d\psi=\int\frac{1}{1+u^2(1-a)}\frac{du}{1+u^2}.$$

The integrand can be resolved into partial fractions

$$+\frac{1}{a}\frac{1}{1+u^2}-\frac{1}{a}\frac{1}{\dfrac{1}{1-a}+u^2}.$$

Hence the indefinite integral is

$$\int \frac{\sqrt{1-x^2}}{1-ax^2}\,dx = \begin{cases} \frac{1}{a}\tan^{-1} u \mp \frac{\sqrt{1-a}}{a}\tan^{-1}(\pm u\sqrt{1-a}) & \text{for } a \leqq 1, \\ \frac{1}{a}\tan^{-1} u \pm \frac{\sqrt{a-1}}{a}\log\frac{1 \pm u\sqrt{a-1}}{1 \mp u\sqrt{a-1}} & \text{for } a \geqq 1, \end{cases}$$

where, if $\sqrt{1-x^2}$ be positive, the value $+\frac{x}{\sqrt{1-x^2}}$ is to be substituted for u.

In the case when $a<1$ the integral over a libration of x is :

$$(3) \qquad \oint \frac{\sqrt{1-x^2}}{1-ax^2}\,dx = \int_0^{2\pi} \frac{\cos^2\psi}{1-a\sin^2\psi}\,d\psi = \frac{2\pi}{a}(1-\sqrt{1-a}).$$

If it is only necessary to find the values of the definite integral

$$\mathrm{J} = \oint \mathrm{R}(x, \sqrt{-\mathrm{A}x^2+2\mathrm{B}x-\mathrm{C}})\,dx,$$

the method of complex integration is usually the most convenient.

If x be represented in the complex plane, the function R can be pictured on a Riemann surface of two sheets with branch points at the roots e_1 and $e_2 (e_1 > e_2)$ of the radicand. The path of integration encloses the line joining the two roots. If it goes from e_2 to e_1 $(dx>0)$ in that sheet of the surface where the root is positive, it goes from e_1 to $e_2 (dx<0)$ in the sheet with the negative root (see, for example, fig. 42).

The simplest way of evaluating the integral is to distort the path of integration and separate it into individual contours, each of which encloses one pole of the function. With the direction of rotation indicated in fig. 42, J is then equal to the negative sum of the residues of the integrand in these poles (the residue is $2\pi i$ times the coefficient of $1/(x-a)$ in the Laurent expansion in the neighbourhood of the pole a ; we will use the symbol Res_a for the residue at the pole a) :

$$\mathrm{J} = -\sum \mathrm{Res}\left[\mathrm{R}(x, \sqrt{-\mathrm{A}x^2+2\mathrm{B}x-\mathrm{C}})\right].$$

Let us consider a few types of integrals.

Group 1.

$$(4) \qquad \begin{aligned} \mathrm{J} &= \oint x^\alpha (\sqrt{-\mathrm{A}x^2+2\mathrm{B}x-\mathrm{C}})^\beta dx \\ &= \oint x^{\alpha+\beta}\left(\sqrt{-\mathrm{A}+2\frac{\mathrm{B}}{x}-\frac{\mathrm{C}}{x^2}}\right)^\beta dx. \end{aligned}$$

The constants A, B, C are supposed positive. If real roots exist —we shall assume that this is here the case—these lie on the positive real axis. The only possible poles of the integrand are at $x=0$ and $x=\infty$. We have therefore

$$J=-\mathrm{Res}_0\left[x^\alpha(\sqrt{-Ax^2+2Bx-C})^\beta\right]$$
$$-\mathrm{Res}_\infty\left[x^\alpha(\sqrt{-Ax^2+2Bx-C})^\beta\right].$$

The diagrams of the original and deformed paths of integration in this instance are clearly shown in fig. 42, in which the pole $x=\infty$ is represented as if it were at a finite distance. Outside the range e_1, e_2 on the real axis, the root is purely imaginary, and has the sign $+i$ from e_1 to ∞, and $-i$ from $-\infty$ to e_2.

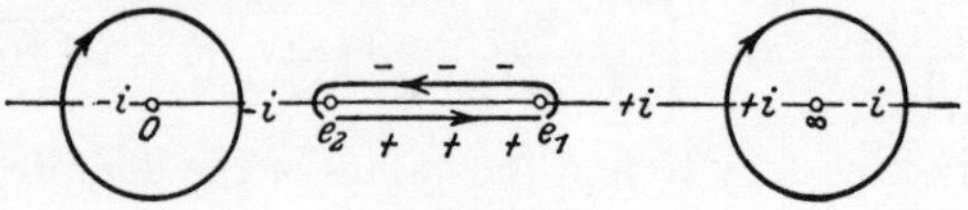

FIG. 42.

We calculate Res_∞ as the Res_0 of the integrand of the integral arising from the substitution $y=1/x$; since in the representation of the x-surface on the y-surface, the direction in which the path of integration is traversed remains unaltered, we have

$$\mathrm{Res}_\infty\ [x^\alpha(\sqrt{-Ax^2+2Bx-C})^\beta]$$
$$=-\mathrm{Res}_0\ [y^{-(\alpha+\beta+2)}(\sqrt{-A+2By-Cy^2})^\beta].$$

The root has sign $-i$ from $1/e_2$ to $y=\infty$, and $+i$ from $-\infty$ to $1/e_1$.

(*a*) $\boldsymbol{\alpha=-1}$, $\boldsymbol{\beta=+1}$:

Taking account of the above determination of sign, the expansions of the integrand necessary for the calculation of the residues at $x=0$ and $y=0$ are

$$-\frac{1}{x}\left(i\sqrt{C}+\frac{B}{i\sqrt{C}}x+\ldots\right)$$

and

$$\frac{1}{y^2}\left(i\sqrt{A}+\frac{B}{i\sqrt{A}}y+\ldots\right)$$

respectively. It follows therefore that

$$\mathrm{Res}_0=2\pi\sqrt{C},$$

$$\mathrm{Res}_\infty=-2\pi\frac{B}{\sqrt{A}}$$

and

$$
(5)\quad \begin{aligned} J_1 &= \oint \frac{1}{x}\sqrt{-Ax^2+2Bx-C}\,dx \\ &= \oint \sqrt{-A+2\frac{B}{x}-\frac{C}{x^2}}\,dx = 2\pi\left(\frac{B}{\sqrt{A}}-\sqrt{C}\right). \end{aligned}
$$

(*b*) $\alpha=-2, \quad \beta=-1$:

For $x=\infty$ the integral is regular. For $x=0$, the expansion of the integrand is

$$
-\frac{1}{x^2}\left(\frac{1}{i\sqrt{C}}+\frac{B}{iC\sqrt{C}}x+\ldots\right),
$$

that is

$$
\mathrm{Res}_0 = -2\pi\frac{B}{C\sqrt{C}}
$$

and

$$
(6)\quad \begin{aligned} J_2 &= \oint \frac{1}{x^2}(\sqrt{-Ax^2+2Bx-C})^{-1}dx \\ &= \oint \frac{1}{x^3}\left(\sqrt{-A+2\frac{B}{x}-\frac{C}{x^2}}\right)^{-1}dx = 2\pi\frac{B}{C\sqrt{C}}. \end{aligned}
$$

(*c*) $\alpha=+2, \quad \beta=-1$:

The integral is regular at $x=0$. The expansion of the corresponding integrand for $y=1/x=0$ is

$$
\frac{1}{y^3}\left[\frac{1}{i\sqrt{A}}+\frac{B}{iA\sqrt{A}}y+\frac{1}{2i}\left(3\frac{B^2}{A^2\sqrt{A}}-\frac{C}{A\sqrt{A}}\right)y^2+\ldots\right],
$$

that is

$$
\mathrm{Res}_\infty = -\frac{\pi}{\sqrt{A}}\left(3\frac{B^2}{A^2}-\frac{C}{A}\right),
$$

consequently

$$
(7)\quad \begin{aligned} J_3 &= \oint \frac{x^2dx}{\sqrt{-Ax^2+2Bx-C}} = \oint \frac{x\,dx}{\sqrt{-A+2\frac{B}{x}-\frac{C}{x^2}}} \\ &= \frac{\pi}{\sqrt{A}}\left(3\frac{B^2}{A^2}-\frac{C}{A}\right). \end{aligned}
$$

Group 2:

(*a*) $\oint \frac{\sqrt{1-x^2}}{1-ax^2}dx$. We can distinguish two possible cases.

1. $a<1$. The poles of the integrand given by the roots of $1-ax^2$ lie outside the path of integration surrounding the zero points ± 1 of the roots (branch points of the integrand); they lie on the real axis for $0<a<1$, and on the imaginary axis for $a<0$. The integral is composed of the residues at

$$x=\pm\sqrt{\frac{1}{a}} \text{ and } x=\infty.$$

The root is positive and imaginary on the positive real axis, and negative and imaginary on the negative real axis; it is positive and real on the negative imaginary axis, and negative and real on the positive imaginary axis. Taking these signs into account, the expansion of the integrand at its poles $\pm\sqrt{\frac{1}{a}}$ commences with

$$-\frac{i}{2a}\sqrt{1-a}\left(x\pm\sqrt{\frac{1}{a}}\right)^{-1}+\cdots.$$

The residues in both poles are the same, viz.:

$$\frac{\pi}{a}\sqrt{1-a}.$$

The contribution of the contour about $x=\infty$ works out to be

$$+\text{Res}_0\left[\frac{1}{y}\frac{\sqrt{y^2-1}}{y^2-a}\right].$$

Since the root is positive and imaginary for positive real values in the neighbourhood of zero, the expansion of the function starts with

$$-\frac{i}{a}\frac{1}{y}+\cdots.$$

This gives for the required contribution $\frac{2\pi}{a}$ and finally

$$\text{(8)} \qquad J_4=\oint\frac{\sqrt{1-x^2}}{1-ax^2}dx=\frac{2\pi}{a}(1-\sqrt{1-a}).$$

2. $a>1$. The poles $\pm\sqrt{\frac{1}{a}}$ fall in the interval $(-1, +1)$ of the real axis and lie therefore inside the path of integration. The integrand does not remain integrable at them, so that this case must be excluded.

(*b*) $$\oint \frac{x^2-AB}{f(x)\sqrt{F(x)}}dx$$

with $$f(x)=(A-x)(x-B), \qquad F(x)=f(x)-ACx.$$

Let A, B, C be positive and real, A>B, and C chosen so that F(x) can assume positive values. The roots α, β of F(x) are then real and lie between A and B.

The integrand possesses simple branch points at α and β: it becomes infinite there, but remains integrable. Simple poles lie

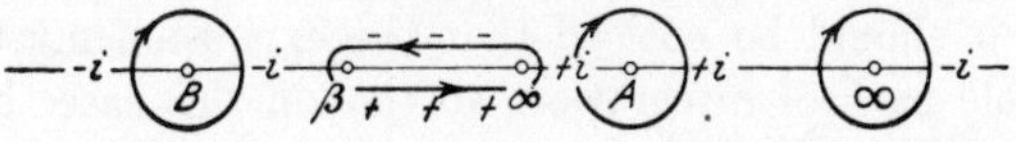

FIG. 43.

at A and B. Again, a circulation about $x=\infty$ will contribute to the integral. The signs of the roots are given in fig. 43. In the neighbourhood of A the expansion of the integrand commences with

$$+i\frac{1}{\sqrt{C}}(x-A)^{-1}+\ldots,$$

in the vicinity of B with

$$-i\sqrt{\frac{B}{AC}}(x-B)^{-1}+\cdots.$$

The residues are therefore

$$\text{Res}_A=-\frac{2\pi}{\sqrt{C}}, \qquad \text{Res}_B=+2\pi\sqrt{\frac{B}{AC}}.$$

Using the substitution $y=1/x$ we find

$$\text{Res}_\infty=-\text{Res}_0\left[\frac{1}{y}\frac{1-ABy^2}{(Ay-1)(1-By)}\cdot\frac{1}{\sqrt{(Ay-1)(1-By)-ACy}}\right],$$

where the root for positive real values of y in the neighbourhood of zero has the sign $+i$. The expansion commences therefore with $-\frac{i}{y}$, and

$$\text{Res}_\infty=+2\pi.$$

Hence

(9) $$J_5=\oint\frac{x^2-AB}{f(x)\sqrt{F(x)}}dx=2\pi\left(\frac{1}{\sqrt{C}}-\sqrt{\frac{B}{AC}}-1\right).$$

In conclusion we will consider one or two other integrals of the form

$$\oint R(x, \sqrt{-Ax^2+2Bx-C+\lambda f(x)})dx,$$

where $\lambda f(x)$ represents a correction term. Under these circumstances the positions of the branch points are not essentially different from those in the integrals of group 1, and the previous figures and determinations of sign and paths of integration remain the same.

In order to carry out the integration we have to expand the integrand in powers of the factor λ of the correction term, and in this connection it should be noticed that the expansion must be valid for the whole path of integration, so that in this case the path of integration must first of all be suitably deformed. Should new branch points be added on account of the correction term, they must be avoided by the deformed path of integration.

The integration may then be carried out by the same process as before, since for the individual terms only the branch points e_1 and e_2, and the poles $x=0$, $x=\infty$ occur.

(a) $$J_6=\oint x^{-1}\sqrt{-Ax^2+2Bx-C+\frac{D}{x}}dx$$
$$=\oint\sqrt{-A+2\frac{B}{x}-\frac{C}{x^2}+\frac{D}{x^3}}dx.$$

For sufficiently small values of D the expansion for $D=0$ holds for the whole path of integration. Let us restrict ourselves to terms of the first order in D :

$$\sqrt{-Ax^2+2Bx-C+\frac{D}{x}}$$
$$=\sqrt{-Ax^2+2Bx-C}+(-Ax^2+2Bx-C)^{-\frac{1}{2}}\frac{D}{2x}+\cdots.$$

Hence

$$J_6=J_1+\frac{D}{2}J_2,$$

or

(10) $$J_6=+2\pi\left(\frac{B}{\sqrt{A}}+\frac{1}{2}\frac{BD}{C\sqrt{C}}-\sqrt{C}\right).$$

(b) $$J_7=\oint\frac{1}{x}\sqrt{-Ax^2+2Bx-C+Dx^3}dx$$
$$=\oint\sqrt{-A+2\frac{B}{x}-\frac{C}{x^2}+Dx}\,dx.$$

The expansion of the square root in powers of D yields

$$\sqrt{-Ax^2+2Bx-C+Dx^3}$$
$$=\sqrt{-Ax^2+2Bx-C}+(-Ax^2+2Bx-C)^{-\frac{1}{2}}\frac{D}{2}x^3+\cdots.$$

Confining ourselves to terms of the first order in D, this leads to

$$J_7=J_1+\frac{D}{2}J_3$$

or

$$J_7=2\pi\left(\frac{B}{\sqrt{A}}-\sqrt{C}\right)+\frac{\pi}{2}\frac{D}{A^{\frac{3}{2}}}\left(3\frac{B^2}{A}-C\right). \tag{11}$$

INDEX

(The numbers refer to pages)